ANALYTIC GEOMETRY

THE APPLETON-CENTURY MATHEMATICS SERIES

Edited by Raymond W. Brink

ANALYTIC GEOMETRY

by

Edwin J. Purcell

PROFESSOR OF MATHEMATICS
UNIVERSITY OF ARIZONA

NEW YORK: APPLETON-CENTURY-CROFTS, INC.

PRINTED IN THE UNITED STATES OF AMERICA
E-72046

PREFACE

~~~~~~

The study of analytic geometry is important not only as a useful preliminary to the calculus but also for its own sake. It presents in short compass a logical system in which the student meets, almost for the first time, the advantages and difficulties of combining algebraic and geometric ideas. The purpose of this book is to help the student overcome the difficulties and realize the advantages of this combination. It is hoped that it will also lead him to share the author's pleasure in the beauty of the ideas involved—their simplicity, generality, and logical perfection.

To these ends, each new topic is thoroughly motivated and put into proper perspective with other topics.

In order to present analytic geometry as a logical system, the book starts with a few simple, explicit assumptions and from them develops the customary material with particular emphasis on the reasoning involved. More often than is customary, statements are justified by numbered references to previous definitions or theorems. It is not expected that the student will look up these references every time. Usually the justifying definition or theorem will occur to him as he reads the statement and its context. But the supporting references are given so that no student shall be mystified by any statement or step in a proof, and also to emphasize the logical consistency of the entire treatment.

It is in the first few lessons that a student often becomes bewildered and loses the opportunity really to *understand* analytic geometry. Exceptional care has been given to this early part. In particular, it is believed that the present book excels in its clear and consistent use of directed and undirected distances and their corresponding notations. Simple definitions are given for positive and negative directions of straight lines in both two- and three-dimensional space. They should do much to give the student a feeling of assurance in some of the thornier problems he encounters.

Conics are presented in the unified manner, using the focus-directrix-eccentricity definition. The treatment of curve-sketching is unusually complete.

It is hoped that the chapters on three-dimensional geometry will be found to be more rigorous, yet easier to understand, than customary.

A word about the numbering: the reference 2.5, for example, is to the fifth section of Chapter 2. The reference 7.12.4 is to the fourth numbered item (definition, theorem, or corollary) in the twelfth section of Chapter 7.

The starred sections are often omitted.

I am happy to have this opportunity to thank Professor Raymond W. Brink, Editor of the Appleton-Century Mathematics Series, for his careful reading of the manuscript and for his many kindly, helpful suggestions.

Tucson, Arizona

E. J. P.

CONTENTS

CONTENTS

Chapter 5

THE CIRCLE

Chapter 6

CONICS

Chapter 7

THE SECOND DEGREE EQUATION

Chapter 8

★ TANGENTS TO CONICS

★ Starred sections and chapters may be omitted.

CONTENTS

CONTENTS

Chapter 13

THE PLANE

Chapter 14

THE STRAIGHT LINE IN SPACE

Chapter 15

SURFACES

ANALYTIC GEOMETRY

1

Cartesian Coordinates

1.1 INTRODUCTION

In high school, algebra and geometry were studied as two different subjects. They seemed to have little in common other than their both being mathematics. Algebra deals with numbers, whereas geometry is concerned with points, lines, planes, and the like.

The Greeks perfected elementary geometry two thousand years ago, but were not much interested in algebra. On the other hand, the Hindus and Arabs cultivated algebra but added little that was new to geometry.

There seemed little connection between algebra and geometry until the seventeenth century when René Descartes, a French mathematician and philosopher, developed a method which associated the numbers of algebra with the points of geometry. By his discoveries, large parts of algebra and geometry were seen to be two aspects of the same thing, somewhat as two different languages may express the same meaning. For example, the algebraic statement "Two distinct equations of the first degree in two variables have a single common solution or none" is equivalent to the geometric theorem "Two distinct lines in the same plane intersect in a single point or are parallel."

Algebra thus became a tool in the study of geometry and geometry helped throw new light on algebra. This study of geometry by means of algebra is called **analytic geometry.**

1.2 DIRECTED LINES

In analytic geometry all **lines** extend indefinitely far in both directions. A line has no ends.

A finite portion of a straight line is called a **line segment.** If A and B are any two points on a line l, the line segment terminated by A and B consists of the points A and B and that part of l which is between A and B (Fig. 1). We will designate it by $\overline{AB}$ or $\overline{BA}$—they are the same.

The student has had experience in measuring the length of an object with a ruler or tape measure and probably has a good intuitive idea of

1

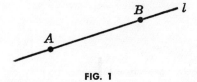

FIG. 1

what is meant by the **length** of a line segment. It is the number of times some convenient unit of measurement is contained in the line segment. We will denote the length of a line segment $\overline{AB}$ by $|AB|$ or $|BA|$—they are the same. In Fig. 2, if the unit of measurement is $\overline{OI}$, then $|AB| = 2$, $|CD| = .7$ and (by the Pythagorean theorem) $|EF| = \sqrt{2}$.

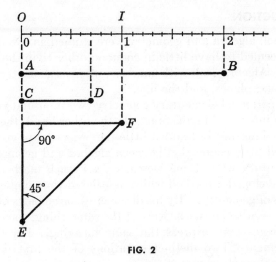

FIG. 2

It made no difference in high school geometry which way we measured a line segment. Once a unit of measurement had been decided upon, the distance from a point A to a point B was always the same positive number as the distance from B to A. But in analytic geometry the direction of measurement must often be taken into account.

A **directed line** is one on which distances measured in one arbitrarily chosen direction are positive while distances measured in the opposite direction are negative. The positive direction on a directed line may be indicated by an arrowhead. Thus in Fig. 3 the distance measured from B to A is positive and the distance from A to B is negative.

The **directed distance** from a point A to a point B is a positive number equal to the length $|AB|$ if the direction from A to B is positive (Fig. 4) and is a negative number equal to $-|AB|$ if the distance from A to B is negative (Fig. 3). The directed distance from A to B is denoted by AB and the directed distance from B to A by BA. Thus $AB = -BA$ or $AB + BA = 0$. In Fig. 3, $AB = -3$ and $BA = 3$.

The **undirected distance** between any two points, A and B, is the length of the line segment $\overline{AB}$.   It is the absolute value of the directed distance from A to B or from B to A and is always a positive number.   In Fig. 3, $|AB| = |BA| = 3$.

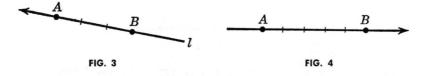

FIG. 3   FIG. 4

Notice that while $\overline{AB}$ represents a geometric concept (the line segment itself, not its length), the symbols AB and $|AB|$ represent numbers.

For example, in Fig. 4 the line on points A and B is indefinite in extent and the arrowhead shows that its positive direction is from A to B. $\overline{AB}$ or $\overline{BA}$ is the line segment terminated by A and B and is not a number.   The directed distance from A to B is $AB = 5$, and the directed distance from B to A is $BA = -5$.   The undirected distance between the points A and B is $|AB| = |BA| = 5$.

A fundamental characteristic of directed lines is stated in the

1.2.1 Principle.   *If A and B are any two points on a directed line, then* $AB = -BA$.

Another important property of directed lines (Fig. 5) may be stated as follows:

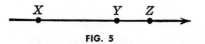

FIG. 5

1.2.2 Principle.   *If X, Y, and Z are any three points on a directed line, in that order when reading in the positive direction, then*

$$XY + YZ = XZ.$$

The student should make a sketch and convince himself of the reasonableness of these two assumptions.

We are now ready for the first theorem.

1.2.3 Theorem.   *If A, B, and C are any three points on a directed line, then*

$$AB + BC = AC,$$

no matter what the relative positions of the points.

Proof: Reading in the positive direction on the line, there are exactly six possible orders for the three points, namely, ABC, ACB, BAC, BCA, CAB, and CBA.

For the first arrangement, ABC, the validity of the theorem follows at once from 1.2.2.

Consider now the second arrangement, ACB (Fig. 6).

FIG. 6

$$AC + CB = AB \qquad \text{(by 1.2.2)}.$$

But
$$CB = -BC \qquad \text{(by 1.2.1)}.$$

Therefore
$$AC + (-BC) = AB,$$

or
$$AC = AB + BC,$$

which proves the theorem for the case ACB.

The proofs of the remaining four cases are similar and are left for the student. They are necessary in order to complete the proof of 1.2.3.

EXERCISES

1. Which of the following statements have no meaning? Why?

    (a) $\overline{AB} = 13$;   (b) $BA = -13$;   (c) $|BA| = 13$;

    (d) $AB = 13$;   (e) $\overline{BA} = -13$;   (f) $|AB| = 13$.

2. Put into words: "If $CD = 6$, then $DC = -6$ and $|CD| = |DC| = 6$."

3. Prove Theorem 1.2.3 when the arrangement of the points is B,A,C, reading from left to right.

4. Prove Theorem 1.2.3 for the arrangement B,C,A.

5. Prove Theorem 1.2.3 for the arrangement C,A,B.

6. Prove Theorem 1.2.3 for the arrangement C,B,A.

1.3   RECTANGULAR CARTESIAN COORDINATES

It was pointed out in Section 1.1 that Descartes' invention of analytic geometry was based on a correspondence between the real numbers of algebra and the points of geometry. Such a correspondence will now be described.

Consider two mutually perpendicular directed lines. One is called the **x-axis** and the other the **y-axis.** Their intersection, O, is the origin. Choose any convenient unit of length, OI.

In our figures we will follow the usual practice of showing the x-axis as a horizontal line whose positive direction is to the right and the y-axis as a vertical line whose positive direction is upward. All lines parallel to a co-ordinate axis are directed and have the same positive direction as that axis. Thus the positive direction on any horizontal line is to the right, and on any vertical line it is upward.

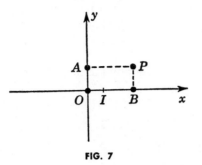

FIG. 7

Each point, P, in the plane has two numbers associated with it, its **x-coordinate**, or **abscissa**, and its **y-coordinate**, or **ordinate** (Fig. 7).

1.3.1 Definition. *The **x-coordinate**, or **abscissa**, of any point, P, in the plane is the directed distance from the y-axis to the point P. The **y-coordinate**, or **ordinate**, of P is the directed distance from the x-axis to P.*

In Fig. 7, the x-coordinate, or abscissa, of P is AP; and the y-coordinate, or ordinate, of P is BP.

Whenever we speak of the distance from a line to a point we of course mean the shortest distance, that is, the distance measured perpendicular to the given line.

When the coordinates of a point are written, the x-coordinate always appears first. Thus the Cartesian coordinates of a given point are an **ordered pair** of numbers. They are enclosed in parentheses and are separated by a comma. For example (Fig. 8), if P is 3 units to the right of the y-axis and 5 units above the x-axis, its coordinates are (3, 5).

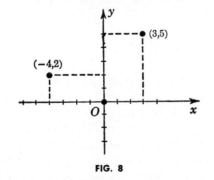

FIG. 8

Clearly this process can be reversed. Given the coordinates $(-4, 2)$, the point is located 4 units to the left of the y-axis and 2 units above the x-axis (Fig. 8).

This establishes a **one-to-one correspondence** between the points of the plane and ordered pairs of real numbers, for to each point of the plane there corresponds a unique ordered pair of real numbers (its rectangular Cartesian coordinates) and to each ordered pair of real numbers there corresponds a unique point. Incidentally, all numbers used in this course are real numbers.

The much-used phrase "the point P whose coordinates are (x, y)" will be symbolized by $P:(x, y)$.

To **plot** a point is to locate it, relative to a pair of coordinate axes, by means of its known coordinates.

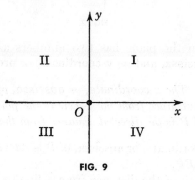

FIG. 9

Coordinate axes divide the plane into four regions called quadrants. The numbering of the quadrants is shown in Fig. 9.

1.3.2 NOTE. The student should acquire the habit of making a drawing *first* when attempting to solve a problem in analytic geometry. There are three reasons for this: (1) it trains him to see the interrelationship between algebra and geometry; (2) a sketch often suggests a method of solution; and (3) the drawing provides a rough check on the correctness of his algebraic results. Coordinate paper, with equally spaced horizontal and vertical rulings, is a convenience in plotting points.

EXERCISES

1. Plot the points whose coordinates are: $(1, 3)$, $(-6, 2)$, $(-3, -2)$, $(0, 0)$, $(8, 0)$, $(\sqrt{2}, 4)$, $(-\sqrt{3}, \sqrt{10})$, and $(-2\pi, -3)$. Label each point with its coordinates (enclosed in parentheses, of course).

2. Plot and label the points whose coordinates are: $(4, 5)$, $(-5, -5)$, $(2, -7)$, $(0, 4)$, $(-5, 1)$, $(1, \sqrt{5})$, $(\pi, 6)$, and $(-\sqrt{2}, \pi)$.

3. Can you plot the point whose coordinates are $(\sqrt{-4}, 3)$? Explain.

4. What signs do the coordinates of a point in the first quadrant have? The second quadrant? The third? The fourth?

5. Plot the points whose coordinates are $(0, 2)$, $(0, -6)$, $(0, 3)$, $(0, 8)$, $(0, -1)$. Where do they all lie?

   6. What is common to the coordinates of all points on the
   (a) x-axis;
   (b) line parallel to the y-axis and 2 units to the left of it;
   (c) line through the origin, bisecting the first and third quadrants?
   7. What is common to the coordinates of points on the
   (a) y-axis;
   (b) line parallel to the x-axis and 5 units above it;
   (c) line through the origin bisecting the second and fourth quadrants?
   8. What is common to the coordinates of all points on a line parallel to the x-axis?
   9. What is common to the coordinates of all points on a line parallel to the y-axis?
   10. (a) Draw $\overline{AB}$ when the coordinates of A are $(2, 3)$ and the coordinates of B are $(-4, 2)$.
   (b) Draw the line determined by A and B.
   11. Plot the points $A:(3, 2)$ and $B:(7, 2)$. Draw $\overline{AB}$. Find AB and BA.
   12. Given the points $A:(-1, -3)$ and $B:(-6, -3)$, draw $\overline{AB}$ and find AB.
   13. Given $A:(2, -2)$ and $B:(2, 8)$, draw $\overline{AB}$. Find AB and $|AB|$.
   14. Given $A:(2, -4)$ and $B:(-3, -4)$, draw $\overline{AB}$. Find AB and $|AB|$.
   15. Draw the triangle whose vertices are $A:(1, 2)$, $B:(4, 2)$, and $C:(4, 6)$. Find $|AB|$ and $|BC|$. Use the Pythagorean theorem to find $|AC|$.
   16. Draw the triangle whose vertices are $A:(2, -1)$, $B:(2, -5)$, and $C:(-6, -5)$ and find AB, BC, and $|CA|$.

1.4 ABSOLUTE VALUES

In the Cartesian coordinate system, all lines are directed lines. But a first course in analytic geometry is based on the student's previous knowledge of high school geometry and the line segments there were undirected. For this reason we must sometimes work with undirected distances. Since undirected distances are the absolute values of directed distances (see 1.2), we will conclude this chapter with a review of the concept of **absolute value.**

The symbol $|N|$ is used to represent the absolute value of the real number N.

The absolute value of any positive number is that number itself. For example, $|2| = 2$, $|\frac{3}{5}| = \frac{3}{5}$, and $|\pi| = \pi$.

The absolute value of zero is zero.

The absolute value of a negative number is the negative of that negative number. For example, $|-3| = 3$, $|-\frac{4}{9}| = \frac{4}{9}$, and $|-1.414| = 1.414$.

This is summarized in the

1.4.1 Definition. *The **absolute value** of any real number, N, is N itself if N is positive or zero, and is $-N$ if N is negative.*

1.4.2 Corollary. *The absolute value of any real number is always positive or zero.*

It is easy to prove the

1.4.3 Theorem. *If N is any real number, then $N^2 = |N|^2$.*

Proof. If N is positive or zero, $N = |N|$ (by 1.4.1) and, squaring both members, we have $N^2 = |N|^2$.

If N is negative, then $-N = |N|$ (by 1.4.1). Squaring both members gives $(-N)^2 = |N|^2$ or $N^2 = |N|^2$.

For example, $(-7)^2 = |-7|^2$ or $49 = 49$.

Recall that every positive number has two distinct square roots. For example, the square roots of 4 are $+2$ and -2. Students sometimes forget that the radical sign means only one of these square roots—the positive one. Thus $\sqrt{4}$ is 2, never -2. Had the other square root been wanted, we would have written $-\sqrt{4}$ which is -2. We restate from algebra the

1.4.4 Definition. *Let K be any positive number or zero. Then $\sqrt{K}$, which may be read "**radical K**," is the non-negative number whose square is K.*

1.4.5 Theorem. *If N is any real number, then $\sqrt{N^2} = |N|$.*

Proof. N is real and therefore N^2 is positive or zero. Hence $\sqrt{N^2}$ is the non-negative number whose square is N^2 (by 1.4.4).

But $|N|^2 = N^2$ (by 1.4.3). Thus $|N|$ is the non-negative number whose square is N^2. Therefore $\sqrt{N^2} = |N|$.

For example, $\sqrt{(-3)^2} = \sqrt{9} = 3$, not -3.

EXERCISES

1. What are the values of $|2|$, $|-4|$, $|3 - 3|$, and $|-\pi|$?

2. What are the values of $|-3|^2$, $|(-3)^2|$, $|5 - 7|$, and $-|-2|$?

3. What are the values of $\sqrt{(-2)^2}$, $\sqrt{9}$, $\sqrt{(-5)^2}$, and $-\sqrt{(-3)^2}$?

4. Find the values of $\pm\sqrt{1/4}$, $-\sqrt{(-8)^2}$, $\sqrt{(-7)^2}$, and $-\sqrt{36}$.

2

The Basic Tools

The geometry studied in high school was Euclidean geometry, and two basic concepts in that geometry are distance and angle.

To apply algebra to the study of geometry, we need algebraic formulas for the distance between two points whose coordinates are known and the magnitude of the angle between two lines whose directions are given. Such formulas, and a few related theorems, are the basic tools of analytic geometry. We will now proceed to develop them.

2.1 DIRECTED LENGTH OF HORIZONTAL AND VERTICAL LINE SEGMENTS

The first basic tool of analytic geometry is a pair of formulas for the directed length of line segments which are parallel to a coordinate axis.

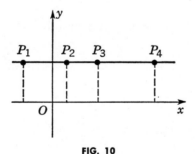

FIG. 10

We observed in Exercise 8 of 1.3 that all points on a line parallel to the x-axis have equal y-coordinates (Fig. 10). This is really a corollary to our definition of the y-coordinate of a point (1.3.1).

2.1.1 Corollary. *A line is parallel to the x-axis if and only if all points on the line have equal y-coordinates.*

Similarly,

9

2.1.2 Corollary. *A line is parallel to the y-axis if and only if all points on the line have equal x-coordinates.*

We now seek a formula for the directed length of a horizontal line segment, the coordinates of whose endpoints are known.

Throughout this book we will indicate the coordinates of a general point P in the plane by (x, y). When definite points enter the discussion they may be symbolized by $P_1:(x_1, y_1)$, $P_2:(x_2, y_2)$, etc., read "the point P-one with coordinates x-one, y-one, etc."

2.1.3 Theorem. *If $P_1:(x_1, y_1)$ and $P_2:(x_2, y_2)$ are two points on a line parallel to the x-axis, then*

$$P_1P_2 = x_2 - x_1.$$

Proof. Denote the intersection of the given line through P_1 and P_2 with the y-axis by K (Fig. 11).

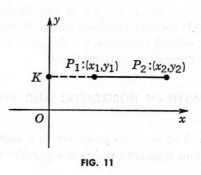

FIG. 11

Since K, P_1, and P_2 are three points on a directed line, then

$$KP_1 + P_1P_2 = KP_2 \qquad \text{(by 1.2.3)}.$$

But the given line is parallel to the x-axis and thus perpendicular to the y-axis. Therefore

$$KP_1 = x_1 \quad \text{and} \quad KP_2 = x_2 \qquad \text{(by 1.3.1)}.$$

Substituting above, we have

$$x_1 + P_1P_2 = x_2,$$

or

$$P_1P_2 = x_2 - x_1,$$

which completes the proof.

2.1.4 Corollary. *If $P_1:(x_1, y_1)$ and $P_2:(x_2, y_2)$ are two points on a line parallel to the x-axis, then*

$$|P_1P_2| = |x_2 - x_1|.$$

2.1.5 NOTE. It is important for the student to realize that the above theorem and proof are valid no matter where the points P_1 and P_2 are placed, if only the line joining them is parallel to the x-axis. For, in examining the proof step by step, we see that the given line which is parallel to the x-axis must intersect the y-axis somewhere, and we can always designate that point of intersection by K. Since K, P_1, and P_2 are three points on a directed line, $KP_1 + P_1P_2 = KP_2$, *no matter what the relative positions of the three points* (by 1.2.3). The rest of the proof of 2.1.3 is elementary algebra.

The student is advised to place the given points in several positions relative to the y-axis and retrace the above proof, observing that not a letter or a comma need be changed in the proof. It is only essential that the line joining the given points be parallel to the x-axis. For example, try it with Fig. 12.

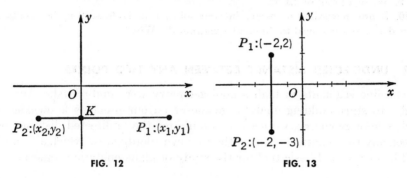

FIG. 12 FIG. 13

2.1.6 Theorem. *If P_1:(x_1, y_1) and P_2:(x_2, y_2) are two points on a line parallel to the y-axis, then*

$$P_1P_2 = y_2 - y_1.$$

The proof is analogous to that of 2.1.3 and is left for the student.

2.1.7 Corollary. *If P_1:(x_1, y_1) and P_2:(x_2, y_2) are two points on a line parallel to the y-axis, then*

$$|P_1P_2| = |y_2 - y_1|.$$

Example. Find the directed distance from the point whose coordinates are $(-2, 2)$ to the point whose coordinates are $(-2, -3)$.

Solution. Designating the given points by P_1 and P_2 respectively, we have $x_1 = -2$, $y_1 = 2$, $x_2 = -2$ and $y_2 = -3$. Since the x-coordinates are equal, $\overline{P_1P_2}$ is parallel to the y-axis (2.1.2). Substituting in 2.1.6, we have

$$P_1P_2 = (-3) - (2).$$

That is, $P_1P_2 = -5$ (Fig. 13).

EXERCISES

1. Where do all points lie for which $x = 2$?

2. Where do all points lie for which $y = -5$?

3. Given the points $A:(2, -5)$ and $B:(-4, -5)$. Draw $\overline{AB}$ and use the theorems of this section to find AB and BA.

4. Draw the right triangle whose vertices are $A:(1, 3)$, $B:(5, 6)$ and $C:(5, 3)$. Using the theorems of this section find $|AC|$ and $|CB|$. Then find $|AB|$ by means of the Pythagorean theorem.

5. In Exercise 4 let the right triangle be $A:(-2, 8)$, $B:(3, -4)$ and $C:(-2, -4)$.

6. Draw the right triangle whose vertices are $P_1:(1, 1)$, $P_2:(4, 2)$ and $P_3:(4, 1)$. Find $|P_1P_2|$.

7. What is the undirected distance between $P_1:(-1, -3)$ and $P_2:(2, 1)$?

8. Prove Theorem 2.1.3 when P_1 and P_2 are both in the third quadrant. Must your proof differ from that given in the text for 2.1.3? Why?

9. Write a proof of 2.1.6.

10. Is any rewording necessary in your solution of Exercise 9 if the points in your diagram are moved to different quadrants? Why?

2.2 UNDIRECTED DISTANCE BETWEEN ANY TWO POINTS

The line segments in high school geometry were undirected. Accordingly, to start building analytic geometry on our previous knowledge of high school geometry, we need a formula for the undirected distance between any two points in terms of their known coordinates. Such a formula will be our second basic tool for the study of plane analytic geometry.

2.2.1 Theorem. *The undirected distance between any two points,* $P_1:(x_1, y_1)$ *and* $P_2:(x_2, y_2)$ *is*

$$|P_1P_2| = \sqrt{(x_2 - x_1)^2 + (y_2 - y_1)^2}.$$

Proof. If $\overline{P_1P_2}$ is not parallel to either axis, draw a line through P_1 parallel to the x-axis and a line through P_2 parallel to the y-axis (Fig. 14).

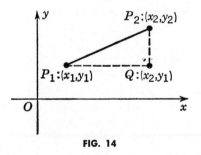

FIG. 14

Designate their intersection by Q. The coordinates of Q are (x_2, y_1) (by 2.1.1 and 2.1.2).

Then, by the Pythagorean theorem,*

---

* The Pythagorean theorem, like all the theorems of high school geometry, deals with undirected distances and thus we must write $|P_1Q|$ and $|QP_2|$, not P_1Q and QP_2.

$$|P_1P_2|^2 = |P_1Q|^2 + |QP_2|^2.$$

But $|P_1Q| = |x_2 - x_1|$ and $|QP_2| = |y_2 - y_1|$ (by 2.1.4 and 2.1.7).
Therefore

$$|P_1P_2|^2 = |x_2 - x_1|^2 + |y_2 - y_1|^2$$
$$= (x_2 - x_1)^2 + (y_2 - y_1)^2 \qquad \text{(by 1.4.3),}$$

whence

$$|P_1P_2| = \sqrt{(x_2 - x_1)^2 + (y_2 - y_1)^2}.$$

Should $\overline{P_1P_2}$ be parallel to the x-axis, then $y_1 = y_2$ (by 2.1.1) and the formula to be proved becomes $|P_1P_2| = \sqrt{(x_2 - x_1)^2}$, which is $|P_1P_2| = |x_2 - x_1|$ (by 1.4.5). But this is verified by 2.1.4.

Similarly, if $\overline{P_1P_2}$ is parallel to the y-axis, $x_1 = x_2$ (by 2.1.2) and the formula becomes $|P_1P_2| = \sqrt{(y_2 - y_1)^2} = |y_2 - y_1|$, which is the same as 2.1.7. This completes the proof of 2.2.1.

Here again, as in 2.1.5, it is essential to understand that the proof of our theorem is valid no matter how P_1 and P_2 are located relative to the coordinate axes. There are three possible cases. In the most general case, the segment $\overline{P_1P_2}$ is oblique to the coordinate axes; in the other two cases, $\overline{P_1P_2}$ is parallel to one or the other of the axes. The proofs of the theorem for the latter two cases are direct applications of the corollaries 2.1.4 and 2.1.7,

$$|P_1P_2| = |x_2 - x_1| \quad \text{and} \quad |P_1P_2| = |y_2 - y_1|,$$

which, as we have shown, hold for all possible positions of P_1 and P_2 on lines parallel to the x- and y-axes, respectively. If $\overline{P_1P_2}$ is not parallel to either axis, the proof uses only these same two corollaries, the Pythagorean theorem, and a little elementary algebra. Since the corollaries are general for all appropriate positions of P_1 and P_2, and the Pythagorean theorem has no reference whatever to the axes, our theorem (2.2.1) is also completely general.

This generality and complete indifference to position, relative to the coordinate axes, will hold in our proofs of all future theorems unless it is specifically stated to the contrary.

EXERCISES

Make a sketch for each exercise.

1. Use theorem 2.2.1 to find the undirected distance between the points

(a) $(2, 1)$ and $(4, -5)$; (b) $(1, -2)$ and $(-5, -3)$;

(c) $(-3, 2)$ and $(6, -1)$; (d) $(0, 0)$ and $(-1, -9)$.

2. By means of 2.2.1 find the undirected distance between the points

(a) $(1, -5)$ and $(-2, 1)$; (b) $(4, 4)$ and $(-3, 0)$;

(c) $(-6, -3)$ and $(2, 1)$; (d) $(0, -7)$ and $(4, 0)$.

3. Find the perimeter of the triangle whose vertices are $(1, 2)$, $(3, 7)$, and $(-2, 1)$.

4. What is the perimeter of the triangle whose vertices are $(0, 0)$, $(-1, -5)$, and $(-6, 2)$?

5. Prove that the triangle whose vertices are $(1, 1)$, $(5, 4)$, and $(-2, 5)$ is isosceles.

6. Prove that the triangle whose vertices are $(-3, 0)$, $(1, 0)$, and $(-1, 2\sqrt{3})$ is equilateral.

7. Prove that the quadrilateral whose vertices are $(-6, -2)$, $(-2, -1)$, $(-1, 3)$, and $(-5, 2)$ is a rhombus.

8. Prove that the quadrilateral whose vertices are $(-2, 6)$, $(4, 3)$, $(1, -3)$, and $(-5, 0)$ is a square.

9. Prove that the quadrilateral whose vertices $(-2, -1)$, $(5, -4)$, $(-1, -18)$, and $(-8, -15)$ is a rectangle.

10. Prove that the quadrilateral whose vertices are $(-1, 1)$, $(6, 1)$, $(4, -2)$, and $(-3, -2)$ is a parallelogram.

11. Prove that the points $(-5, 7)$, $(2, 6)$, and $(1, -1)$ lie on a circle whose center is $(-2, 3)$.

12. Express by an equation in x and y the statement that a point $P:(x, y)$ is on the perpendicular bisector of the line segment from $(1, -5)$ to $(-2, 2)$.

13. Prove that the points $(-8, -2)$, $(-5, 0)$, and $(4, 6)$ lie on the same straight line.

14. Prove that the point $(3, 0)$ is on the line determined by the points $(-3, 4)$ and $(6, -2)$.

15. Express in analytic language (that is, by means of an equation in x and y) the statement that a point $P:(x, y)$ is always at a distance of 6 units from the point $(3, 2)$. On what geometric figure must P lie?

16. Express in analytic language the statement that a point $P:(x, y)$ is always equidistant from the points $(-6, 0)$ and $(1, 3)$. What geometric figure do the totality of such points P form?

17. Make a diagram with P_1 in the third quadrant and P_2 in the second. With this figure follow the steps of the proof of Theorem 2.2.1 in the text. What rewording is necessary? Why?

18. Make a diagram with P_1 in the fourth quadrant and P_2 in the third quadrant. With this figure follow the steps of the proof of Theorem 2.2.1. What rewording is necessary? Why?

2.3   SLOPE OF A LINE

We recall that in Cartesian coordinates the positive direction on any line parallel to the x-axis is to the right (1.3). On all other lines *the positive direction is defined to be upward*. Thus in Fig. 15 the positive direction on each line is as indicated by the arrowhead.

It is clear that whenever two lines intersect, many angles are formed. In order to avoid confusion when speaking of the angle between two lines we make the following definition.

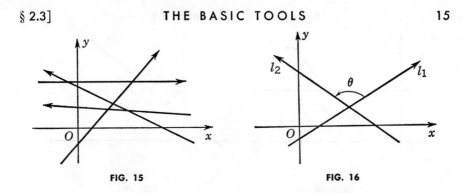

FIG. 15　　　　　　　　FIG. 16

2.3.1 Definition. *The **angle between two intersecting lines** is the small-est non-negative angle whose vertex is the point of intersection of the given lines and whose sides extend in the positive direction along the given lines.*

Thus in Fig. 16 the angle between the lines l_1 and l_2 is θ.

Now consider any line l. Through any point of l draw a line h parallel to the x-axis (Figs. 17a and 17b).

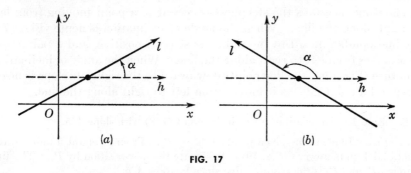

(a)　　　　　　　　(b)

FIG. 17

2.3.2 Definition. *The angle α between the lines l and h is called the **angle of inclination** of l.*

Observe that the value of the angle of inclination of a horizontal line is $0°$ and that for every line

2.3.3　　　　　　　　　$0° \leqslant \alpha < 180°.$

To show that the value of the angle of inclination of a given line, l, is unique, draw another line, h', parallel to h (Fig. 18). By 2.3.2, α' is also an angle of inclination of l. But $\alpha = \alpha'$ (Appendix 3). Thus the value of α is unique for l.

We are now prepared to define the important concept of the slope of a straight line.

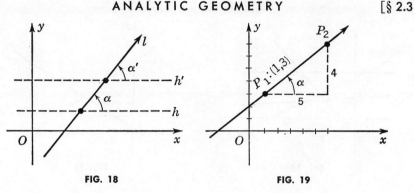

FIG. 18   FIG. 19

2.3.4 Definition. *The **slope** of any line not parallel to the y-axis is the tangent of its angle of inclination; in symbols,*

$$m = tan\ \alpha.$$

A vertical line does not possess a slope, since tan 90° does not exist. All other lines have slopes.

The slope measures the steepness of ascent of a point moving from left to right along the line. When the angle of inclination is acute (Fig. 17a) the line points upward to the right, its slope is positive, and a point rises as it moves from left to right along the line. When the angle of inclination is obtuse (Fig. 17b), the line points downward to the right, its slope is negative, and a point falls as it moves from left to right along the line.

Example 1. Draw a line through the point $(1, 3)$ with slope $4/5$.

Solution. Indicate the given point $(1, 3)$ by P_1. From P_1 count 5 units to the right and 4 units upward (Fig. 19). Designate the new position by P_2. The line through P_1 and P_2 is the required line since $\tan \alpha = 4/5$.

Example 2. Draw a line through $(2, 4)$ with slope -3.

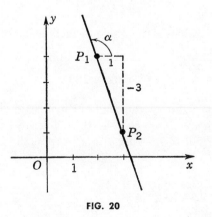

FIG. 20

Solution.   The slope -3 can be written $-3/1$.   Designate the given point $(2, 4)$ by P_1 and locate P_2 one unit to the right of P_1 and 3 units down (Fig. 20). The line through P_1 and P_2 is the required line.

2.4 THE SLOPE FORMULA

Our third basic tool for plane analytic geometry is a formula for the slope of a straight line.   It will enable us to determine the direction of a line when we know the coordinates of any two points on it.

2.4.1 Theorem.   *The slope, m, of the non-vertical line through the points P_1:(x_1, y_1) and P_2:(x_2, y_2) is*

$$m = \frac{y_2 - y_1}{x_2 - x_1}.$$

Proof. P_1 is either lower than P_2 or higher than P_2, or else P_1P_2 is horizontal.   That is, $y_1 < y_2$, $y_1 > y_2$ or $y_1 = y_2$.

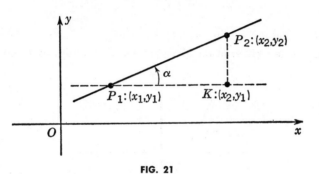

FIG. 21

CASE I. $y_1 < y_2$.

Through P_1 draw a horizontal line and through P_2 a vertical line (Fig. 21).   Their intersection is K:(x_2, y_1) (by 2.1.1 and 2.1.2).
Then

$$m = \tan \alpha \qquad \text{(by 2.3.4)}$$

$$= \frac{KP_2}{P_1K} \qquad \text{(Appendix, 8)}$$

$$= \frac{y_2 - y_1}{x_2 - x_1} \qquad \text{(by 2.1.3 and 2.1.6)}.$$

CASE II. $y_1 > y_2$.

In this case P_2 becomes the lower and P_1 the higher of the two points (Fig. 22).   Therefore by interchanging y_1 and y_2, and also x_1 and x_2 in Case I, we have

$$m = \frac{y_1 - y_2}{x_1 - x_2} = \frac{y_2 - y_1}{x_2 - x_1}.$$

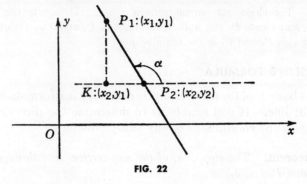

FIG. 22

CASE III. $y_1 = y_2$.

The line is parallel to the x-axis (by 2.1.1) and thus its **angle of inclination** and slope are zero.   Since substitution of $y_1 = y_2$ in $(y_2 - y_1)/(x_2 - x_1)$ gives zero, the theorem is verified for Case III.

This completes the proof of 2.3.4.

Example.   Find the slope of the line through the points $(0, -3)$ and $(-2, 1)$.

Solution.   Denote either of the given points, say $(0, -3)$, by P_1 and the other,

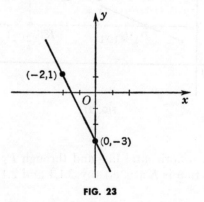

FIG. 23

$(-2, 1)$, by P_2 (Fig. 23).   Substituting their coordinates in the slope formula (2.4.1), we obtain

$$m = \frac{(1) - (-3)}{(-2) - (0)} = -2.$$

The desired slope is -2.

EXERCISES

Make a sketch for each exercise.

1. Draw the line through the point $(5, 3)$ with

(a) slope $2/3$;   (b) slope 7;

(c) slope $-1/2$;   (d) slope $-\sqrt{2}$.

2. Draw the line through the point $(-2, -4)$ with

    (*a*) slope -5;   (*b*) slope 3.5;

    (*c*) slope $3/5$;   (*d*) slope $-2/9$.

3. Find the slope of the line through

    (*a*) $(2, 1)$ and $(5, 7)$;   (*b*) $(3, 2)$ and $(8, -1)$;

    (*c*) $(-6, -2)$ and $(-1, -8)$;   (*d*) $(-1, 3)$ and $(7, 11)$.

4. Find the slope of the line through

    (*a*) $(1, 3)$ and $(6, 4)$;   (*b*) $(3, -2)$ and $(-2, 2)$;

    (*c*) $(-4, -5)$ and $(7, 1)$;   (*d*) $(-8, -3)$ and $(2, -5)$.

5. Using a table of trigonometric functions find, to the nearest degree, the angles of inclination of the lines of Exercise 3.

6. Use a table of trigonometric functions to find, to the nearest degree, the angles of inclination of the lines in Exercise 4.

7. Find the slopes of the sides of the triangle whose vertices are $(-4, 2)$, $(1, -5)$, and $(8, 3)$.

8. Find the slopes of the sides of the triangle whose vertices are $(-7, 1)$, $(-4, 5)$, and $(3, -2)$.

9. Using slopes only, determine whether the points $(-3, 2)$, $(4, 4)$, and $(8, 5)$ lie on the same straight line.

10. By means of the slope formula alone determine whether the points $(-1, 0)$, $(11, 3)$, and $(-9, -2)$ lie on the same straight line.

11. By means of the slope formula, put into analytic language (that is, express by means of an equation in x and y) the statement that the slope of the line joining the point $(1, 3)$ to a point $P{:}(x, y)$ is always equal to 2. On what geometric figure must P lie?

12. Use the slope formula to put into analytic language the statement that the slope of the line joining the point $(-3, 2)$ to a point $P{:}(x, y)$ is always equal to -1. On what geometric figure must all such points P lie?

13. A line has slope $-1/8$ and passes through the point $(-5, 2)$. Find the coordinates of its point of intersection with the x-axis.

14. A line with slope $2/5$ passes through the point $(3, -4)$. Find the coordinates of its point of intersection with the y-axis.

15. The x-coordinate of a point P is 3. The slope of the line segment joining P to the point $(-1, 4)$ is -2. Find the y-coordinate of P.

16. The y-coordinate of a point P is -1. The slope of the line joining P to the point $(3, 5)$ is $-1/2$. What is the x-coordinate of P?

2.5 PARALLEL AND PERPENDICULAR LINES

Our fourth and fifth basic tools for plane analytic geometry are theorems which enable us to tell when two given lines are parallel to each other and when they are perpendicular to each other.

2.5.1 Theorem. *Two non-vertical lines are parallel if and only if their slopes are equal.*

Proof. Denote the two given non-vertical lines by l_1 and l_2, their angles of inclination by α_1 and α_2, and their slopes by m_1 and m_2, respectively (Fig. 24).

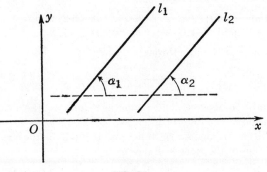

FIG. 24

If l_1 and l_2 are parallel, then $\alpha_1 = \alpha_2$ (Appendix, 3). Therefore $\tan \alpha_1 = \tan \alpha_2$, or $m_1 = m_2$.

Conversely, since $0° \leqslant \alpha_1 < 180°$ and $0° \leqslant \alpha_2 < 180°$ (by 2.3.3), it follows that if $m_1 = m_2$ so that $\tan \alpha_1 = \tan \alpha_2$, then $\alpha_1 = \alpha_2$. Therefore l_1 is parallel to l_2 (Appendix, 4).

2.5.2 Theorem. *Two non-vertical lines are perpendicular if and only if the slope of one is the negative of the reciprocal of the slope of the other.*

Proof. Given two non-vertical lines which are perpendicular to each other. Denote by l_1 the line with the smaller angle of inclination α_1, and let the other line be l_2 with angle of inclination α_2. Their slopes are m_1 and m_2, respectively. Through the point of intersection of l_1 and l_2 draw a horizontal line (Fig. 25).

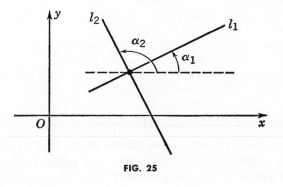

FIG. 25

Since l_1 is perpendicular to l_2,

$$\alpha_2 = \alpha_1 + 90°.$$

Therefore,

$$\tan \alpha_2 = \tan (\alpha_1 + 90°)$$

$$= -\cot \alpha_1 \qquad \text{(Appendix, 9)}$$

$$= -\frac{1}{\tan \alpha_1}.$$

That is,

$$m_2 = -\frac{1}{m_1} \quad \text{and} \quad m_1 = -\frac{1}{m_2},$$

which proves that if two non-vertical lines are perpendicular to each other, then the slope of each is the negative of the reciprocal of the slope of the other.

Moreover, if l_1 and l_2 are two lines having angles of inclination α_1 and α_2 and slopes m_1 and m_2, respectively, such that

$$m_2 = -\frac{1}{m_1},$$

then

$$\tan \alpha_2 = -\frac{1}{\tan \alpha_1}$$

$$= -\cot \alpha_1.$$

Therefore (by Appendix, 10) α_1 and α_2 differ by some odd multiple of 90°. But since $0° \leqslant \alpha_1 < 180°$ and $0° \leqslant \alpha_2 < 180°$, this implies that one of the angles α_1 and α_2 is just 90° greater than the other and l_1 and l_2 are perpendicular to each other.

This completes the proof of 2.5.2.

Example. Show that line through the points $(8, 7)$ and $(2, -3)$ is perpendicular to the line through $(1, 4)$ and $(6, 1)$.

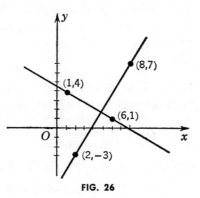

FIG. 26

Solution. Call either line, say the first, l_1 and denote the other by l_2 (Fig. 26). Then

$$m_1 = \frac{7 - (-3)}{8 - 2} = \frac{5}{3} \qquad \text{(by 2.4.1)}$$

and

$$m_2 = \frac{4 - 1}{1 - 6} = \frac{-3}{5} \qquad \text{(by 2.4.1)}.$$

Since $-3/5$ is the negative reciprocal of $5/3$, the lines are perpendicular (by 2.5.2).

EXERCISES

Make a sketch for each exercise.

1. Find the slope of a line parallel to the line joining $(-1, 4)$ and $(3, 7)$.

2. Find the slope of a line perpendicular to the line joining $(-3, -1)$ and $(8, -5)$.

3. Find the slopes of the six lines determined by the four points whose coordinates are $(-2, 3)$, $(2, -1)$, $(6, 2)$, and $(3, 7)$. Which of the lines are parallel or perpendicular to each other?

4. Using slopes, prove that the triangle whose vertices are $(-1, -3)$, $(2, -1)$, and $(-2, 5)$ is a right triangle.

5. By means of slopes, prove that the triangle whose vertices are $(3, -4)$, $(9, -4)$, and $(6, 2)$ is isosceles.

6. Using slopes, prove that the quadrilateral whose vertices are $(1, -4)$, $(8, -2)$, $(-4, 16)$, and $(-3, 2)$ is a trapezoid.

7. By means of slopes, prove that the quadrilateral whose vertices are $(4, 0)$, $(7, 5)$, $(-2, 3)$, and $(-5, -2)$ is a parallelogram.

8. Express by an equation the statement that the line joining the point $(-1, 3)$ to a point $P:(x, y)$ is perpendicular to the line connecting the origin to $(-1, 3)$. On what geometric figure must P lie?

2.6 ANGLE BETWEEN TWO LINES

In Section 2.3, we saw that the positive direction on any horizontal line is to the right and on all other lines it is upward. We then defined the angle between two lines to be the smallest non-negative angle formed by their positive directions (2.3.1).

We will now prove the

2.6.1 Theorem. *If l_1 and l_2 are two intersecting lines with slopes m_1 and m_2, respectively, and if θ is the angle between l_1 and l_2, then*

$$tan \; \theta = \frac{m_2 - m_1}{1 + m_1 m_2},$$

provided l_2 is the line with the greater angle of inclination, and $\theta \neq 90°$.

Proof. Denote the angles of inclination of l_1 and l_2 by α_1 and α_2, respectively (Fig. 27). Clearly

$$\theta = \alpha_2 - \alpha_1.$$

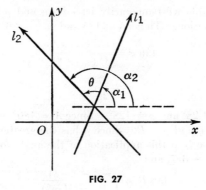

FIG. 27

Therefore

$$\tan \theta = \tan (\alpha_2 - \alpha_1)$$

$$= \frac{\tan \alpha_2 - \tan \alpha_1}{1 + \tan \alpha_1 \tan \alpha_2}$$

$$= \frac{m_2 - m_1}{1 + m_1 m_2}.$$

This formula fails only when $1 + m_1 m_2 = 0$; that is, when $m_1 = -1/m_2$. But in that case l_1 and l_2 are perpendicular to each other (2.5.2) and $\theta = 90°$.

Example.   Find, to the nearest degree, the interior angles of the triangle whose vertices are $A\!:\!(-4, 2)$, $B\!:\!(3, -4)$, and $C\!:\!(1, 3)$.

Solution.   Let p denote the line through A and B, q the line through B and C, and r the line through C and A (Fig. 28).

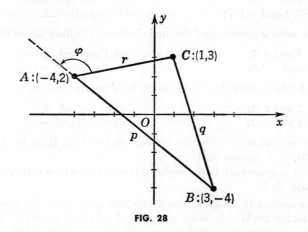

FIG. 28

By the slope formula (2.4.1), the slope of p is $-6/7$, the slope of q is $-7/2$, and the slope of r is $1/5$.

The angle between r and p (see 2.3.1) is φ, and $A = 180° - \varphi$.   In applying the angle formula (2.6.1) we temporarily let r be l_1 and p be l_2, since p has the greater angle of inclination. Thus $m_1 = 1/5$ and $m_2 = -6/7$, and

$$\tan \varphi = \frac{-\frac{6}{7} - \frac{1}{5}}{1 + \frac{1}{5}(-\frac{6}{7})}$$

$$= -\frac{37}{29}.$$

Therefore $\tan \varphi \doteq -1.28^*$ and $\varphi \doteq 128°$. Since $A = 180° - \varphi$, we have $A \doteq 52°$.

The angle between q and p is B. Since p has the greater angle of inclination, we let q be l_1 and p be l_2 in this application of the angle formula (2.6.1). Thus $m_1 = -7/2$ and $m_2 = -6/7$, and

$$\tan B = \frac{-\frac{6}{7} - (-\frac{7}{2})}{1 + (-\frac{7}{2})(-\frac{6}{7})}$$

$$= \frac{37}{56}.$$

That is, $\tan B \doteq .661$ and therefore $B \doteq 33°$.

Angle $C \doteq 180° - (52° + 33°) = 95°$.

EXERCISES

Make a sketch for each exercise.

1. Find the tangent of the angle between the lines whose slopes are

    (a) 1/2 and 2/3;   (b) −1/3 and 4/5;

    (c) 1.4 and −.6;   (d) −3/4 and −5/2.

2. Find the tangent of the angle between the lines whose slopes are

    (a) 4/9 and 1/3;   (b) −2/7 and 5/3;

    (c) −3/4 and −1/7;   (d) .8 and −2.2.

3. To the nearest degree, find the angle between the lines whose slopes are

    (a) 1/5 and 3/4;   (b) 1 and −1/3;

    (c) .7 and −1.5;   (d) −1/9 and −1/2.

4. Find, to the nearest degree, the angle between the lines whose slopes are

    (a) 5/2 and 2/3;   (b) −1.3 and .6;

    (c) 1/4 and −2;   (d) −3/5 and −2.

5. To the nearest degree, find the interior angles of the triangle whose vertices are (−2, −3), (−5, 4), and (6, 1).

6. Calculate approximately the angles of the triangle whose vertices are (3, −4), (−4, −2), and (5, 5).

7. The tangent of the angle between two lines is 2/3 and the slope of the line having the smaller angle of inclination is 1/4. Find the slope of the other line.

8. If the tangent of the angle between two lines is −4/9 and the slope of the line with the smaller angle of inclination is 3/7, find the slope of the other line.

* The symbol "$\doteq$" means "is approximately equal to."

9. Use 2.6.1 to prove that the triangle whose vertices are $(-2, 3)$, $(6, 9)$, and $(4, 11)$ is isosceles.

10. By means of 2.6.1 show that the triangle whose vertices are $(-2, -5)$, $(10, 0)$, and $(3, 7)$ is isosceles.

11. Denote the line through $(2, 1)$ and $(4, -3)$ by q. What is the slope of a line l such that the angle between q and l is 45°? (Two solutions.)

12. If t is the line through $(-1, -3)$ and $(7, 2)$, find the slope of the line l so that the angle between l and t is 60°. (One solution.)

13. What is the slope of the line which bisects the angle A of the triangle whose vertices are $A:(-1, 1)$, $B:(-9, 9)$, and $C:(7, 5)$?

14. Find the slope of the bisector of the angle A of the triangle whose vertices are $A:(3, -2)$, $B:(-3, 1)$, and $C:(9, 4)$.

2.7 MIDPOINT FORMULAS

In applying the analytic method to problems in elementary geometry, it is sometimes useful to have formulas for the coordinates of the midpoint of a line segment in terms of the coordinates of its endpoints.

To derive such formulas, we need the following property of directed lines.

2.7.1 Principle. *If P is the midpoint of any directed line segment, $\overline{AB}$, then $AP = PB$ (Fig. 29).*

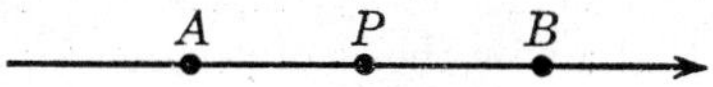

FIG. 29

We will now prove the

2.7.2 Theorem. *The coordinates of the midpoint, $P:(x, y)$, of the line segment whose endpoints are $P_1:(x_1, y_1)$ and $P_2:(x_2, y_2)$ are*

$$x = \frac{x_1 + x_2}{2}, \quad y = \frac{y_1 + y_2}{2}.$$

Proof. Through P_1 draw a line parallel to the x-axis and through P_2 a line parallel to the y-axis (Fig. 30). Call their intersection Q. The coordinates of Q are (x_2, y_1) (by 2.1.1 and 2.1.2).

From P draw a perpendicular to $\overline{P_1Q}$ intersecting it in R. The coordinates of R are (x, y_1) (by 2.1.1 and 2.1.2).

Since P is the midpoint of $\overline{P_1P_2}$ (given), R is the midpoint of $\overline{P_1Q}$ (Appendix, 5).

Therefore

$$P_1R = RQ \qquad \text{(by 2.7.1)}.$$

But $P_1R = x - x_1$ and $RQ = x_2 - x$ (by 2.1.3). Substituting above, we

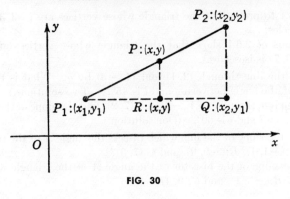

FIG. 30

have

$$x - x_1 = x_2 - x.$$

Solving this equation for x, we obtain

$$x = \frac{x_1 + x_2}{2}.$$

The proof of the formula for y is analogous and is left for the student.

Example. Prove analytically that the line segment joining the midpoints of the non-parallel sides of any trapezoid is equal to half the sum of the parallel sides.

Solution. Our proof must include every trapezoid, not merely some particular one. It is well to notice that a wise choice of position for the coordinate axes will often simplify the algebra.

Draw a general trapezoid. A good position for the coordinate axes is shown in Fig. 31. If we denote the length of the parallel sides by a and b, the altitude by h,

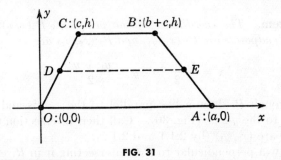

FIG. 31

and the x-coordinate of C by c, the vertices will be O:$(0, 0)$ A:$(a, 0)$, B:$(b + c, h)$ and C:(c, h). We wish to prove that the length of the line segment joining the midpoints, D and E, of $\overline{OC}$ and $\overline{AB}$ is equal to $\frac{1}{2}(a + b)$.

By the midpoint formulas (2.7.2), the coordinates of D are $(\frac{1}{2}c, \frac{1}{2}h)$ and the coordinates of E are $(\frac{1}{2}(a + b + c), \frac{1}{2}h)$. Since the y-coordinates of D and E are equal, $\overline{DE}$ is horizontal and (by 2.1.4)

$$|DE| = |\tfrac{1}{2}(a + b + c) - \tfrac{1}{2}c|$$
$$= \tfrac{1}{2}(a + b),$$

which completes the proof.

The symbols a, b, and h represent any positive numbers and c is any real number. Therefore we have proved the theorem for all trapezoids, not just a particular one. In Exercises 9, 11 and 12, below, general proofs are wanted.

EXERCISES

Make a sketch for each exercise.

1. Find the coordinates of the midpoint of the line segment joining

　(a) $(1, 2)$ and $(5, 4)$;　　　　　　(b) $(2, 1)$ and $(4, -3)$;

　(c) $(-3, 2)$ and $(-4, -3)$;　　　　(d) $(2, -5)$ and $(1, -7)$.

2. Find the coordinates of the midpoint of the line segment joining

　(a) $(3, 2)$ and $(7, 8)$;　　　　　　(b) $(-4, 5)$ and $(2, 7)$;

　(c) $(0, 0)$ and $(\sqrt{2}, 5)$;　　　　(d) $(-3, -1)$ and $(-6, 4)$.

3. If one end of a line segment is at $(-4, 3)$ and if its midpoint is $(1, -1)$, find the coordinates of its other endpoint.

4. One end of a diameter of a circle is $(-2, -7)$ and its center is $(3, 0)$. Find the coordinates of the other end of the diameter.

5. The center of a circle is at $(1, -3)$. Find the undirected distance from the center to the chord whose endpoints are $(-3, 0)$ and $(1, 2)$.

6. Find the slope of the line through the origin and the midpoint of the line segment joining $(-2, -3)$ and $(1, 8)$.

7. A triangle has vertices $(1, -3)$, $(6, 2)$, and $(8, -4)$. Prove that the line segment joining the midpoints of any two sides of the triangle is parallel to the third side. (Three cases.)

8. Prove that $(-1, 1)$, $(1, 4)$, $(3, -2)$, and $(1, -5)$ are the vertices of a parallelogram and that its diagonals bisect each other.

9. Prove analytically (that is, by the methods of analytic geometry) that the diagonals of any parallelogram bisect each other.

10. The vertices of a quadrilateral are $(5, -7)$, $(-1, 1)$, $(5, 3)$, and $(7, -1)$. Prove that the line segments joining the midpoints of the sides of this quadrilateral form a parallelogram.

11. Prove analytically that the lines joining in succession the midpoints of the sides of any quadrilateral form a parallelogram.

12. Prove analytically that two medians of any isosceles triangle are equal.

3

The Two Fundamental Problems

~~~~~~

Although analytic geometry has grown enormously since Descartes' time, the elementary part which constitutes a first course depends essentially on two fundamental problems.

3.1   THE FIRST FUNDAMENTAL PROBLEM: LOCUS OF AN EQUATION

The first fundamental problem of plane analytic geometry is, being given an equation in x and y, to draw its **locus**.

3.1.1 Definition.   *The **locus** of an equation is the totality of points whose coordinates satisfy the equation.*

Consider the equation

$$x - 2y - 6 = 0.$$

Not every point belongs to the locus of this equation. For example, the point P:(3, 2) is not on the locus because the coordinates $x = 3$, $y = 2$ fail to satisfy the equation, but the point Q:(4, −1) *is* on the locus because $x = 4$, $y = -1$ do satisfy the equation. While repeated trials of random pairs of numbers may disclose points of the locus, a more systematic procedure is available. Substituting zero for y in the equation and simplifying, we obtain $x = 6$. That is, the coordinates (6, 0) satisfy the equation and therefore P:(6, 0) belongs to the locus (by 3.1.1). When $y = 1$, $x = 8$ and P:(8, 1) belongs to the locus. These results are included in the accompanying **table of values**.

x	y
−6	−6
−4	−5
−2	−4
0	−3
2	−2
4	−1
6	0
8	1
10	2
12	3
14	4
16	5

Are the points of this locus scattered over the plane or do they form some familiar pattern? In other words, what does the locus look like?

Draw a pair of coordinate axes and plot the points whose coordinates are listed in the table of values. They appear to lie on a straight line (Fig.

28

32). Indeed, it will be proved in Chapter 4 that the locus of this equation, like that of every other first degree equation in x and y, is a straight line.

Next, consider the equation

$$x^2 + y^2 = 9.$$

What is its locus? When zero is substituted for x in this equation, $y = \pm 3$ and the points whose coordinates are $(0, 3)$ and $(0, -3)$ belong to the locus.

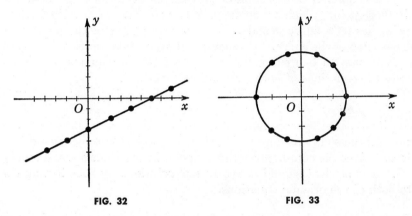

FIG. 32   FIG. 33

When $x = 1$, $y = \pm\sqrt{8}$ and therefore $(1, \sqrt{8})$ and $(1, -\sqrt{8})$ lie on the locus. These values are included in the accompanying table.

The points, when plotted, seem to lie on a circle (Fig. 33). Between any two points on the circle lie indefinitely many other points on the locus. In Chapter 5 we will prove that this locus is a circle whose center is at the origin and whose radius is 3.

There also exist equations that have no locus. For example, the equation $x^2 + y^2 = -1$ has no locus. The coordinates of any point in the plane are real numbers and the square of a real number is never

x	y
0	± 3
± 1	$\pm\sqrt{8}$
± 2	$\pm\sqrt{5}$
$\pm\sqrt{5}$	± 2
$\pm\sqrt{8}$	± 1
± 3	0

negative. Moreover, the sum of two non-negative numbers cannot be -1 and thus no point exists whose coordinates satisfy $x^2 + y^2 = -1$. In this course, however, we will be chiefly concerned with equations that have loci.

In plane analytic geometry the locus, if any, of an equation in x and y is often called a **curve**. In this sense a straight line is considered to be a curve.

3.1.2 Corollary. *A point lies on a curve if and only if the coordinates of the point satisfy the equation of the curve.*

3.2 INTERSECTIONS

Two curves lying in the same plane may or may not intersect. For example, a straight line can cut a circle in two points, be tangent to it, or miss it completely.

By the **points of intersection** of two curves we mean those points and only those points which are common to two curves. We saw in 3.1.2 that a point lies on a curve if and only if the coordinates of the point satisfy the equation of the curve. It follows that a point lies on two curves, that is, is common to two curves, if and only if the coordinates of the point satisfy the equations of both curves simultaneously.

Therefore, *to find the coordinates of the points of intersection of two curves, solve the equations of the two curves simultaneously.* The real pairs of solutions, if any, are the coordinates of the points common to both curves. Of course all the solutions may be imaginary in which case the curves fail to intersect since the coordinates of every point in the plane are real numbers (1.3). The student should check all real solutions by substituting them into both of the original equations.

Example. Find the coordinates of the points of intersection of the line $x - 2y - 6 = 0$ and the circle $x^2 + y^2 = 9$ (Figs. 32 and 33).

Solution. Rewriting the equation of the line as $x = 2y + 6$ and substituting in the equation of the circle, we obtain $(2y + 6)^2 + y^2 = 9$ or $5y^2 + 24y + 27 = 0$. The left member of this equation can be factored, giving $(y + 3)(5y + 9) = 0$, or $y = -3$ and $y = -9/5$. Substituting each of these values of y in $x = 2y + 6$ above, we obtain $x = 0$ and $x = 12/5$, respectively. Thus the coordinates of the points of intersection of the line and the circle are $(0, -3)$ and $(12/5, -9/5)$.

EXERCISES

Make a table of values for each of the following equations, plot the corresponding points and draw a smooth curve through them. If no pair of real coordinates satisfy the equation, state that the equation has no locus.

1. $x - 3y - 2 = 0$.
2. $x + 2y - 4 = 0$.
3. $3x - 5y + 2 = 0$.
4. $2x + y + 4 = 0$.
5. $x = 3$.
6. $y = -6$.
7. $x = 0$.
8. $y = 0$.
9. $x^2 + y^2 = 25$.
10. $x^2 + y^2 = -25$.
11. $y^2 = 4x$.
12. $x^2 + 2y = 0$.
13. $4x^2 + 9y^2 - 36 = 0$.
14. $25x^2 + 9y^2 - 175 = 0$.

15. Find the coordinates of the point of intersection of the lines whose equations are given in Exercises 1 and 3.

16. Find the point of intersection of the lines in Exercises 2 and 4.

17. Find the coordinates of the points of intersection of the line in Exercise 5 with the circle in Exercise 9.

18. Find the points of intersection of the curves in Exercises 11 and 12.

3.3   FACTORABLE EQUATIONS

When an equation is written with *all* of its non-zero terms in the left member, it sometimes happens that the left member can be factored.   In such event the equation is said to be **factorable.**   For example, the equation

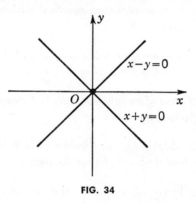

FIG. 34

$x^2 - y^2 = 0$ can be written $(x - y)(x + y) = 0$ and is therefore factorable.

It is an axiom of algebra that the product of two factors is equal to zero if and only if at least one of its factors is zero.   It follows that the coordinates of a point satisfy $x^2 - y^2 = 0$ if and only if they satisfy $x - y = 0$ or $x + y = 0$ or both.   Therefore the entire locus of $x^2 - y^2 = 0$ consists of the loci of $x - y = 0$ and $x + y = 0$, a pair of lines through the origin (Fig. 34).

3.3.1 Theorem.   *The locus of a factorable equation consists of the loci of the equations formed by setting the separate factors equal to zero.*

When an equation is factorable and its locus consists of two or more parts, the locus is said to be **degenerate.**

EXERCISES

Sketch the loci of the following factorable equations:

1. $3x^2 - xy = 0$.

2. $xy - y^2 = 0$.

3. $2x^2 + xy - y^2 = 0$.

4. $3x^2 - 5xy - 2y^2 = 0$.

5. $x^3 + xy^2 - x = 0$.

6. $xy^2 - y^3 - 9x^2 + 9xy = 0$.

3.4 OPERATIONS ON AN EQUATION

We have seen that the locus of an equation consists of those points and only those points whose coordinates satisfy the equation (3.1.1). Therefore, *a locus is unchanged by any operation on its equation which leaves the totality of its solutions unaltered.*

It was shown in algebra that the same expression, variable or constant, may be added to, or subtracted from, both sides of an equation without affecting its solutions, and that both members of an equation may be multiplied or divided by the same non-zero *constant* without changing its solutions. Thus we have the

3.4.1 Theorem. *The same expression may be added to, or subtracted from, both sides of an equation without affecting its locus.*

3.4.2 Corollary. *Terms of an equation may be transposed from one member to the other without affecting the locus.*

3.4.3 Theorem. *Multiplication or division of both sides of an equation by the same non-zero constant does not change the locus.*

For example, the locus of each of the following three equations, $x = 3y - 1$, $x - 3y + 1 = 0$, and $10x - 30y + 10 = 0$, is the same straight line.* It goes through the point $(-1, 0)$ and its slope is $\frac{1}{3}$.

However, we also learned in algebra that multiplication of both sides of an equation by an expression containing a variable sometimes introduces extraneous solutions. For example, if we multiply both members of the equation

$$\frac{y}{x - 1} = 7$$

by $x - 1$ we obtain $y = 7x - 7$ whose locus is a straight line which crosses the axes at $(1, 0)$ and $(0, -7)$ (Fig. 35). But $(1, 0)$ cannot be a point on the locus of the original equation because substitution of 1 for x in the original equation makes the denominator of the left member zero, and division by zero is impossible. The locus of the original equation consists of all points on the line except $(1, 0)$.

Closely related to this is the useful process of squaring both members of an equation to remove a radical. None of the original locus is lost but sometimes new loci are introduced. For example, the locus of $x = y$ is a straight line through the origin whose angle of inclination is 45°. If we square both sides, the equation becomes $x^2 = y^2$. Transposing the right

---

* In this sense a locus has many equivalent equations. But for simplicity we will say "the equation of a locus."

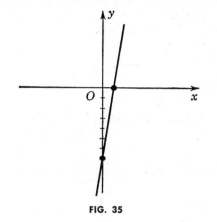

FIG. 35

member to the left side we obtain $x^2 - y^2 = 0$. The new left member is the difference of two squares and can be factored. The equation becomes $(x - y)(x + y) = 0$, the locus of which consists of the original locus of $x - y = 0$ and the extraneous locus of $x + y = 0$, which is another line through the origin (Fig. 34).

The student should be on the lookout for extraneous loci whenever he has occasion to square both members of an equation.

These results are summarized in the

3.4.4 Theorem. *Raising both members of an equation to the same power never loses any part of the original locus but sometimes introduces new loci.*

An equation in the form of a polynomial in x and y, equated to zero, will be said to be in **polynomial form.** All such equations in this course will have real coefficients.

Now recall that the degree of any particular term of a polynomial in x and y is the sum of the exponents of x and of y appearing in that term. Thus, the terms $2x^2$ and $7xy$ are each of degree 2 while $3x^2y^3$ is of degree 5.

3.4.5 Definition. *The **degree** of an algebraic equation is the highest of the degrees of the individual terms, after the equation has been reduced to polynomial form.*

For example, the degree of $2x^2 - 3xy^4 + x^7y^2 = 0$ is 9. The degree of $y = 1/x$ is 2 since in polynomial form this equation becomes $xy = 1$.

EXERCISES

In Exercises 1–7 compare the loci of each pair of equations.
1. $x - y = 0$ and $10x - 10y = 0$.
2. $2x - y + 2 = 0$ and $4x - 2y + 4 = 0$.

3. $y/x = 1$ and $y = x$.

4. $2x/(y - 2) = 3$ and $2x = 3y - 6$.

5. $y = 2x$ and $y^2 = 4x^2$.

6. $y = \sqrt{4 - x^2}$ and $y^2 = 4 - x^2$.

7. $y = 2\sqrt{x}$ and $y^2 = 4x$.

8. $x = \sqrt{2y}$ and $x^2 = 2y$.

Determine the degree of each of the following equations:

9. $x^2 + y^2 - 36 = 0$.

10. $xy^3 - 3x^5y^2 - 29 = 0$.

11. $y = 1/2x^3$.

12. $x - 3y^2 = 1/x$.

13. $(3x^2 - 2y)/xy = 14x^3y - 1$.

14. $y = x^{\frac{1}{3}}$.

3.5 INTERCEPTS

The easiest points to locate when sketching a curve are usually its points of intersection, if any, with the coordinate axes.

All points on the x-axis have zero for their y-coordinate, and conversely. Therefore, *to find the **x-intercepts** of a curve*, that is, the x-coordinates of the points of intersection of the curve with the x-axis, *substitute $y = 0$ in the equation of the curve and find the corresponding values of x.*

Similarly, *to find the **y-intercepts** of a curve, put $x = 0$ in the equation of the curve and find the corresponding values of y.*

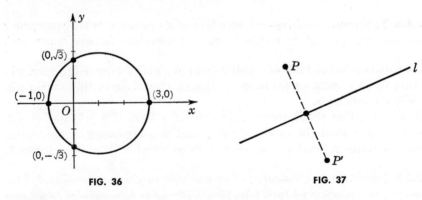

FIG. 36   FIG. 37

Example 1.   Find the intercepts of the curve whose equation is

$$x^2 + y^2 - 2x - 3 = 0.$$

Solution.   Putting $y = 0$ in the equation we have

$$x^2 - 2x - 3 = 0 \quad \text{or} \quad (x - 3)(x + 1) = 0,$$

and the x-intercepts are 3 and -1.   Putting $x = 0$ in the given equation, we have $y^2 - 3 = 0$, and the y-intercepts are $\sqrt{3}$ and $-\sqrt{3}$ (Fig. 36).

If an equation in polynomial form contains no constant term, every term will contain either x or y or both.   Thus $(0, 0)$ will satisfy the equation.

In other words, the locus goes through the origin.   Moreover, this argument can be reversed.   Therefore, we have the

3.5.1 Theorem.   *The locus of an equation in polynomial form goes through the origin if and only if its equation contains no constant term.*

For example, the locus of $x^2 + y^2 - 2x + 3y = 0$ is a circle which goes through the origin, while the locus of $x - 2y + 15 = 0$ is a straight line which does not.

3.6   SYMMETRY

Very often considerable labor can be saved in curve sketching by first testing the equation for certain **symmetries.**

3.6.1 Definition.   *Two points, P and P', are said to form a* **symmetric pair** *with respect to a line l if the line segment, $\overline{PP'}$, is bisected perpendicularly by l (Fig. 37).   Each of the points, P and P', is the* **symmetric partner** *of the other with respect to l.   A point on l is its own symmetric partner.*

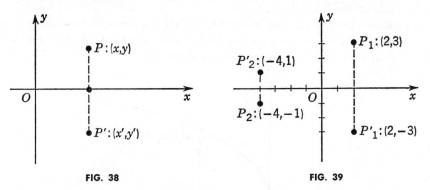

FIG. 38   FIG. 39

Now consider any point $P:(x, y)$ not on the x-axis (Fig. 38).   Its symmetric partner with respect to the x-axis is clearly $P':(x, -y)$, for $\overline{PP'}$ is perpendicular to the x-axis (by 2.1.2) and is bisected by the x-axis.

3.6.2 Corollary.   *Two points, P and P', form a symmetric pair with respect to the x-axis if and only if their x-coordinates are equal and the y-coordinate of one is the negative of the y-coordinate of the other.*

For example, the points $P_1:(2, 3)$ and $P_1':(2, -3)$ are symmetric with respect to the x-axis, as are $P_2:(-4, -1)$ and $P_2':(-4, 1)$ (Fig. 39).
Similar considerations with respect to the y-axis give us the

3.6.3 Corollary.   *Two points, P and P', are symmetric with respect to the y-axis if and only if their y-coordinates are equal and the x-coordinate of one is the negative of the x-coordinate of the other (Fig. 40).*

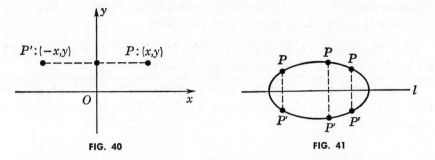

FIG. 40   FIG. 41

The concept of symmetry is extended to curves by the

3.6.4 Definition.   *A curve is **symmetric** with respect to a line if the symmetric partner (with respect to the line) of every point on the curve also lies on the curve* (Fig. 41).

Notice that if we fold the paper along a line of symmetry, the part of the curve on one side of the line will exactly coincide with the part on the other side of the line.

It follows from 3.6.2 and 3.6.4 that a curve is symmetric with respect to the x-axis if, whenever a pair of coordinates (x, y) satisfy the equation, $(x, -y)$ also satisfy the equation, and conversely.

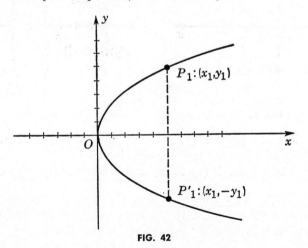

FIG. 42

For example (Fig. 42), let $P_1:(x_1, y_1)$ be any point on the locus of

(1) $y^2 - 4x = 0.$

That is, let

(2) $y_1^2 - 4x_1 = 0$ (by 3.1.2).

Then P_1':$(x_1, -y_1)$, the symmetric partner of P_1 with respect to the x-axis, is also on the locus because substitution of $(x_1, -y_1)$ in the left member of (1) gives $(-y_1)^2 - 4x_1$ which reduces to $y_1{}^2 - 4x_1$, and this is equal to zero by (2). Therefore the curve is symmetric with respect to the x-axis (by 3.6.4).

An equation is said to remain **essentially unchanged** as long as its locus is not altered. Thus we can change the sign of *every* term in an equation yet leave the equation essentially unchanged, since this is equivalent to multiplying through by -1 which does not affect the locus (by 3.4.3).

3.6.5 Corollary. *A curve is symmetric with respect to the x-axis if and only if substitution of $-y$ for y throughout the equation leaves the equation essentially unchanged.*

3.6.6 Corollary. *The locus of an equation in polynomial form is symmetric with respect to the x-axis if the equation contains no odd power of y.*

Similarly, from 3.6.3 and 3.6.4 we have the

3.6.7 Corollary. *A curve is symmetric with respect to the y-axis if and only if substitution of $-x$ for x throughout the equation leaves the equation essentially unchanged.*

3.6.8 Corollary. *The locus of an equation in polynomial form is symmetric with respect to the y-axis if the equation contains no odd power of x.*

Example. Sketch the curve whose equation is $x^2 - y^2 + 1 = 0$.

Solution. This equation is in polynomial form. Since it contains a constant term, its locus does not go through the origin (by 3.5.1).

Substituting zero for y in the equation we get $x = \pm\sqrt{-1}$, which are imaginary. Therefore the curve does not intersect the x-axis.

Substitution of zero for x in the given equation yields $y = \pm 1$. Therefore the curve intersects the y-axis in the points $(0, 1)$ and $(0, -1)$.

Since the equation contains no odd power of either x or y, the curve is symmetric with respect to both of the coordinate axes (by 3.6.6 and 3.6.8).

It is interesting to notice that the curve does not exist in the horizontal band where $-1 < y < 1$. For if we solve the equation for x in terms of y we get $x = \pm\sqrt{y^2 - 1}$; any value of y for which $|y| < 1$ makes $y^2 - 1$ negative and $\sqrt{y^2 - 1}$ imaginary. Thus no real value of x corresponds to any value of y between -1 and 1, and the curve has no points in the horizontal band between the lines $y = -1$ and $y = 1$.

With all this information at our disposal, we need only plot a few points, say, $(1, \sqrt{2})$ and $(2, \sqrt{5})$. By symmetry it follows that the points $(1, -\sqrt{2})$, $(-1, \sqrt{2})$, $(-1, -\sqrt{2})$, $(2, -\sqrt{5})$, $(-2, \sqrt{5})$, and $(-2, -\sqrt{5})$ are also on the curve (Fig. 43).

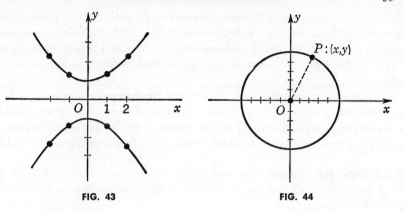

FIG. 43   FIG. 44

EXERCISES

Test for symmetry with respect to the coordinate axes and find the intercepts. Then, using as few other points as possible, sketch the curve.

1. $x^2 + y^2 - 64 = 0$.   2. $x^2 - 8y = 0$.

3. $x^2 + y^2 + 4x - 12 = 0$.   4. $2x + 7y = 0$.

5. $x^2 - y^2 = 4$.   6. $4x^2 - 9y^2 - 36 = 0$.

7. $y = 1/x$.   8. $25x^2 + 4y^2 - 100 = 0$.

9. $2x - y^2 = 0$.   10. $9x^2 + 16y^2 - 72x = 0$.

11. $y^2 = x^3$.   12. $y = x^3$.

13. $x^4 + y^4 = 81$.   14. $y = 1/x^2$.

15. $y = x^2 - 5x + 4$.   16. $x^2 - 3y^2 = 0$.

17. $x^3 + xy^2 - 16x = 0$.   18. $y^2 = x^3 - x$.

3.7   THE SECOND FUNDAMENTAL PROBLEM: EQUATION OF A LOCUS

The second fundamental problem in plane analytic geometry is to find the equation of a locus from its geometric description. We seek an equation in x and y which is satisfied by the coordinates of all points on the locus and by no others.

Example 1. Find the equation of the locus of points whose undirected distance from the origin is 5.

Solution. The locus is a circle, but for our present purpose it is not important to be able to recognize the locus from its given description. After drawing a pair of coordinate axes, select a point in general position whose undirected distance from the origin is 5 (Fig. 44). Label this point $P:(x, y)$. Be careful not to choose P in a special position, such as where the locus cuts an axis, because of the danger of assuming special properties for P not enjoyed by all points on the locus.

P is on the locus if and only if the undirected distance between the origin and

P is 5. That is, if and only if

$$|OP| = 5.$$

Translate this geometric equation into algebraic language by means of one of the basic tools developed in Chapter 2. In this instance we clearly need the formula for the undirected distance between two points (2.2.1). We obtain

$$\sqrt{x^2 + y^2} = 5.$$

Finally, simplify this equation by squaring both members and transposing the constant term. The desired equation of the locus is

$$x^2 + y^2 - 25 = 0.$$

Example 2.   Find the equation of the locus of points whose undirected distances from the two fixed points, $A:(1, 4)$ and $B:(5, 2)$, are equal.

Solution.   Draw the coordinate axes and plot $A:(1, 4)$ and $B:(5, 2)$. The locus is a straight line (Fig. 45). In fact, it is the perpendicular bisector of $\overline{AB}$, as we learned in high school. Select a point in general position, equidistant from A and B, and label it $P:(x, y)$.

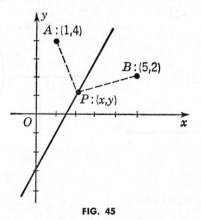

FIG. 45

P is on the locus if and only if the undirected distance between A and P is equal to the undirected distance between B and P; that is, if and only if

$$|AP| = |BP|.$$

Using the formula for the undirected distance between two points (2.2.1), we rewrite this geometric equation in algebraic language, obtaining

$$\sqrt{(x - 1)^2 + (y - 4)^2} = \sqrt{(x - 5)^2 + (y - 2)^2}.$$

Squaring both members and simplifying, we find the desired equation of the locus to be

$$2x - y - 3 = 0.$$

Despite minor variations from problem to problem, a procedure for finding the equation of a locus when its geometric description is known can be summarized as follows.

3.7.1 Procedure for finding the equation of a locus.

(1) *Draw a pair of coordinate axes and mark a point in non-special position which fulfills the given geometric conditions. Label it $P:(x, y)$.*

(2) *From the verbal description of the locus write a geometric equation involving P which is true for all points on the locus and for no points off the locus.*

(3) *Use one or more of the basic tools developed in Chapter 2 to transform the geometric equation found in step (2) into an equation in x and y, and simplify. The resulting equation is the desired equation of the locus.*

Example 3. Find the equation of the straight line through the point $A:(2, 3)$ with slope 4.

Solution. Draw the straight line through the given point $A:(2, 3)$ with slope 4 (see Example 2, Section 2.3). Mark a point $P:(x, y)$ in general position on the line and distinct from A (Fig. 46).

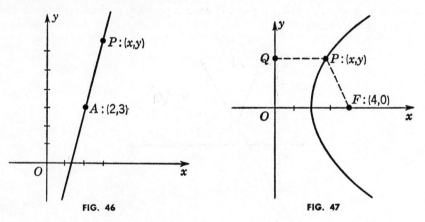

FIG. 46   FIG. 47

Then P is on the line if and only if

$$(\text{slope of } \overline{AP}) = 4.$$

Translating this geometric equation into algebraic language by means of the formula for the slope of a line segment (2.4.1), we obtain

$$\frac{y - 3}{x - 2} = 4.$$

Multiplying both members by $x - 2$ and simplifying, we get the desired equation of the locus,

$$4x - y - 5 = 0.$$

Example 4. Find the equation of the locus of points which are equidistant from the y-axis and from the point $F:(4, 0)$.

Solution. Draw the coordinate axes and mark the point $F:(4, 0)$. Choose a point $P:(x, y)$ in general position whose undirected distance from F is equal to its undirected distance from the y-axis. Drop a perpendicular from P to the y-axis and call its foot Q.

Then P is on the locus if and only if

$$|QP| = |FP|.$$

Translating this geometric equation into algebraic language by means of the basic tools 2.1.4 and 2.2.1, we have

$$|x - 0| = \sqrt{(x - 4)^2 + y^2}.$$

Simplifying, we find the desired equation of the locus to be

$$y^2 - 8x + 16 = 0.$$

In cases like this where we do not recognize the locus from its given verbal description, it is interesting to sketch the locus from its equation. It turns out to be a parabola (Fig. 47).

EXERCISES

In each of the following exercises, after obtaining the equation, sketch the locus from the equation.

1. Find the equation of the locus of points, P, whose undirected distance from the origin is 3.

2. Find the equation of the locus of points, P, whose undirected distance from the point $(2, 3)$ is 5. Name the locus.

3. Find the equation of the circle whose center is at $(0, 2)$ and whose radius is 2.

4. Find the equation of the circle whose center is the fixed point (a, b) and whose radius is r.

5. Find the equation of the locus of points, P, whose directed distance from the y-axis is 6. Name the locus.

6. Find the equation of the vertical line 2 units to the left of the y-axis.

7. Find the equation of the vertical line whose directed distance from the y-axis is k.

8. Find the equation of the locus of points, P, such that the line segment joining the origin to P always has slope 2. Name the locus.

9. Find the equation of the locus of points, P, such that the line segment joining $(1, 3)$ to P always has slope -1. Name the locus.

10. Find the equation of the line through the point $(-2, 1)$ and with slope 5.

11. Find the equation of the line through the fixed point (a, b) and with slope m.

12. Find the equation of the locus of points whose undirected distance from the point $(4, 0)$ is equal to their undirected distance from the y-axis. This locus is called a parabola.

13. Find the equation of the locus of points whose undirected distance from the point $(2, 0)$ is equal to their undirected distance from the line $x = -2$. The locus is a parabola.

14. Find the equation of the locus of points whose undirected distance from the point $(0, 3)$ is equal to their undirected distance from a horizontal line 3 units below the x-axis. The locus is a parabola.

15. Find the equation of the locus of points whose undirected distance from the point $(k, 0)$ is equal to their undirected distance from the line $x = -k$. The locus is a parabola.

16. Find the equation of the locus of points whose undirected distance from the point $(3, 0)$ is $1/2$ their distance from the y-axis. This locus is called an ellipse.

17. Find the equation of the locus of points whose undirected distance from the point $(0, 5)$ is $1/4$ their undirected distance from the x-axis. This locus is an ellipse.

18. Find the equation of the locus of points whose undirected distance from the point $(3, 0)$ is twice their undirected distance from the y-axis. This locus is called a hyperbola.

19. Find the equation of the locus of points whose undirected distance from the point $(0, 4)$ is three times their undirected distance from the x-axis. The locus is a hyperbola.

20. Given the two points, $A:(-2, 0)$ and $B:(0, -2)$, find the equation of the locus of points P such that the slope of $\overline{AP}$ is one half the slope of $\overline{BP}$.

21. The point A has coordinates $(4, 0)$. Find the equation of the locus of points P such that the slope of $\overline{OP}$ is always one half the slope of $\overline{AP}$.

22. The coordinates of a point A are $(1, -2)$. Find the equation of the locus of points P such that the product of the slopes of $\overline{OP}$ and $\overline{AP}$ is always equal to 1.

4

The Straight Line

~~~~~~

Having established a coordinate system in Chapter 1, developed the basic tools in Chapter 2, and discussed the two fundamental problems in Chapter 3, we are now ready to proceed with the study of plane analytic geometry.

It is natural to start with simple things and build to more complex situations. From the point of view of our first fundamental problem (3.1), we would expect to begin with the simplest equation in x and y, that of the first degree, and investigate its locus. From the point of view of the second fundamental problem (3.7), we would start with the simplest curve, the straight line, and determine its equation.

Happily, it turns out that every first degree equation in x and y has for its locus a straight line and every straight line has a first degree equation.

4.1 EQUATION OF A LINE

In seeking the equation of every straight line, two cases must be considered—vertical lines (which do not have slopes) and non-vertical lines.

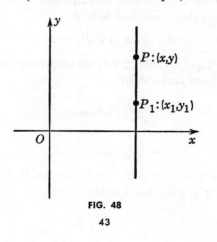

FIG. 48

43

4.1.1 Theorem. *The equation of the line through a point, P_1:(x_1, y_1), and parallel to the y-axis is $x = x_1$.*

Proof. Draw the line through the given point, P_1:(x_1, y_1), and parallel to the y-axis (Fig. 48). Choose any point on the line and label it P:(x, y). By 2.1.2, P is on the locus if and only if

$$x = x_1,$$

which completes the proof.

For example, the equation of the vertical line through the point $(-7, 4)$ is $x = -7$ or $x + 7 = 0$.

All non-vertical lines have slopes. A characteristic property of non-vertical lines is that if P_1:(x_1, y_1) is a definite point on the line and P:(x, y) is any other point on the line, then the slope of the line segment $\overline{P_1P}$ is the same for all positions of P on the line (Fig. 49).

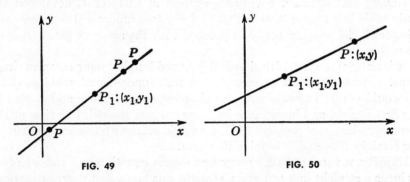

FIG. 49　　　　　　　　FIG. 50

4.1.2 Theorem. *The equation of the line through a point, P_1:(x_1, y_1), with slope m, is*

$$y - y_1 = m(x - x_1).$$

Proof. Through the given point P_1:(x_1, y_1) draw the line with slope m (Fig. 50). Indicate by P:(x, y) any other point.
Then $P.(x, y)$ is on the line if and only if

$$(\text{the slope of } \overline{P_1P}) = m.$$

By means of the slope formula (2.4.1) we transform this geometric equation into algebraic form and obtain

$$\frac{y - y_1}{x - x_1} = m,$$

or

$$y - y_1 = m(x - x_1).$$

That the locus of $y - y_1 = m(x - x_1)$ contains P_1 is easily verified by substituting x_1, y_1 for x, y in this equation.

The equation in 4.1.2 is called the **point-slope form** of the equation of a straight line.

Example 1. Find the equation of the line through the point whose coordinates are $(-1, -2)$, having slope 3 (Fig. 51).

Solution. Here $x_1 = -1, y_1 = -2$ and $m = 3$. Substituting in (4.1.2), we have $y - (-2) = 3\{x - (-1)\}$, or $3x - y + 1 = 0$.

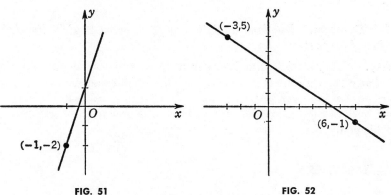

FIG. 51   FIG. 52

Example 2. Write the equation of the line through the two points whose coordinates are $(6, -1)$ and $(-3, 5)$.

Solution. Designating the given points by P_1 and P_2, respectively (Fig. 52), and using the slope formula (2.4.1), we find

$$m = \frac{5 - (-1)}{-3 - 6} = \frac{-2}{3}.$$

Substituting $m = -2/3$ and the coordinates of P_1:$(6, -1)$ in 4.1.2, we obtain

$$y - (-1) = -2/3 \, (x - 6).$$

Upon simplification, this equation becomes

$$2x + 3y - 9 = 0.$$

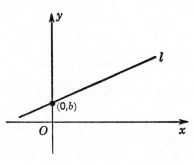

FIG. 53

Example 3. Find the equation of the line whose slope is m and whose y-intercept is b.

Solution. Since the y-intercept is b, one point on the line is $(0, b)$ (see 3.5). Let this be the point P_1 (Fig. 53). Using 4.1.2, we have $y - b = m(x - 0)$ or

$$y = mx + b.$$

This equation is sometimes called the **slope-intercept form** of the equation of a straight line.

4.1.3 Theorem. *In plane analytic geometry, every straight line has an equation of the first degree.*

Proof. Every straight line is either vertical or non-vertical. The equation of any vertical line is $x = x_1$ and the equation of any non-vertical line is $y - y_1 = m(x - x_1)$ (by 4.1.1 and 4.1.2). Since x_1, y_1 and m are constants, both of these equations are of the first degree in the variables x and y. This completes the proof.

EXERCISES

Make a sketch for each exercise.

1. Find the equation of the line through the point $(2, -5)$, having slope 4.

2. Find the equation of the line through the point $(-3, 1)$ with slope -2.

3. Find the equation of the vertical line whose x-intercept is -5.

4. Find the equation of the horizontal line whose y-intercept is 6.

5. Find the equation of the line with slope -3, whose y-intercept is 1.

6. Find the equation of the line whose slope is 2 and whose x-intercept is -11.

7. Find the equation of the line through the points $(-4, -3)$ and $(2, -1)$.

8. Find the equation of the line joining $(-3, 5)$ to the origin.

9. Find the equation of the line whose x-intercept is 2 and whose y-intercept is 7.

10. Find the equation of the line whose x-intercept is -5 and whose y-intercept is 1.

11. Find the equation of the line through the origin and perpendicular to the line joining $(-5, 1)$ and $(2, 4)$.

12. Find the equation of the line through $(-1, 4)$ and perpendicular to the line in Exercise 9.

13. Find the equation of the line through $(1, -4)$ and parallel to the line in Exercise 1.

14. Find the equation of the line through $(-2, 7)$ and parallel to the line in Exercise 10.

15. Given the points $A:(1, 3)$ and $B:(4, -1)$, find the equation of the line through the midpoint of $\overline{AB}$ and perpendicular to $\overline{AB}$.

16. Find the equation of the perpendicular bisector of the line segment joining the points $(-2, -1)$ and $(5, 5)$.

17. Find the coordinates of the point on the line $3x - y + 3 = 0$ which is equidistant from the points $A:(2, 4)$ and $B:(6, -2)$. (Hint: find the point of intersection of the given line and the perpendicular bisector of the line segment $\overline{AB}$.)

18. Find the coordinates of the center of the circle through the points $A:(0, 0)$, $B:(2, 4)$, and $C:(-4, 6)$. (Hint: find the intersection of the perpendicular bisectors of the line segments $\overline{AB}$ and $\overline{BC}$.)

4.2 LOCUS OF ANY FIRST DEGREE EQUATION

We have just seen that every straight line has an equation of the first degree. Is the locus of every first degree equation a straight line?

A first degree equation in the variables x and y may contain terms involving x alone, terms involving y alone, constant terms, and no others (by 3.4.5). The most general form of such an equation is

$$Ax + By + C = 0.$$

All first degree equations in x and y can be so expressed. For example, in $5x - 7y - 12 = 0$ we have $A = 5$, $B = -7$ and $C = -12$. In the equation $y = 2$ we have $A = 0$, $B = 1$ and $C = -2$. Throughout this course, A, B, and C are always real numbers.

4.2.1 Theorem. *In plane analytic geometry, the locus of every first degree equation in x and y is a straight line.*

Proof. Every first degree equation in x and y can be written in the form $Ax + By + C = 0$. Now B is either zero or not zero.

CASE I. $B = 0$. Then $A \neq 0$ since otherwise C would also be zero and there would be no equation. Dividing both members by A, we have $x + C/A = 0$, or

$$x = -\frac{C}{A}$$

which (by 4.1.1) is the equation of a vertical line through a fixed point whose x-coordinate is $-C/A$.

CASE II. $B \neq 0$. Solving $Ax + By + C = 0$ for y, we obtain

$$y = -\frac{A}{B}x - \frac{C}{B}$$

which (by Example 3, Section 4.1) is the equation of the line with slope $-A/B$ and y-intercept equal to $-C/B$.

$Ax + By + C = 0$ is called the **general form** of the equation of a straight line. All other forms can be obtained from it. It is because of 4.2.1 that first degree equations are often referred to as **linear equations.**

From Case II in the proof of 4.2.1 we have the

4.2.2 Corollary. *If $B \neq 0$, the straight line whose equation is*

$$Ax + By + C = 0$$

has the slope $-A/B$.

The student should acquire the habit of reading the slope of a line directly from its general equation by means of 4.2.2. For example, the slope of $2x - 7y + 15 = 0$ is $\frac{2}{7}$ and the slope of $x + 2y = 9$ is $-\frac{1}{2}$.

Theorems 2.5.1 and 2.5.2 can be combined with 4.2.2 to give the following two corollaries.

4.2.3 Corollary. *Two non-vertical lines whose equations are*

$$A_1x + B_1y + C_1 = 0 \quad and \quad A_2x + B_2y + C_2 = 0$$

are parallel (or coincident) if and only if

$$\frac{A_1}{B_1} = \frac{A_2}{B_2}.$$

4.2.4 Corollary. *Two non-vertical lines whose equations are*

$$A_1x + B_1y + C_1 = 0 \quad and \quad A_2x + B_2y + C_2 = 0$$

are perpendicular if and only if

$$\frac{A_1}{B_1} = \frac{-B_2}{A_2}.$$

For example, the lines whose equations are $2x + 3y - 1 = 0$ and $4x + 6y + 11 = 0$ are parallel to each other and the lines whose equations are $2x + 3y - 1 = 0$ and $12x - 8y + 7 = 0$ are perpendicular to each other. However, the equations $x - 5y + 2 = 0$ and $2x - 10y + 4 = 0$ represent the same line (by 3.4.3).

EXERCISES

By inspection, tell which of the equations in Exercises 1–14 of Section 3.2 represent straight lines. Then use Theorem 4.2.2 to determine their slopes.

4.3 AN IMPORTANT METHOD

A straight line is determined whenever the values of the coefficients, A, B, and C, in its general equation, $Ax + By + C = 0$, are known. Indeed, since division of both sides of the equation by the same non-zero coefficient does not affect the locus (by 3.4.3), only two ratios of the coefficients are essential. If, for instance, $C \neq 0$, the general equation can be rewritten

$$\frac{A}{C}x + \frac{B}{C}y + 1 = 0,$$

from which it is evident that the values of the two ratios, A/C and B/C, are sufficient to determine a unique line. For example, if $A/C = 2$ and $B/C = -\frac{1}{3}$, the above equation becomes $2x + (-\frac{1}{3})y + 1 = 0$, or $6x - y + 3 = 0$.

Two appropriate geometric conditions are sufficient to determine a line—for example, the requirement that it pass through two given points. An important method of analytic geometry uses given geometric conditions to determine the ratios of coefficients. It is explained in the following examples.

Although not always the shortest way to solve these first elementary problems, the power of the method is such as to make it nearly indispensable for later work.

Example 1. Find the equation of the line through the two points, $P_1:(6, -1)$ and $P_2:(-3, 5)$.

Solution (See Fig. 50). We could, of course, proceed as in Example 2 of 4.1. Instead, we will determine suitable values for the coefficients A, B, and C in the general equation of the straight line,

(1) $$Ax + By + C = 0.$$

Since the point P_1 lies on the line, its coordinates $(6, -1)$ satisfy the general equation of the line (by 3.1.2). That is,

(2) $$A(6) + B(-1) + C = 0.$$

Again, the point P_2 is on the line and therefore its coordinates $(-3, 5)$ satisfy the general equation of the line. Thus

(3) $$A(-3) + B(5) + C = 0.$$

Dividing both members of the equations (2) and (3) by one of the coefficients, say C, we have

$$\frac{6A}{C} - \frac{B}{C} + 1 = 0,$$

$$\frac{-3A}{C} + \frac{5B}{C} + 1 = 0.$$

Solving these two simultaneous equations for the two unknowns, A/C and B/C, we find

$$\frac{A}{C} = -\frac{2}{9} \quad \text{and} \quad \frac{B}{C} = -\frac{1}{3} = -\frac{3}{9},$$

or

$$A : B : C = -2 : -3 : 9.$$

We now substitute these values for A, B, and C in the general equation (1) and obtain

$$-2x - 3y + 9 = 0,$$

or

$$2x + 3y - 9 = 0.$$

The student should verify that the coordinates of the given points satisfy this equation.

Example 2. Using the general form of the equation of a line, find the equation of the line whose slope is $-2/3$ and which passes through the point $(4, 7)$ (Fig. 54).

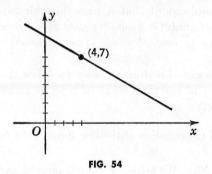

FIG. 54

Solution. By 4.2.2, the slope of the line is $-A/B$. Therefore

$$\frac{A}{B} = \frac{2}{3}$$

and the equation of the line is of the form

(1) $$2x + 3y + C = 0.$$

Since the given point lies on the line, its coordinates $(4, 7)$ must satisfy (1) (by 3.1.2). That is,

$$2(4) + 3(7) + C = 0,$$

or

$$C = -29.$$

Substituting this result in (1), we find the desired equation to be

$$2x + 3y - 29 = 0.$$

EXERCISES

Make a sketch for each exercise.

Using the given geometric conditions to determine values for A, B and C in $Ax + By + C = 0$, find the equations of the following lines:

1. Through the origin and the point $(4, 3)$.
2. Through $(0, 2)$ and $(-5, 0)$.
3. With x-intercept -4 and y-intercept 7.
4. With x-intercept 6 and y-intercept -1.
5. Through the point $(-1, -2)$ with slope $2/3$.

6. Through the origin with slope π.

7. Through the point $(2, -3)$ and parallel to the line $x - 5y + 2 = 0$.

8. Through the point $(-4, -6)$ and parallel to the line $2x + 3y + 6 = 0$.

9. Through the point $(2, -3)$ and perpendicular to the line $x - 5y + 2 = 0$.

10. Through the point $(7, 4)$ and perpendicular to the line $2x + 3y - 5 = 0$.

4.4 DIRECTED DISTANCE FROM A LINE TO A POINT

We are now in a position to derive another important basic tool, namely, a formula for the directed distance from a line to a point.

To accomplish this we will first find a formula for the *undirected* distance between a line and a point, and from that develop the desired formula for the *directed* distance.   By "the distance from a line to a point" we of course mean the shortest distance, that is, the perpendicular distance.

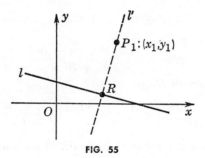

FIG. 55

Consider a point $P_1:(x_1, y_1)$ and a line l which is not parallel to either axis (Fig. 55).   Through P_1 draw a line l' perpendicular to l and denote their intersection by R.

The undirected distance $|RP_1|$ is found by substituting the coordinates of P_1 and of R in the undirected distance formula (2.2.1).   We know the coordinates of P_1, and we can find the coordinates of R, which is the point of intersection of the lines l and l', by solving the equations of l and l' simultaneously for x and y (3.2).

The general equation of l is

(1) $$Ax + By + C = 0,$$

in which we assume that B is positive.   There is no loss of generality in this assumption, since both sides of an equation may be multiplied by -1 without affecting the locus (3.4.3).

The slope of l is $-A/B$ (by 4.2.2) and therefore the slope of l' is B/A (by 2.5.2).

The equation of the line l', through the point $P_1:(x_1, y_1)$ with slope B/A, is

$$y - y_1 = \frac{B}{A}(x - x_1) \qquad \text{(by 4.1.2)},$$

or

$$(2) \qquad\qquad Bx - Ay - (Bx_1 - Ay_1) = 0.$$

Multiplying both members of the equation (1) by A, and both members of the equation (2) by B, and then adding the resulting equations member by member, we obtain

$$(A^2 + B^2)x + AC - B(Bx_1 - Ay_1) = 0,$$

from which

$$x = \frac{B^2x_1 - ABy_1 - AC}{A^2 + B^2}.$$

Similarly, if we multiply the equation (1) through by B and the equation (2) through by A, and then subtract the resulting equations member by member, we get

$$(A^2 + B^2)y + BC + A(Bx_1 - Ay_1) = 0,$$

or

$$y = -\frac{ABx_1 - A^2y_1 + BC}{A^2 + B^2}.$$

Thus the coordinates of R are

$$(3) \qquad \left(\frac{B^2x_1 - ABy_1 - AC}{A^2 + B^2}, \; -\frac{ABx_1 - A^2y_1 + BC}{A^2 + B^2}\right).$$

Substituting the coordinates of P_1 and of R in the square of the distance formula, we have

$$|RP_1|^2 = \left(x_1 - \frac{B^2x_1 - ABy_1 - AC}{A^2 + B^2}\right)^2 + \left(y_1 + \frac{ABx_1 - A^2y_1 + BC}{A^2 + B^2}\right)^2$$

$$= \left(\frac{A^2x_1 + B^2x_1 - B^2x_1 + ABy_1 + AC}{A^2 + B^2}\right)^2$$

$$+ \left(\frac{A^2y_1 + B^2y_1 + ABx_1 - A^2y_1 + BC}{A^2 + B^2}\right)^2$$

$$= \frac{A^2(Ax_1 + By_1 + C)^2 + B^2(Ax_1 + By_1 + C)^2}{(A^2 + B^2)^2}$$

$$= \frac{(A^2 + B^2)(Ax_1 + By_1 + C)^2}{(A^2 + B^2)^2}$$

$$= \frac{(Ax_1 + By_1 + C)^2}{A^2 + B^2}.$$

Therefore the undirected distance between the line l and the point $P_1:(x_1, y_1)$ is

$$(4) \qquad\qquad |RP_1| = \frac{|Ax_1 + By_1 + C|}{\sqrt{A^2 + B^2}}.$$

To find the *directed* distance RP_1, we need to know the positive direction on the line through R and P_1. We recall the definition given in Section 2.3: *In rectangular Cartesian coordinates the **positive direction** on lines parallel to the x-axis is to the right, and on all other lines the **positive direction** is upward.* Thus RP_1 is positive if P_1 is higher than R and negative if P_1 is lower than R.

Notice in Fig. 55 that P_1 is higher than R if and only if the y-coordinate of P_1 is greater than the y-coordinate of R. (This is really the analytic definition of what we mean by the word *higher*.)

Therefore the directed distance from R to P_1 is positive if and only if the y-coordinate of P_1 is greater than the y-coordinate of R. That is, RP_1 is positive if and only if

$$y_1 > -\frac{ABx_1 - A^2y_1 + BC}{A^2 + B^2}.$$

Multiplying both sides of this inequality by the positive quantity $A^2 + B^2$, and then transposing all terms to the left member, we have

$$B(Ax_1 + By_1 + C) > 0.$$

Dividing both members of this inequality by the positive constant B gives

$$Ax_1 + By_1 + C > 0.$$

Thus RP_1 is positive if and only if $Ax_1 + By_1 + C$ is positive. Moreover, we also know that RP_1 is zero if and only if P_1 is on l, that is, if and only if $Ax_1 + By_1 + C = 0$ (by 3.1.2). Therefore RP_1 is positive, zero, or negative according as $Ax_1 + By_1 + C$ is positive, zero, or negative. From this and from (4) it follows that the directed distance from l to P_1 is

(5) $$RP_1 = \frac{Ax_1 + By_1 + C}{\sqrt{A^2 + B^2}}.$$

We assumed above that l was oblique to the coordinate axes. If l is parallel to the x-axis (Fig. 56), drop a perpendicular from P_1 to l and call its foot R. Then the equation of l is $By + C = 0$, and the coordinates of R are $(x_1, -C/B)$ (by 2.1.1 and 2.1.2). Therefore

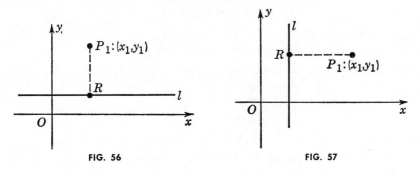

FIG. 56   FIG. 57

$$RP_1 = y_1 + \frac{C}{B} \qquad \text{(by 2.1.6)}$$

$$= \frac{By_1 + C}{B},$$

which is the same as (5) with $A = 0$. Therefore (5) is valid not only when l is oblique to the axes but also when l is horizontal.

If l is vertical (Fig. 57), $B = 0$ and the equation of l is $Ax + C = 0$, where A is assumed to be positive. Drop a perpendicular from P_1 to l and call its foot R. The coordinates of R are $(-C/A, y_1)$ (by 2.1.1 and 2.1.2). Therefore

$$RP_1 = x_1 + \frac{C}{A} \qquad \text{(by 2.1.3)}$$

$$= \frac{Ax_1 + C}{A},$$

which is the same as (5) when $B = 0$. Thus (5) is true for all positions of l, provided that either B is positive or else $B = 0$ and A is positive.

This completes the proof of the

4.4.1 Theorem. *Given a point P_1:(x_1, y_1) and a line l whose equation is $Ax + By + C = 0$, in which either B is positive or else $B = 0$ and A is positive. Then the directed distance from l to P_1 is*

$$\frac{Ax_1 + By_1 + C}{\sqrt{A^2 + B^2}}.$$

Example 1. Find the directed distance from the line $3x - 2y + 6 = 0$ to the point $(1, -4)$.

Solution. Since B, the coefficient of y in the given equation, is negative, we multiply both members by -1 and obtain

$$-3x + 2y - 6 = 0.$$

By 4.4.1, the directed distance from this line to the point $(1, -4)$ is

$$\frac{-3(1) + 2(-4) - 6}{\sqrt{13}} = \frac{-17}{\sqrt{13}} \doteq -4.7$$

Example 2. Find the undirected distance between the parallel lines whose equations are $x + 2y - 4 = 0$ and $x + 2y + 1 = 0$.

Solution. Designate the given lines by l_1 and l_2, respectively (Fig. 58). Select any convenient point on l_1, say $(4, 0)$ where it cuts the x-axis. Then (by 4.4.1) the directed distance from l_2 to the point $(4, 0)$ is

$$\frac{4 + 2(0) + 1}{\sqrt{5}} \doteq \sqrt{5}.$$

Therefore the undirected distance between the two lines is $\sqrt{5}$.

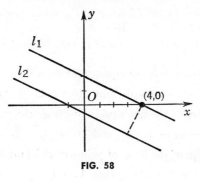

FIG. 58

EXERCISES

Make a sketch for each exercise.

1. Find the directed distance from the line $3x - 4y + 12 = 0$ to the point $(4, 1)$.

2. Find the directed distance from the line $5x + 2y + 10 = 0$ to the point $(-1, -2)$.

3. Find the radius of the circle with center at the origin and tangent to the line $4x - 3y + 30 = 0$.

4. A triangle has vertices $A:(1, 3)$, $B:(6, -2)$, and $C:(-2, 1)$. Find the length of the altitude from A.

5. Find the area of the triangle whose vertices are $(10, 2)$, $(13, 0)$, and $(1, -5)$.

6. Show that the area of the triangle whose vertices are $A:(x_1, y_1)$, $B:(x_2, y_2)$, and $C:(x_3, y_3)$, reading counterclockwise, is

$$\tfrac{1}{2}[x_1(y_2 - y_3) - y_1(x_2 - x_3) + (x_2y_3 - x_3y_2)].$$

7. By expanding the following determinant and comparing with Exercise 6, show that the area of the triangle whose vertices are $A:(x_1, y_1)$, $B:(x_2, y_2)$, and $C:(x_3, y_3)$, reading counterclockwise, is

$$A = \frac{1}{2}\begin{vmatrix} x_1 & y_1 & 1 \\ x_2 & y_2 & 1 \\ x_3 & y_3 & 1 \end{vmatrix}.$$

8. Find the undirected distance between the parallel lines $x + 2y - 2 = 0$ and $3x + 6y - 14 = 0$.

9. Find the undirected distance between the parallel lines $2x - 3y + 6 = 0$ and $4x - 6y - 5 = 0$.

10. Find the equation of the line which bisects the acute angles formed by the lines $8x + y - 5 = 0$ and $4x - 7y + 2 = 0$. (Hint: find the equation of the locus of points whose directed distances from the two given lines are equal.)

11. Find the equation of the line which bisects the obtuse angles formed by the lines in Exercise 10. (Hint: find the equation of the locus of points whose directed distance from one of the given lines is the negative of their directed distance from the other given line.)

12. Find the equation of the bisector of the acute angles formed by the lines $4x - 3y + 8 = 0$ and $5x + 12y - 15 = 0$.

13. Find the equation of the bisector of the obtuse angles formed by the lines in Exercise 12.

14. Find the equation of the line equidistant from the parallel lines

$$5x + 8y - 10 = 0 \quad \text{and} \quad 10x + 16y + 49 = 0.$$

15. Find the equation of the line equidistant from the parallel lines

$$2x - 3y - 2 = 0 \quad \text{and} \quad 6x - 9y - 26 = 0.$$

16. Find the equation of the locus of points equidistant from the line

$$3x + 4y + 12 = 0$$

and from the point $(1, 0)$.

17. Find the equation of the locus of points equidistant from the line

$$x + y - 2 = 0$$

and from the point $(0, -3)$.

18. Find the equation of the locus of points whose undirected distance from the origin is twice their undirected distance from the line $3x + 4y - 24 = 0$.

4.5   FAMILIES OF LINES

Consider the equation

(1) $$x - 2y + k = 0.$$

If $k = 0$, this equation becomes $x - 2y = 0$ which represents a straight line having slope $1/2$ and passing through the origin. If $k = 1$, the equation (1) is $x - 2y + 1 = 0$, the locus of which is a line with slope $1/2$ whose

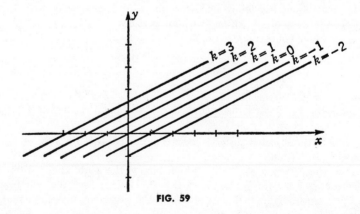

FIG. 59

x-intercept is -1. If $k = 2$, the equation (1) is $x - 2y + 2 = 0$, a line with slope $1/2$ whose x-intercept is -2. For each value of k, (1) represents a line with slope $1/2$. The totality of such lines is called the **family** or

system of lines with slope $1/2$. The arbitrary constant k is called the parameter of the family. Fig. 59 shows the locus of (1) for several values of the parameter.

Again, the equation $y - 2 = k(x - 3)$ (by 4.1.2) represents the family of lines through the point $(3, 2)$. Here the parameter k is the slope. Several lines of this family are shown in Fig. 60, each labeled with the corresponding value of the parameter.

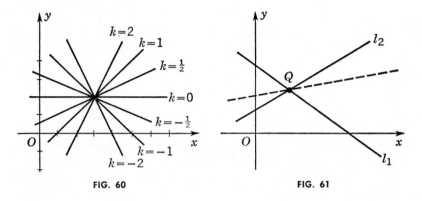

FIG. 60   FIG. 61

In analytic geometry we sometimes wish to write the equation of a line through the point of intersection of two given lines. But the equations of the two given lines may be such that the algebra involved in finding the coordinates of their common point is tedious. The following theorem enables us to write the equation of a line through the point of intersection of two given lines without ever finding the coordinates of that point. The method used in its proof has much wider application.

4.5.1 Theorem. *If $A_1x + B_1y + C_1 = 0$ and $A_2x + B_2y + C_2 = 0$ are two intersecting lines, then for each value of the parameter k, the equation*

$$(A_1x + B_1y + C_1) + k(A_2x + B_2y + C_2) = 0$$

represents a line through the point of intersection of the two given lines.

Proof. Indicate the given lines by l_1 and l_2, respectively, and their point of intersection by Q (Fig. 61).

The equation

(1) $$(A_1x + B_1y + C_1) + k(A_2x + B_2y + C_2) = 0$$

can be rewritten

(2) $$(A_1 + kA_2)x + (B_1 + kB_2)y + (C_1 + kC_2) = 0.$$

The coefficients of x and y in (2) cannot both be zero for any particular value of k. For if they were, we would have

$$A_1 + kA_2 = 0 \quad \text{and} \quad B_1 + kB_2 = 0,$$

or

$$k = -\frac{A_1}{A_2} \quad \text{and} \quad k = -\frac{B_1}{B_2}.$$

That is,

$$\frac{A_1}{A_2} = \frac{B_1}{B_2}$$

and l_1 would be parallel to l_2 (by 4.2.3). But we were given that l_1 and l_2 are intersecting lines. Therefore the coefficients of x and y in (2) cannot both be zero for any value of k.

In other words, the equation (2) is of the first degree in the variables x and y for all values of k. Hence the equation (2), and therefore the equation (1), represents a straight line for each value of the parameter k (by 4.2.1).

Since Q is the point of intersection of l_1 and l_2, Q is on both of the lines l_1 and l_2. Therefore the coordinates of Q satisfy the equations of l_1 and l_2 (by 3.1.2). That is, the coordinates of Q make both $A_1x + B_1y + C_1$ and $A_2x + B_2y + C_2$ zero. But this means that if we substitute the coordinates of Q for x and y in (1) we obtain

$$(0) + k(0) = 0,$$

which is true for all values of k. In other words, the coordinates of Q satisfy the equation (1) for each value of k. Therefore for each value of the parameter k, the line represented by the equation (1) goes through the point Q.

It is also easy to prove that every line through Q, with one exception, is included in the lines given by the equation (1). The method of proof is similar to that used in solving Example 1, below. Thus (1) *is the equation of the family of lines through the point of intersection of the two given lines, l_1 and l_2.*

The one exception to the above statement is the line l_2 itself. For no value of k does the equation (1) become $A_2x + B_2y + C_2 = 0$.

Example 1. Find the equation of the line through the point of intersection of the two lines, $3x - 7y + 21 = 0$ and $2x + y - 1 = 0$, and passing through the point $(2, 1)$.

Solution. Let Q denote the point of intersection of the two given lines (Fig. 62). The equation of the family of lines through Q is

(1) $$(3x - 7y + 21) + k(2x + y - 1) = 0.$$

For each value of k, the equation (1) represents a line through Q. We seek the particular value of k which makes the corresponding line of the family (1) go through the point $(2, 1)$.

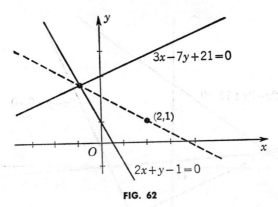

$3x - 7y + 21 = 0$

(2,1)

$2x + y - 1 = 0$

FIG. 62

The point $(2, 1)$ is on the line if and only if the coordinates $(2, 1)$ satisfy the equation of the line. Substitution of the coordinates $(2, 1)$ for x and y in (1) gives

$$[3(2) - 7(1) + 21] + k[2(2) + (1) - 1] = 0,$$

or

$$k = -5.$$

If we substitute -5 for k in (1), we obtain

$$(3x - 7y + 21) - 5(2x + y - 1) = 0,$$

or

$$7x + 12y - 26 = 0,$$

which is the desired equation.

Example 2. Find the equation of the line through the point of intersection of the two lines, $2x - 3y + 11 = 0$ and $x + 7y - 1 = 0$, and perpendicular to a third line, $2x - y - 6 = 0$.

Solution. The family of lines through the point of intersection of the two given lines (Fig. 63) is

(1) $(2x - 3y + 11) + k(x + 7y - 1) = 0.$

If we collect terms, this becomes

$$(2 + k) x + (-3 + 7k) y + (11 - k) = 0.$$

For each value of k, the slope of this line is $-(2 + k)/(-3 + 7k)$ (by 4.2.2). The slope of the third given line is 2. These two lines will be perpendicular if the slope of one is the negative of the reciprocal of the slope of the other (by 4.2.4). That is,

$$\frac{-(2 + k)}{-3 + 7k} = -\frac{1}{2},$$

or $k = 7/5$.

Substituting this value of k in (1), we find the equation of the line of the family (1) which is perpendicular to the third given line to be

$$(2x - 3y + 11) + \frac{7}{5} (x + 7y - 1) = 0,$$

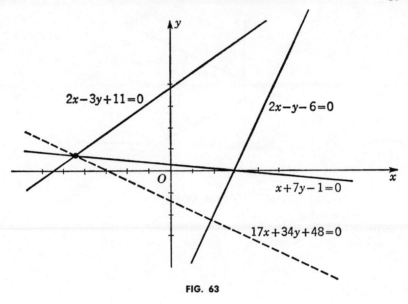

FIG. 63

or

$$17x + 34y + 48 = 0.$$

EXERCISES

Draw three members of each of the families of lines in Exercises 1–8 and label each line with the corresponding value of the parameter. Tell what is common to all lines in each family.

1. $y = 2x + k$.   **2.** $x = k$.

3. $(y - 2) = k(x + 5)$.   **4.** $kx + 4y - 7 = 0$.

5. $x + ky + 2 = 0$.   **6.** $3x - 2y + k = 0$.

7. $mx - y - 4\sqrt{m^2 + 1} = 0$. (Hint: What is the directed distance from this line to the origin?)

8. $mx - y + 2\sqrt{m^2 + 1} = 0$.

9. Write the equation of the family of lines parallel to the line

$$2x - 6y + 10 = 0.$$

Draw several lines of the family and label each with the corresponding value of the parameter.

10. For what value of your parameter in Exercise 9 does the corresponding line go through the point $(2, -3)$? Use that value of the parameter to find the equation of that particular line.

11. Write the equation of the family of lines perpendicular to the line

$$3x + y - 6 = 0.$$

Draw several members and label each with the corresponding value of the parameter.

12. For what value of the parameter in Exercise 11 does the corresponding line go through the origin?   Write the equation of that line.

13. Find the equation of the line which passes through the point $(2, -1)$ and also through the point of intersection of the lines

$$3x + 7y - 5 = 0 \text{ and } 19x + 11y - 3 = 0.$$

Make a sketch.

14. Find the equation of the line through the point of intersection of the two lines, $9x + 13y - 41 = 0$ and $5x - 8y - 10 = 0$, and passing through the point $(-1, -1)$.   Make a sketch.

15. Find the equation of the line perpendicular to the line $12x + 5y - 60 = 0$ and passing through the point of intersection of the lines $5x - 6y + 11 = 0$ and $4x + 7y - 2 = 0$.   Make a sketch.

16. Find the equation of the line through the point of intersection of the two lines, $3x - 2y - 9 = 0$ and $2x + y - 2 = 0$, and perpendicular to the line $x - y + 4 = 0$.   Make a sketch.

17. Find the equation of the line whose slope is $2/3$ and which passes through the point of intersection of the lines $x + 4y + 3 = 0$ and $5x - y - 7 = 0$.   Make a sketch.

18. Find the equation of the line whose slope is $-1/2$ and which passes through the point of intersection of the lines $4x - 5y - 10 = 0$ and $4x - 7y + 14 = 0$. Make a sketch.

19. Find the equation of the line whose y-intercept is -4 and which passes through the point of intersection of the lines

$$2x - 7y + 4 = 0 \quad \text{and} \quad 7x + 5y - 13 = 0.$$

Make a sketch.

20. Find the equation of the line whose x-intercept is 2 and which passes through the point of intersection of the lines $4x - 3y + 6 = 0$ and $10x - 28y - 35 = 0$. Make a sketch.

5

The Circle

~~~~~~

After the straight line, the circle is in many respects the simplest curve. Indeed, under primitive conditions it is easier to draw a circle than a straight line, since a forked stick would do for a compass but a straightedge is more difficult to come by.

5.1 EQUATION OF A CIRCLE

5.1.1 Definition. *A circle is the locus of points whose undirected distances from a fixed point are equal.*

The fixed point is called the **center** of the circle and the constant undirected distance is the **radius**.

Designate the center by C with coordinates (a, b), and the radius by r.

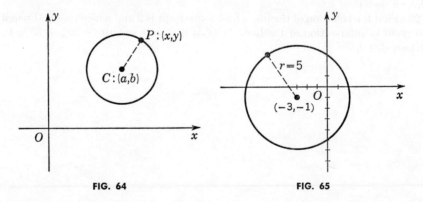

FIG. 64 FIG. 65

Draw the circle (Fig. 64) and indicate a general point on it by $P:(x, y)$. P lies on the locus if and only if

$$|CP| = r \qquad \text{(by 5.1.1).}$$

By means of the formula for the undirected distance between two points

(2.2.1), this becomes

$$\sqrt{(x - a)^2 + (y - b)^2} = r.$$

Squaring both members, we have

$$(x - a)^2 + (y - b)^2 = r^2,$$

which proves the

5.1.2 Theorem. *The equation of the circle with center at* (a, b)*, and radius equal to* r *is*

$$(x - a)^2 + (y - b)^2 = r^2.$$

This is called the **center-radius** form of the equation of the circle because it exhibits the coordinates of the center and the value of the radius.

When the center is at the origin, $a = b = 0$ in 5.1.2, and we have the

5.1.3 Corollary. *The equation of the circle whose center is at the origin and whose radius is equal to* r *is*

$$x^2 + y^2 = r^2.$$

Example. Find the equation of the circle whose center is at $(-3, -1)$, with radius equal to 5.

Solution. Substituting $a = -3$, $b = -1$, and $r = 5$ in 5.1.2, we have

$$(x + 3)^2 + (y + 1)^2 = 25,$$

which is the required equation (Fig. 65).

Removing parentheses and collecting terms in the center-radius equation of a circle, 5.1.2, we have

$$x^2 + y^2 - 2ax - 2by + (a^2 + b^2 - r^2) = 0,$$

which is in the form

$$x^2 + y^2 + Dx + Ey + F = 0,$$

wherein $D = -2a$, $E = -2b$, and $F = a^2 + b^2 - r^2$. This is called the **general form** of the equation of a circle. Since every circle has a center and a radius, every circle has a center-radius equation (5.1.2). Therefore all circles are included in the general equation.

5.1.4 Theorem. *The equation of any circle can be written in the general form*

$$x^2 + y^2 + Dx + Ey + F = 0,$$

where D*,* E*, and* F *are real numbers.*

EXERCISES

Make a sketch for each exercise.

In each of the Exercises 1 to 8, write the equation of the circle with center at C and radius equal to r, first in the center-radius form and then in the general form.

1. C:$(5, 2)$, $r = 3$.   **2.** C:$(-4, 7)$, $r = 7$.

3. C:$(0, -8)$, $r = 8$.   **4.** C:$(-2, -3)$, $r = 1$.

5. C:$(11, 0)$, $r = 5$.   **6.** C:$(6, -1)$, $r = 4$.

7. C:$(12, -5)$, $r = 13$.   **8.** C:$(-3, -4)$, $r = 5$.

9. Find the equation of the circle whose center is $(1, 4)$ and which passes through the point $(-2, -3)$.

10. Find the equation of the circle whose center is $(-3, 7)$ and which goes through the origin.

11. Find the equation of the circle with center at $(3, 2)$ and tangent to the y-axis.

12. Find the equation of the circle whose center is $(-5, -2)$ and which is tangent to the x-axis.

13. Find the equation of the circle with center at $(4, 0)$ and tangent to the line $2x - y + 1 = 0$.

14. Find the equation of the circle with center at $(-5, -3)$ and tangent to the line $5x + 12y - 4 = 0$.

15. A circle has its center on the x-axis and passes through the points $(1, 3)$ and $(5, 5)$. Find its equation.

16. Find the equation of the circle which passes through the points $(5, 4)$ and $(13, -8)$, and whose center is on the y-axis.

17. A circle is tangent to the line $4x - 3y + 10 = 0$ at the point $(-1, 2)$ and also is tangent to the line $3x + 4y - 30 = 0$ at $(6, 3)$. Find the equation of the circle.

18. Find the equation of the circle which is tangent to the line $x - 4y + 3 = 0$ at the point $(5, 2)$, and is also tangent to the line $4x + y - 5 = 0$ at the point $(2, -3)$.

19. Find the equation of the circle which passes through the three points $(10, -6)$, $(11, -1)$, and $(3, 11)$.

20. Find the equation of the circle through the points $(0, 2)$, $(3, 3)$, and $(7, 1)$.

5.2   LOCUS OF $x^2 + y^2 + Dx + Ey + F = 0$

Since the equation of every circle can be expressed in the general form

$$x^2 + y^2 + Dx + Ey + F = 0,$$

it is natural to ask whether the locus of such an equation is always a circle. This equation can be rewritten

$$(x^2 + Dx) + (y^2 + Ey) = -F.$$

Completing the squares in the parentheses by adding $D^2/4$ and $E^2/4$ to both members of the equation, we have

$$\left(x^2 + Dx + \frac{D^2}{4}\right) + \left(y^2 + Ey + \frac{E^2}{4}\right) = \frac{D^2}{4} + \frac{E^2}{4} - F,$$

or

(1) $$\left(x + \frac{D}{2}\right)^2 + \left(y + \frac{E}{2}\right)^2 = \frac{D^2 + E^2 - 4F}{4}.$$

Comparison of (1) with 5.1.2 shows that if $D^2 + E^2 - 4F$ is positive, the locus is a **circle** with center at $(-D/2, -E/2)$ and radius equal to $\sqrt{D^2 + E^2 - 4F}/2$.

If $D^2 + E^2 - 4F$ is zero, the equation (1) becomes

$$\left(x + \frac{D}{2}\right)^2 + \left(y + \frac{E}{2}\right)^2 = 0,$$

the locus of which is a single point, the center; for the coordinates of the center, $(-D/2, -E/2)$, clearly satisfy this equation. Moreover, the substitution of any other coordinates than these for x and y will make at least one of the expressions $(x + D/2)^2$ and $(y + E/2)^2$ positive, and since neither one of them is ever negative their sum cannot be zero. This locus is called a **point-circle**. It may be thought of as the limit of a circle whose radius decreases and approaches zero. From this point of view, the designation "curve" is still appropriate for the locus.

When $D^2 + E^2 - 4F$ is negative in (1), the radius is imaginary. No real coordinates satisfy (1) and the equation has no locus. This situation is sometimes described by saying that the circle is **imaginary.**

5.2.1 Theorem.   *The locus of the equation*

$$x^2 + y^2 + Dx + Ey + F = 0$$

is a circle, a point-circle, or is imaginary.

This theorem is restated in the following test for circles.

5.2.2 Corollary.   *The locus, if any, of a second degree equation is a circle (or a point-circle) if the coefficients of x^2 and y^2 are equal and the xy-term is missing.*

In drawing a circle whose general equation is given, the student is advised to use the method of completing the squares to find the coordinates of the center and the radius. He should not bother to memorize the formulas for the center and the radius.

Example 1.   Draw the locus of the equation $x^2 + y^2 + 10x - 4y - 7 = 0$.

Solution. By 5.2.2 the locus, if any, is a circle or a point-circle. The given equation can be rewritten

$$(x^2 + 10x) + (y^2 - 4y) = 7.$$

Completing the squares in the parentheses by adding 25 and 4 to both sides of the equation, we obtain

$$(x^2 + 10x + 25) + (y^2 - 4y + 4) = 7 + 25 + 4,$$

or

$$(x + 5)^2 + (y - 2)^2 = 36.$$

Comparison of this equation with 5.1.2 shows the coordinates of the center to be $(-5, 2)$ and the radius to be 6. It is now easy to draw the circle (Fig. 66).

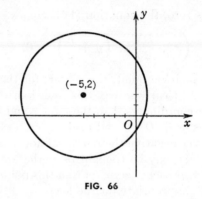

FIG. 66

Example 2. Name the locus of $4x^2 + 4y^2 - 24x - 32y + 99 = 0$.

Solution. By 5.2.2, if this equation has a locus it is a circle or a point-circle. Dividing both members by 4, we obtain

$$x^2 + y^2 - 6x - 8y + \frac{99}{4} = 0,$$

which may be rewritten

$$(x^2 - 6x) + (y^2 - 8y) = \frac{-99}{4}.$$

Completing the squares in the terms involving x and y, we have

$$(x^2 - 6x + 9) + (y^2 - 8y + 16) = 9 + 16 - \frac{99}{4},$$

or

$$(x - 3)^2 + (y - 4)^2 = \frac{1}{4}.$$

The locus is a circle with center at $(3, 4)$ and radius $1/2$.

EXERCISES

Tell which of the equations in Exercises 1 to 4 has for its locus a circle.

1. $x^2 - y^2 + 2x + 64 = 0$.

2. $x^2 + 3xy + y^2 - 15x + 10y - 20 = 0$.

3. $4x^2 + 4y^2 - 4x - 24y + 21 = 0$.

4. $x^2 + y^2 + 9 = 0$.

In Exercises 5 to 10, find the center and radius of each circle.   Make a sketch.

5. $x^2 + y^2 + 14x - 4y + 52 = 0$.

6. $x^2 + y^2 - 8x + 4y - 29 = 0$.

7. $x^2 + y^2 + 20y + 64 = 0$.

8. $9x^2 + 9y^2 - 72x - 6y + 1 = 0$.

9. $x^2 + y^2 - 4x - 12y + 40 = 0$.

10. $4x^2 + 4y^2 + 24x + 20y - 39 = 0$.

11. Find the equation of the line which is tangent to the circle

$$x^2 + y^2 - 8x + 6y + 8 = 0$$

at the point $(3, 1)$.   Make a sketch.

12. Find the equation of the tangent line to the circle $x^2 + y^2 + 2x - 4y - 8 = 0$ at the point $(2, 4)$.   Make a sketch.

13. Find the equation of the circle whose center is on the x-axis and which is tangent to the circle $x^2 + y^2 - 6x - 12y - 7 = 0$ at the point $(-3, 2)$.   Make a sketch.

14. Find the equation of the circle whose center is on the y-axis and which is tangent to the circle $x^2 + y^2 - 10x + 6y + 14 = 0$ at the point $(1, -1)$.   Make a sketch.

15. Find the equations of the lines with slope 2 which are tangent to the circle $x^2 + y^2 + 4x - 8y - 25 = 0$.   (Two solutions.)   Make a sketch.

16. Find the equations of the two lines with slope 4/3 which are tangent to the circle $x^2 + y^2 - 6x + 2y - 15 = 0$.   Make a sketch.

17. Find the equation of the circle which is concentric with the circle

$$x^2 + y^2 + 8x + 2y + 8 = 0$$

and which passes through the point $(1, 7)$.   Make a sketch.

18. Find the equation of the circle which is concentric with the circle

$$x^2 + y^2 - 4x + 10y = 0$$

and which passes through the point $(-2, 3)$.   Make a sketch.

5.3   DETERMINING COEFFICIENTS FROM GIVEN GEOMETRIC CONDITIONS

The method discussed in 4.3 of using given geometric conditions to determine the coefficients of an equation begins to show its power in problems involving circles.

We are familiar with two forms of the equation of a circle—the general form and the center-radius form.

In the general equation,

$$x^2 + y^2 + Dx + Ey + F = 0,$$

there are three essential coefficients, D, E, and F.   Whenever the values of D, E, and F are known, the locus (if any) is a unique circle. Three independent equations in the unknown D, E, and F are sufficient to determine their values, and three appropriate geometric conditions, such as the requirement that the circle pass through three given points, give rise to these equations.

Similarly, there are also three essential constants, h, k, and r, in the center-radius equation,

$$(x - h)^2 + (y - k)^2 = r^2.$$

Three geometric conditions can lead to three equations in h, k, and r, and their values, when substituted in the center-radius equation, define a circle.

The student must decide from the given geometric conditions which of the two forms of the equation to use.

Example 1. Find the equation of the circle through the points whose coordinates are $(-2, -1)$, $(0, 3)$, and $(4, 2)$ (Fig. 67).

Solution. We will determine the values of D, E, and F in the general equation

(1) $$x^2 + y^2 + Dx + Ey + F = 0.$$

The point $(-2, -1)$ is on the circle and therefore its coordinates must satisfy (1)

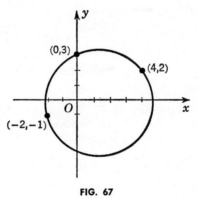

FIG. 67

(by 3.1.2). That is, $(-2)^2 + (-1)^2 + D(-2) + E(-1) + F = 0$, or

(2) $$-2D - E + F + 5 = 0.$$

Similarly, the point $(0, 3)$ is on the circle and its coordinates also satisfy (1). Thus

(3) $$3E + F + 9 = 0.$$

Again, $(4, 2)$ is on the circle, and therefore

(4) $$4D + 2E + F + 20 = 0.$$

Solving equations (2), (3), and (4) simultaneously, we find $D = -8/3$, $E = 1/3$, and $F = -10$. Substituting these results in (1), we find the desired equation of the circle to be $x^2 + y^2 - \frac{8}{3}x + \frac{1}{3}y - 10 = 0$ or $3x^2 + 3y^2 - 8x + y - 30 = 0$. Of course, there are other ways of solving this problem.

Example 2. Find the equations of the circles through the origin and tangent to both of the lines $x - 3y + 4 = 0$ and $3x - y - 20 = 0$.

Solution. Using the center-radius form,

(1) $$(x - h)^2 + (y - k)^2 = r^2,$$

we seek three equations in h, k, and r in order to determine their values.

Since the circle goes through the origin, the coordinates $(0, 0)$ must satisfy (1) (by 3.1.2). That is,

(2) $$h^2 + k^2 = r^2.$$

By 4.4.1, the directed distance from the given tangent line, $x - 3y + 4 = 0$,

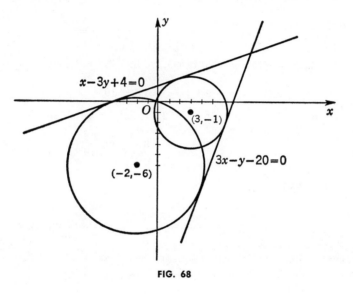

FIG. 68

to the unknown center, (h, k), is

(3) $$\frac{-h + 3k - 4}{\sqrt{10}}.$$

Similarly, the directed distance from the other tangent line, $3x - y - 20 = 0$, to the center, (h, k), is

(4) $$\frac{-3h + k + 20}{\sqrt{10}}.$$

Now (3) is a negative number, since it measures a directed distance downward, while (4) is a positive number, measuring a directed distance upward (Fig. 68). Therefore, (3) is equal to the negative of (4). That is,

$$\frac{-h + 3k - 4}{\sqrt{10}} = -\frac{-3h + k + 20}{\sqrt{10}},$$

or

(5) $$h - k - 4 = 0.$$

The absolute value of (3) is the length of the radius. That is,

(6) $$\left| \frac{-h + 3k - 4}{\sqrt{10}} \right| = r,$$

or, if we square both members and collect terms,

(7) $$h^2 + 9k^2 - 6hk + 8h - 24k + 16 = 10r^2.$$

Equations (2), (5), and (7) are three equations in h, k, and r. To solve them for h, k, and r, we first eliminate r^2 between (2) and (7), obtaining

(8) $$9h^2 + k^2 + 6hk - 8h + 24k - 16 = 0.$$

Solving (5) and (8) simultaneously for h and k we obtain two sets of solutions, $h = 3$, $k = -1$, and $h = -2$, $k = -6$. Substituting each of these sets of solutions in (6), we find $r = \sqrt{10}$ and $r = 2\sqrt{10}$, respectively.

Thus, there are two circles which satisfy the given geometric conditions. Substituting $h = 3$, $k = -1$, $r = \sqrt{10}$ in (1), we find the equation of the first circle to be

$$(x - 3)^2 + (y + 1)^2 = 10.$$

Substituting $h = -2$, $k = -6$, and $r = 2\sqrt{10}$ in (1), we obtain the equation of the second circle,

$$(x + 2)^2 + (y + 6)^2 = 40.$$

EXERCISES

Make a sketch for each exercise.

1. Find the equation of the circle which passes through the three points $(3, -1)$, $(2, 6)$, and $(-1, 7)$.

2. Find the equation of the circle through the points $(-5, 1)$, $(2, 2)$, and $(4, -2)$.

3. Find the equation of the circle circumscribed about the triangle whose vertices are $(-8, 4)$, $(-3, 5)$, and $(9, -3)$.

4. Find the equation of the circle circumscribed about the triangle whose vertices are $(-11, -7)$, $(6, 0)$, and $(7, 5)$.

5. Find the equation of the circle which passes through the points $(2, 4)$ and $(1, -1)$, with radius $\sqrt{13}$.

6. Find the equation of the circle through $(-3, 3)$ and $(2, -2)$, having radius $\sqrt{53}$.

7. Find the equation of the circle whose center is on the line $x - 2y - 2 = 0$ and which is tangent to both coordinate axes.

8. Find the equation of the circle whose center is on the line $x - y - 3 = 0$ and which is tangent to both of the lines $4x - 3y + 14 = 0$ and $3x + 4y - 27 = 0$. (Two solutions.)

9. Find the equation of the circle inscribed in the triangle formed by the coordinate axes and the line $3x + 4y - 18 = 0$.

10. Find the equation of the circle which is tangent to the coordinate axes and also to the line $12x - 5y - 60 = 0$.

11. Find the equation of the circle through the points $(-1, 3)$ and $(4, 2)$, with center on the line $x - y + 3 = 0$.

12. Find the equation of the circle which passes through the points $(-2, -3)$ and $(5, 4)$, and whose center is on the line $x - 4y - 12 = 0$.

13. Find the equation of the circle which is tangent to both coordinate axes and which passes through the point $(4, -2)$. (Two solutions.)

14. Find the equation of the circle through the point $(-3, -6)$ and which is tangent to both of the coordinate axes.

15. Find the equation of the circle which is tangent to the lines $x = -4$ and $y = 8$, and whose center is on the line $4x - 5y - 7 = 0$.

16. Find the equation of the circle inscribed in the triangle formed by the three lines, $3x - 4y + 5 = 0$, $5x + 12y + 41 = 0$, and $4x - 3y - 26 = 0$.

★5.4 A FAMILY OF CIRCLES

Consider two circles whose equations are

$$(1) \qquad x^2 + y^2 + Dx + Ey + F = 0$$

and

$$(2) \qquad x^2 + y^2 + D'x + E'y + F' = 0,$$

wherein D, E, F, D', E', and F' are constants. Then the equation

$$(3) \quad (x^2 + y^2 + Dx + Ey + F) + k(x^2 + y^2 + D'x + E'y + F') = 0,$$

in which k is a parameter, represents a family of circles. For equation (3) can be rewritten

$$(4) \quad (1 + k)x^2 + (1 + k)y^2 + (D + kD')x + (E + kE')y + (F + kF') = 0$$

or, if $k \neq -1$,

$$(5) \qquad x^2 + y^2 + \frac{(D + kD')}{1 + k} x + \frac{(E + kE')}{1 + k} y + \frac{(F + kF')}{1 + k} = 0,$$

whose locus (if any) is a circle for each value of k except $k = -1$ (by 5.2.2).

For example, if the given circles are $x^2 + y^2 + 4x - 4y - 1 = 0$ and $x^2 + y^2 - 4x - 6y + 9 = 0$, the equation of the family is

$$(x^2 + y^2 + 4x - 4y - 1) + k(x^2 + y^2 - 4x - 6y + 9) = 0,$$

in which k is the parameter. The circle corresponding to $k = 1$ is $x^2 + y^2 - 5y + 4 = 0$ and the circle corresponding to $k = -4$ is $3x^2 + 3y^2 - 20x - 20y + 37 = 0$. Fig. 69 shows these circles, along with several other members of the family.

If $k = -1$ in (3), the equation (4) becomes

$$(6) \qquad (D - D')x + (E - E')y + (F - F') = 0,$$

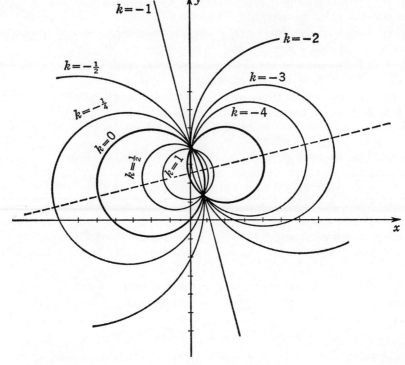

FIG. 69

which represents a straight line (4.2.1).   This line is called the **radical axis** of the system of circles (3).

The coordinates of the center of the circle (1) are $(-D/2, -E/2)$ and the coordinates of the center of the circle (2) are $(-D'/2, -E'/2)$ (by 5.2). Therefore the slope of the line joining them is $(E - E')/(D - D')$ (by 2.4.1).   But the slope of the radical axis (6) is $-(D - D')/(E - E')$ (by 4.2.2), which is the negative reciprocal of the slope of the line joining the centers of the circles, (1) and (2).   Therefore the radical axis is perpendicular to the line joining the centers of the given circles, (1) and (2).

The equation of the line joining the centers of the circles (1) and (2) is (by 4.1.2)

(7) $2(E - E')x - 2(D - D')y + (ED' - E'D) = 0.$

Let k_1 be any particular value of the parameter k in (5), except -1.   Then (by 5.2) the coordinates of the center of the circle of the system (5) which corresponds to $k = k_1$ are

$$\left(-\frac{D + k_1 D'}{2(1 + k_1)}, -\frac{E + k_1 E'}{2(1 + k_1)}\right).$$

But these coordinates satisfy the equation (7), as may be verified. Therefore the centers of all circles of the system (3) lie on the line joining the centers of the two given circles, (1) and (2). This line is called the **line of centers** of the system of circles (3). Combining this result with that of the preceding paragraph, we see that *the radical axis* (6) *is perpendicular to the line of centers of the system of circles* (3).

Let $P_1:(x_1, y_1)$ be a point common to both the circles (1) and (2). Then (by 3.1.2)

$$x_1{}^2 + y_1{}^2 + Dx_1 + Ey_1 + F = 0$$

and

$$x_1{}^2 + y_1{}^2 + D'x_1 + E'y_1 + F' = 0,$$

and therefore

(8) $(x_1{}^2 + y_1{}^2 + Dx_1 + Ey_1 + F) + k(x_1{}^2 + y_1{}^2 + D'x_1 + E'y_1 + F') = 0$

for all values of k, since (8) is really $0 + k(0) = 0$. But (8) shows that the point $P_1:(x_1, y_1)$ is on every member of the family (3) (by 3.1.2). Therefore, any point common to the two given circles, (1) and (2), is common to every member of the family (3), including the radical axis.

The equations of any two particular members of the family (3), obtained by assigning the two distinct, arbitrary values, k_1 and k_2, to the parameter k, are

(9) $(x^2 + y^2 + Dx + Ey + F) + k_1(x^2 + y^2 + D'x + E'y + F') = 0$

and

(10) $(x^2 + y^2 + Dx + Ey + F) + k_2(x^2 + y^2 + D'x + E'y + F') = 0.$

Let $P_1:(x_1, y_1)$ be a point common to (9) and (10). Then (by 3.1.2)

(11) $(x_1{}^2 + y_1{}^2 + Dx_1 + Ey_1 + F)$
$$+ k_1(x_1{}^2 + y_1{}^2 + D'x_1 + E'y_1 + F') = 0$$

and

(12) $(x_1{}^2 + y_1{}^2 + Dx_1 + Ey_1 + F)$
$$+ k_2(x_1{}^2 + y_1{}^2 + D'x_1 + E'y_1 + F') = 0.$$

Subtracting (12) from (11), member by member, we have

$$(k_1 - k_2)(x_1{}^2 + y_1{}^2 + D'x_1 + E'y_1 + F') = 0$$

or, since $k_1 \neq k_2$,

(13) $$x_1{}^2 + y_1{}^2 + D'x_1 + E'y_1 + F' = 0.$$

But (13) tells us that P_1 is on the original circle (2) (by 3.1.2). Again, multiplying both members of (11) by k_2 and both members of (12) by k_1, and then subtracting the resulting equations member by member, we have

(14) $$x_1{}^2 + y_1{}^2 + Dx_1 + Ey_1 + F = 0,$$

which tells us that P_1 is on the circle (1) (by 3.1.2). Therefore, if any two members of the family (3) intersect in a point P_1, the original circles (1) and (2) also intersect in P_1. From this, and from the result in the preceding paragraph, it follows that:

If the circles (1) and (2) intersect in two points, all circles of the family (3) intersect in the same two points and the radical axis contains their common chord.

If the circles (1) and (2) are tangent to each other, all circles of the system (3) are tangent to each other at that same point, and the radical axis is their common tangent.

If the circles (1) and (2) fail to intersect, no circles of the system (3) intersect each other, and none intersects the radical axis.

We are now in a better position to understand the process, learned mechanically in college algebra, for solving two simultaneous equations of the same type as (1) and (2). We were told in algebra to subtract (2) from (1), member by member, and then solve the resulting linear equation simultaneously with one of the original equations. But subtracting (2) from (1) is the same as letting $k = -1$ in the equation (3) of the family of circles, thus obtaining the (linear) equation of the radical axis (6). Since the radical axis goes through any point common to the two given circles, finding the coordinates of the points of intersection of the radical axis and one of the given circles is equivalent to finding the coordinates of the points of intersection of the two given circles.

Example. Find the equation of the circle through the point $(-1, 5)$ and also passing through the points of intersection of the circles $x^2 + y^2 + 4x - 4y - 1 = 0$ and $x^2 + y^2 - 4x - 6y + 9 = 0$.

Solution (see Fig. 69). The family of circles through the points of intersection of the two given circles is

$$(x^2 + y^2 + 4x - 4y - 1) + k(x^2 + y^2 - 4x - 6y + 9) = 0.$$

We seek the value of k which will make the corresponding circle of this family go through the point $(-1, 5)$. But the point $(-1, 5)$ is on the circle if and only if its coordinates satisfy the above equation (by 3.1.2). Therefore

$$((-1)^2 + 5^2 + 4(-1) - 4(5) - 1) + k((-1)^2 + 5^2 - 4(-1) - 6(5) + 9) = 0,$$

or $k = -1/9$. Substituting $k = -1/9$ in the equation of the family, we obtain

$$4x^2 + 4y^2 + 20x - 15y - 9 = 0,$$

which is the desired equation.

EXERCISES

Make a sketch for each exercise.

1. Given the family of circles $x^2 + y^2 - 12x + 11 + k(x^2 + y^2 - 9) = 0$ draw the circles of this family for which $k = 5, 2, 1/2, 0, -1$, and -3.

2. Draw the circles of the family $x^2 + y^2 - 4y + k(x^2 + y^2 + 6y) = 0$ corresponding to $k = 5, 2, 1/2, 0, -1$, and -3.

3. Find the coordinates of the points of intersection (if any) of the pair of circles

(a) $x^2 + y^2 - 4x - 2y - 20 = 0$ and
$x^2 + y^2 - 16x - 14y + 100 = 0$;

(b) $x^2 + y^2 + 4x - 2y - 4 = 0$ and
$x^2 + y^2 - 4x + 10y + 13 = 0$.

4. Find the coordinates of the points of intersection (if any) of the circles

(a) $x^2 + y^2 + 4x - 9 = 0$ and $x^2 + y^2 - 4x - 8y + 15 = 0$;

(b) $x^2 + y^2 + 4x + 2y - 4 = 0$ and $x^2 + y^2 - 8x + 12 = 0$.

5. Find the equation of the circle which goes through the points of intersection of the circles $x^2 + y^2 - 2x - 8y + 8 = 0$ and $x^2 + y^2 - 10x - 2y + 10 = 0$ and also through the point $(-1, 1)$.

6. Find the equation of the circle through the point $(1, 3)$ and also through the points of intersection of the two circles $x^2 + y^2 - 6x + 8y - 11 = 0$ and $x^2 + y^2 - 10x + 2y + 10 = 0$.

7. Find the equation of the circle through the points of intersection of the circles $x^2 + y^2 + 6x - 4y - 3 = 0$ and $x^2 + y^2 - 4x - 8y + 11 = 0$ and having its center on the line $2x - 3y - 6 = 0$.

8. Find the equation of the circle with center on the x-axis and which passes through the points of intersection of the circles $x^2 + y^2 + 12x + 4y + 24 = 0$ and $x^2 + y^2 + 2x - 6y - 15 = 0$.

9. Prove that the circles $x^2 + y^2 - 6x - 8y + 16 = 0$ and $x^2 + y^2 - 4 = 0$ are tangent to each other. Then find the equation of the circle which is tangent to both the given circles at their common point and which passes through the point $(2, 2)$.

10. Prove that the circles $x^2 + y^2 - 5 = 0$ and $x^2 + y^2 + 6x - 12y + 25 = 0$ are tangent to each other. Find the equation of the circle which is tangent to the given circles at their point of tangency and passes through the point $(-5, 1)$.

11. Prove that the radical axes of any three circles, taken in pairs, intersect in the same point (the **radical center**) or are parallel.

12. (a) If $P:(x, y)$ is a point external to the circle $x^2 + y^2 + Dx + Ey + F = 0$, and T is the point of tangency of a tangent from P to the circle, prove that

$$|PT| = \sqrt{x^2 + y^2 + Dx + Ey + F}.$$

(Hint: The center of the circle is

$$S:(-D/2, -E/2),$$

and the radius is given by $r^2 = (D^2 + E^2 - 4F)/4$. Also, $|PS|^2 = r^2 + |PT|^2$.)

(b) Denote the point of tangency of a tangent from a point P to the circle $x^2 + y^2 + Dx + Ey + F = 0$ by T, and the point of tangency of a tangent from P to the circle $x^2 + y^2 + D'x + E'y + F' = 0$ by T'. Prove that the locus of points, P, such that $|PT| = |PT'|$, is the radical axis of the two circles.

5.5   TRANSLATION

When a circle of radius 5, say, has its center at $(2, 3)$, its equation is $(x - 2)^2 + (y - 3)^2 = 25$ (by 5.1.2), or

$$x^2 + y^2 - 4x - 6y - 12 = 0.$$

The same circle, when its center is at the origin, has the much simpler equation,

$$x^2 + y^2 - 25 = 0.$$

The position of the coordinate axes has nothing whatever to do with the size or shape of the curve, but it does affect the algebraic representation

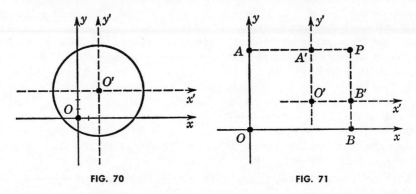

FIG. 70   FIG. 71

of the locus.   It is often desirable to be able to choose new coordinate axes, without changing the locus, in order to simplify the equation of a curve.

If new axes are chosen in the plane, every point will have two sets of coordinates—the old ones, (x, y), relative to the old axes and new ones, (x', y'), relative to the new axes. The original coordinates undergo a **transformation.** If the new axes are respectively parallel to the original axes (Fig. 70), the transformation is said to be a **translation.** We seek formulas connecting the two sets of coordinates in a translation.

5.5.1 Theorem.   *If new Cartesian axes are chosen in the plane, respectively parallel to the old axes, so that the new origin has coordinates (h, k) relative to the original axes, then the old coordinates (x, y) and the new coordinates (x', y') of any point in the plane are connected by the equations*

$$x = x' + h, \qquad x' = x - h,$$
$$y = y' + k; \quad \text{or} \quad y' = y - k.$$

Proof.   Let P be any point in the plane (Fig. 71).   Through P draw a line parallel to the x-axis, intersecting the old y-axis in A and the new y'-axis in A'.   Also draw a line through P, parallel to the y-axis, intersecting the old x-axis in B and the new x'-axis in B'.

Since A, A', and P are three points on a directed line,

(1) $$AA' + A'P = AP \qquad \text{(by 1.2.3)}.$$

But the x-coordinate of O' was given as h, and thus the x-coordinate of A' is also h (2.1.2). That is, $AA' = h$. Moreover, by the definition of co-ordinates (1.3.1), $A'P = x'$ and $AP = x$. Substituting in (1), we have $h + x' = x$, or

$$x = x' + h.$$

Similarly,

$$y = y' + k.$$

These are called the **equations of translation.**

Example 1. Find the new coordinates of the point $P:(-5, 7)$ after a translation in which the new origin is at $(3, -2)$.

Solution. The original coordinates of P are $x = -5$ and $y = 7$, and the co-ordinates of the new origin are given as $h = 3$ and $k = -2$ (Fig. 72). Sub-stituting in 5.5.1, we have $x' = -5 - 3$ and $y' = 7 - (-2)$. Therefore the new coordinates of P are $x' = -8$ and $y' = 9$.

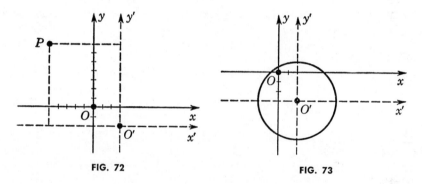

FIG. 72   FIG. 73

Example 2. Given the equation $x^2 + y^2 - 4x + 6y - 3 = 0$, find the new equation of its locus after a translation with new origin at $(2, -3)$.

Solution. By 5.5.1, every point in the plane has old coordinates (x, y) and new coordinates (x', y'), connected by $x = x' + 2$ and $y = y' - 3$. Substituting these expressions for x and y in the given equation, we have

$$(x' + 2)^2 + (y' - 3)^2 - 4(x' + 2) + 6(y' - 3) - 3 = 0.$$

This simplifies to

$$x'^2 + y'^2 - 16 = 0,$$

the locus of which is a circle with center at the new origin and radius 4 (Fig. 73).

EXERCISES

Make a sketch for each exercise, showing both sets of axes.

1. If new axes are chosen respectively parallel to the original axes so that the new origin will have coordinates $(-4, 3)$ with respect to the old axes, find the new coordinates of the points whose old coordinates are: $(1, -3)$, $(2, 5)$, $(-2, 6)$, $(5, 9)$, $(-1, -1)$, $(0, 10)$, $(-16, 0)$, and $(4, -6)$.

2. After a translation with new origin at $(2, -5)$, find the new coordinates of the points whose old coordinates are: $(4, 5)$, $(3, 1)$, $(-6, 4)$, $(0, 6)$, $(-3, 0)$, $(7, -1)$, $(-6, -2)$, and $(5, -4)$.

3. If, after a translation, the point $(-3, 4)$ has new coordinates $(7, 0)$, what are the coordinates of the new origin relative to the original axes?

4. After a translation the point $(-4, -5)$ has new coordinates $(2, -8)$. What are the coordinates of the new origin relative to the original axes?

5. Find the new equation of the line $x - 7 = 0$ after a translation in which the new origin is at $(7, 0)$.

6. Find the new equations of the original axes after a translation with new origin at $(2, -1)$.

7. Find the new equation of the line $2x - 5y + 36 = 0$ after a translation in which the new origin is at $(-3, 6)$.

8. What is the new equation of the line $x + 4y - 12 = 0$ after a translation with new origin at $(5, -1)$?

9. What is the new equation of the line $4x + y - 7 = 0$ after a translation in which the new origin is on the line?

10. Translate so that the new equation of the line $x + 3y + 5 = 0$ will have no constant term.

11. Find the new equation of the circle $x^2 + y^2 + 8x - 2y + 13 = 0$ after a translation in which the new origin is at $(-4, 1)$.

12. What is the new equation of the circle $x^2 + y^2 - 8x + 6y - 11 = 0$ after a translation with new origin at $(4, -3)$?

13. Find the new equation of the locus of $y^2 - 4x - 4y + 8 = 0$ after a translation in which the new origin is at $(1, 2)$. Draw both sets of axes and sketch the locus from the new equation, relative to the new axes.

14. Find the new equation of the locus of $x^2 + 4x + 9y - 23 = 0$ after a translation with new origin at $(-2, 3)$. Draw both sets of axes and sketch the locus from the new equation, relative to the new axes.

15. Find the new equation of the locus of $4x^2 + 9y^2 + 16x - 54y + 61 = 0$ after a translation with new origin at $(-2, 3)$. Sketch the locus and both sets of axes.

16. Find the new equation of the locus of $9x^2 + 16y^2 - 126x + 297 = 0$ after a translation with new origin at $(7, 0)$. Sketch the locus and both sets of axes.

5.6 SIMPLIFICATION OF SECOND DEGREE EQUATIONS BY TRANSLATION

Second degree equations which contain no term involving xy can often be simplified by a translation. Two methods will be explained in the examples.

Example 1. Transform the coordinates so that the new equation of the locus of

$$4x^2 + 9y^2 + 8x - 90y + 193 = 0$$

will contain no first degree terms.

Solution. The given second degree equation contains no xy term but does contain terms in x^2 and y^2. That is, the equation is in the form

$$Ax^2 + Cy^2 + Dx + Ey + F = 0,$$

where $A \neq 0$ and $C \neq 0$. It will be proved in 7.3 that such an equation can always be reduced to the form

$$Ax'^2 + Cy'^2 + F' = 0$$

by an appropriate translation. From the latter equation it is apparent that the locus will be symmetric with respect to the new x'-axis and also with respect to the new y'-axis (by 3.6.6 and 3.6.8).

First Method. The given equation can be rewritten

$$4(x^2 + 2x) + 9(y^2 - 10y) = -193.$$

Completing the squares in the parentheses by adding $4(1) = 4$ and $9(25) = 225$ to both sides of this equation, we get

$$4(x^2 + 2x + 1) + 9(y^2 - 10y + 25) = 36,$$

or

(1) $$4(x + 1)^2 + 9(y - 5)^2 = 36.$$

If we substitute x' for $x + 1$ and y' for $y - 5$ in (1) we obtain

(2) $$4x'^2 + 9y'^2 = 36,$$

which is the desired equation.

The substitution $x' = x + 1$, $y' = y - 5$ is a translation with the new origin at $(-1, 5)$ (by 5.5.1). Drawing both sets of axes (Fig. 74), we graph (2) relative to the new axes after noting that its locus will be symmetric with respect to the new axes (by 3.6.6 and 3.6.8).

Second Method. Substituting the equations of translation, $x = x' + h$ and $y = y' + k$, in the given equation, we have

$$4(x' + h)^2 + 9(y' + k)^2 + 8(x' + h) - 90(y' + k) + 193 = 0.$$

If we expand the parentheses and collect terms, this becomes

(1)　$$4x'^2 + 9y'^2 + (8h + 8)x' + (18k - 90)y'$$
$$+ (4h^2 + 9k^2 + 8h - 90k + 193) = 0.$$

We seek values of h and k so that the equation (1) will contain no first degree terms in either x' or y'. To determine the proper values of h and k, we set the coefficients of x' and y' equal to zero. We get

$$8h + 8 = 0, \qquad 18k - 90 = 0,$$

from which $h = -1$ and $k = 5$. This is equivalent to a translation with the new origin at $(-1, 5)$.

Substituting $h = -1$ and $k = 5$ in (1), we obtain

$$4x'^2 + 9y'^2 = 36.$$

Example 2. Simplify the equation $y^2 - 4x - 12y + 28 = 0$ by a translation.

Solution. The given second degree equation contains no terms in either x^2 or xy. However, it does contain a term in y^2 and also a term in x. It is in the form

$$Cy^2 + Dx + Ey + F = 0,$$

where $C \neq 0$ and $D \neq 0$. As will be proved in 7.3, such an equation can always be reduced to the form

$$Cy'^2 + Dx' = 0$$

by an appropriate translation. The locus will be symmetric with respect to the new x'-axis (by 3.6.6) and will pass through the new origin (by 3.5.1).

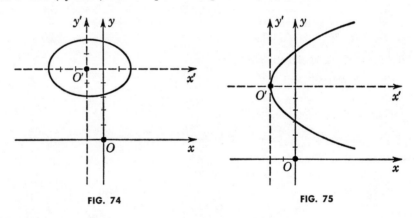

FIG. 74   FIG. 75

First Method. The given equation can be rewritten

$$y^2 - 12y = 4x - 28.$$

Completing the square in the left-hand member by adding 36 to both sides of the equation, we obtain

$$y^2 - 12y + 36 = 4x + 8,$$

or

$$(y - 6)^2 = 4(x + 2).$$

If we let $x' = x + 2$ and $y' = y - 6$, and thus make a translation with the new origin at $(-2, 6)$, the equation becomes

$$y'^2 = 4x'.$$

Fig. 75 shows the graph of this equation, sketched relative to the new axes.

Second Method. Substituting the equations of translation (5.5.1) in the given equation, we have

$$(y' + k)^2 - 4(x' + h) - 12(y' + k) + 28 = 0.$$

Expanding, and collecting terms, we obtain

(1) $$y'^2 - 4x' + (2k - 12)y' + (k^2 - 4h - 12k + 28) = 0.$$

We seek values of h and k so that the resulting equation will contain no first degree term in y' and no constant term. Accordingly, let

$$2k - 12 = 0 \quad \text{and} \quad k^2 - 4h - 12k + 28 = 0,$$

whence $h = -2$ and $k = 6$. Substituting in (1), we have

$$y'^2 - 4x' = 0.$$

EXERCISES

In Exercises 1 to 10 use both methods of translation to simplify the equation. Then draw both sets of axes and sketch the locus.

1. $x^2 + y^2 - 2x + 4y + 4 = 0$.

2. $9x^2 - 16y^2 + 90x + 192y - 495 = 0$.

3. $4x^2 + 9y^2 - 16x + 72y + 124 = 0$.

4. $y^2 - 8x - 6y + 1 = 0$.

5. $5x^2 + 30x - 6y + 3 = 0$.

6. $25x^2 - 4y^2 - 400x - 16y + 1684 = 0$.

7. $y^2 - 10x - 8y - 14 = 0$.

8. $25x^2 + 4y^2 + 150x - 8y + 129 = 0$.

9. $16x^2 + 5y^2 - 128x + 30y + 221 = 0$.

10. $x^2 + 6x - 16y - 71 = 0$.

11. Use the Second Method of translation to reduce $xy + 2x - 3y - 10 = 0$ to an equation with no first degree terms. Then draw both sets of axes and sketch the locus.

12. By means of the Second Method of translation, reduce the equation $xy + 8x - 7y - 59 = 0$ to an equation with no first degree terms. Make a sketch.

13. Use the Second Method of translation to reduce

$$8x^3 - 24x^2 + 24x - y + 1 = 0$$

to an equation containing no second degree term and no constant term. Make a sketch.

14. By means of the Second Method of translation, reduce the equation $x^2y - 8x^2 + 8xy - 64x + 16y - 129 = 0$ to an equation containing no second degree terms and no first degree terms. Make a sketch.

6

Conics

~~~~~~

After the classic Greeks had exhausted the more obvious possibilities of the geometry of lines and circles, they turned to the curves of intersection of a plane and a right circular cone.   Many properties of these conic sections were discovered by Appolonius of Perga, about 200 B.C., using only the elementary methods that were at his disposal.   He was long known as "the great geometer."

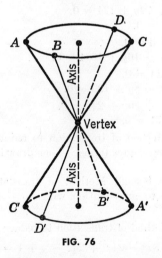

FIG. 76

The cone extends indefinitely far in both directions.   It may be thought of as generated by a moving line which always passes through a fixed point called the **vertex,** and makes a constant angle with a fixed line called the **axis.**   Fig. 76 shows the moving line in several positions, $\overline{AA'}$, $\overline{BB'}$, $\overline{CC'}$, and $\overline{DD'}$; they are called **generators** of the cone.

A **conic section,** as studied by Appolonius, is the curve in which a plane cuts a right circular cone.   There are three types of conic sections according as the cutting plane is parallel to no generator, to one and only one generator, or to two generators.

If the cutting plane is parallel to no generator, it of course cuts all generators. The curve of intersection is called an **ellipse** (Fig. 77). A circle is a limiting case of the ellipse. The ellipse reduces to a single point when the cutting plane goes through the vertex of the cone and contains no generator.

If the cutting plane is parallel to one and only one generator, the curve of intersection is a **parabola** (Fig. 78). Should the cutting plane pass through the vertex of the cone and contain one and only one generator, the parabola degenerates into a straight line. If the vertex of the cone moves far away, the cone approaches the form of a right circular cylinder and the parabola has as a limiting case two parallel lines.

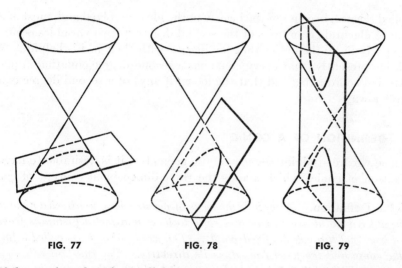

FIG. 77   FIG. 78   FIG. 79

If the cutting plane is parallel to two generators, the curve of intersection is a **hyperbola** (Fig. 79). The hyperbola degenerates into a pair of intersecting lines when the cutting plane goes through the vertex of the cone and contains two generators.

These curves of intersection of a plane and a right circular cone are called conic sections, or **conics** for short.

The purpose of the foregoing historical introduction is to show how the curves known as conic sections got their name. It is not intended as a working definition of conics, for it involves the three-dimensional concept of cone. Since, for the present, we are confining our attention to *plane* analytic geometry, we need a definition of conics which uses only two-dimensional ideas. Such a definition, quite independent of the notion of a cone, will be given in 6.1.1. It can be shown, however, that the two definitions are consistent and that plane sections of a cone are, in fact, truly "conics" as we shall define them.

Conics are studied in analytic geometry because of their importance in

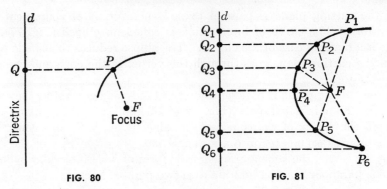

FIG. 80   FIG. 81

applied science, because of the beauty of the ideas involved and, most of all, because algebraic equations of the second degree in two variables occur so frequently in mathematics that familiarity with their loci is helpful.   We will see, presently, that every conic has a second degree equation in plane Cartesian coordinates and that the locus (if any) of a second degree equation is always a conic.

6.1 DEFINITION OF A CONIC

Since we are studying *plane* analytic geometry, it is desirable to have a definition of conics which avoids the three-dimensional concept of cone.

6.1.1 Definition.   *A conic is the locus of points whose undirected distances from a fixed point are in constant ratio to their undirected distances from a fixed line (not through the fixed point).   The fixed point, F, is called a* **focus** *of the conic and the fixed line, d, is its* **directrix.**   *The constant ratio, e, is the* **eccentricity** *of the conic.   If P is a point and Q is the foot of the perpendicular from P to d* (Fig. 80), *then P is on the conic if and only if*

$$|FP| = e|QP|.$$

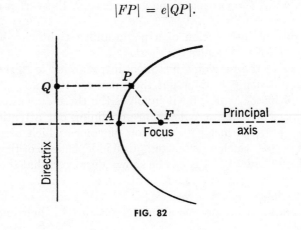

FIG. 82

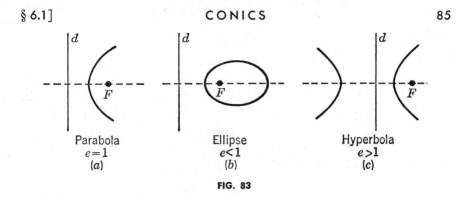

Parabola   Ellipse   Hyperbola
$e = 1$ $e < 1$ $e > 1$
(a) (b) (c)

FIG. 83

In Fig. 81, the undirected distance of each point, P_1, P_2, $\cdots$, P_6, from F is one half of its undirected distance from d. That is, $|FP_1| = \frac{1}{2}|Q_1P_1|$, $|FP_2| = \frac{1}{2}|Q_2P_2|$, $\cdots$, $|FP_6| = \frac{1}{2}|Q_6P_6|$. The locus of all such points is a conic whose eccentricity is one half.

The line through a focus perpendicular to its directrix is called the **principal axis** of the conic. The points of intersection of the conic and its principal axis are the **vertices** of the conic. In Fig. 82, F is a focus, d is its directrix, and A is a vertex.

The eccentricity, e, being a ratio of undirected distances, is a positive number.

6.1.2 Definition. *When $e = 1$, the conic is called a **parabola**. When $e < 1$, the conic is an **ellipse**. When $e > 1$, the conic is a **hyperbola**.*

It is apparent from the figures that a conic is symmetric with respect to its principal axis. This is easy to prove and is left as an exercise for the student.

It also appears that an ellipse or a hyperbola has two vertices, while a parabola has only one (Fig. 83(a), (b), and (c)).

6.1.3 Theorem. *An ellipse or a hyperbola has two vertices, but a parabola has only one vertex.*

Proof. Given a directrix, d, a focus, F, and an eccentricity, e. Denote by Q the intersection of the directrix and the principal axis of the conic (Fig. 84). Let k be the directed distance from the directrix to the focus,

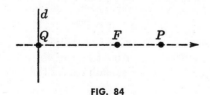

FIG. 84

so that

(1) $$QF = k.$$

We seek the number of vertices of the conic. In other words, we seek the number of points, P, of intersection of the conic with its principal axis. By the definition of a conic (6.1.1), P is on the conic if and only if

$$|FP| = e|QP|.$$

Removing the absolute value signs, we have

(2) $$FP = \pm e(QP).$$

Since P is also on the directed line through Q and F,

$$QP = QF + FP, \qquad \text{(by 1.2.3)}$$

or, by virtue of (1) and (2),

$$QP = k \pm e(QP).$$

If we solve this equation for QP in terms of the constants k and e, we get

$$QP = \frac{k}{1 \pm e}.$$

Thus, if $e \neq 1$, there are two points, P, of intersection of the conic with its principal axis. However, if $e = 1$ there is only one such point since division by zero is excluded in algebra.

Therefore every ellipse or hyperbola has two vertices, while a parabola has only one vertex. This completes the proof.

EXERCISES

1. Turn a sheet of paper so that the long side is horizontal. Draw a vertical line, d, down the center. About two inches to the right of this line and about half-way down the paper mark a fixed point F. Now locate a point on the paper so that its undirected distance from F is equal to its undirected distance from the line d. (By distance from a line we of course mean perpendicular distance.) Locate about 10 other such points and draw a smooth curve through them. Name the curve.

2. As in Exercise 1, draw the vertical line, d, and mark the fixed point, F, to the right of d. Locate a point on the paper so that its undirected distance from F is half its undirected distance from d. Then locate about 10 other such points. Draw a smooth curve through these points. Name the resulting conic.

3. Again, as in Exercise 1, draw d and F. Locate a point on the paper so that its undirected distance from F is twice its undirected distance from d. Then locate about 15 other such points. About half of these points should be to the left of d in this third exercise. Draw smooth curves through these points. Name the conic.

4. Prove the Theorem: Every conic is symmetric with respect to its principal axis. (Hint: Use 3.6.1 and 6.1.1 to show that if P is a point on a conic, its symmetric partner, P', with respect to the principal axis is also on the conic, and therefore, by 3.6.4, the conic is symmetric with respect to its principal axis.)

6.2   THE PARABOLA $(e = 1)$

When $e = 1$ the conic is a parabola and 6.1.1 becomes

6.2.1 Definition. *The locus of points equidistant from the focus and the directrix is a* **parabola.**

We wish to derive an equation of the parabola from its definition. We are given a geometric description of the locus (its definition) and we seek

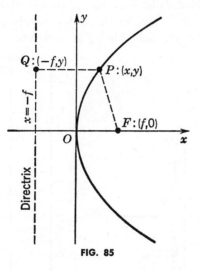

FIG. 85

its equation. This is an application of our second fundamental problem (3.7).

Of course we want the equation to be as simple as possible. We recall that the position of the coordinate axes has no effect on the locus but does affect the simplicity of the equation. Since all conics are symmetric with respect to their principal axis, it is natural to place one of the coordinate axes, say the x-axis, along the principal axis of the conic.

By 6.2.1, the vertex of the parabola is midway between the focus and the directrix. Choose the vertex of the parabola to be the origin of coordinates (Fig. 85). Let $OF = f$. Then the coordinates of the focus are $(f, 0)$ and the equation of the directrix is $x = -f$ (by 2.1.2).

Let $P:(x, y)$ be any point on the parabola. Drop a perpendicular from P to the directrix and indicate its foot by Q. The coordinates of Q are

$(-f, y)$.   Then

$$|FP| = |QP| \qquad \text{(by 6.2.1)}.$$

But $|FP| = \sqrt{(x - f)^2 + y^2}$, and $QP = x - (-f)$ (by 2.1.3).   Therefore

$$\sqrt{(x - f)^2 + y^2} = |x + f|.$$

Squaring both members and collecting terms, we have

$$y^2 = 4fx.$$

This proves the

6.2.2 Theorem.   *The equation of the parabola with focus at $(f, 0)$ and directrix $x = -f$ is*

$$y^2 = 4fx.$$

Since f was the *directed* distance, OF, from the origin to the focus, f can be positive or negative.   Fig. 84 shows the parabola when f is positive, and Fig. 86 shows the parabola when f is negative.

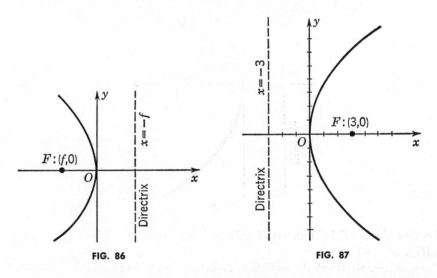

FIG. 86   FIG. 87

A parabola is said to be in **standard position** when its vertex is at the origin and its principal axis is one of the coordinate axes.   The equation of a conic in standard position is called a **standard equation.**   Thus the equation in 6.2.2 is a standard equation of a parabola.

Example.   Find the coordinates of the focus and the equation of the directrix of the parabola $y^2 = 12x$.   Sketch the curve.

Solution.   Comparing the given equation with 6.2.2, we see that $f = 3$.   Therefore the focus is $F:(3, 0)$ and the directrix is $x = -3$.   The parabola has its vertex at the origin, is symmetric with respect to the x-axis and opens to the right (Fig. 87).

An equally simple standard equation of a parabola is obtained by inter-changing the x- and y-axes in the above derivation.   That is, we start by placing the y-axis along the principal axis.

6.2.3 Theorem.   *The standard equation of the parabola with focus at $(0, f)$ and directrix $y = -f$ is*

$$x^2 = 4fy.$$

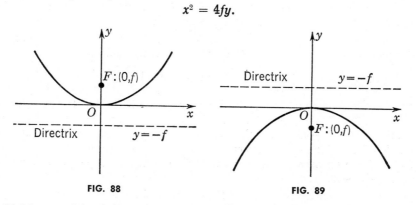

FIG. 88   FIG. 89

If f is a positive number the parabola $x^2 = 4fy$ opens upward as shown in Fig. 88.   If f is negative, the parabola opens downward (Fig. 89).

EXERCISES

Make a sketch for each exercise.

In Exercises 1 to 8, find the coordinates of the focus and the equation of the directrix for each parabola.

1. $y^2 = 2x$.

2. $y^2 = -28x$.

3. $x^2 = 6y$.

4. $x^2 = -16y$.

5. $y^2 - 5x = 0$.

6. $x^2 + 10y = 0$.

7. $3y^2 + 4x = 0$.

8. $2x^2 - 7y = 0$.

In Exercises 9 to 16, find the standard equation of each parabola from the given information.

9. Focus is $(3, 0)$.

10. Directrix is $x = 2$.

11. Directrix is $y + 4 = 0$.

12. Focus is $(0, -2)$.

13. Focus is $(-5, 0)$.

14. Directrix is $y - 6 = 0$.

15. Focus is $(4/3, 0)$.

16. Directrix is $x = -2/11$.

17. Find the equation of the parabola with vertex at the origin and principal axis along the x-axis, if the parabola passes through the point $(3, -1)$.

18. Find the equation of the parabola through the point $(-4, 2)$ if its vertex is at the origin and its principal axis is along the y-axis.

By a translation (see 5.6, Example 2) reduce to standard form the equations of the parabolas in Exercises 19 to 22.   In your sketch of the parabola show both sets of axes.

19. $y^2 - 8x + 4y + 12 = 0.$ **20.** $x^2 + 4x + 7y + 25 = 0.$

21. $y^2 + 2x - 2y - 7 = 0.$ **22.** $x^2 - 4x - 3y + 19 = 0.$

23. Show that by an appropriate translation the equation $(y - k)^2 = 4f(x - h)$ can be reduced to the standard form $y'^2 = 4fx'$. What are the coordinates of the vertex of the parabola relative to the original axes?

24. Show that by an appropriate translation the equation $(x - h)^2 = 4f(y - k)$ can be reduced to the standard form $x'^2 = 4fy'$. Find the coordinates of the vertex and of the focus, relative to the original axes.

In Exercises 25 to 28 sketch the parabolas whose (nonstandard) equations are given. What are the coordinates of the vertex of each parabola?

25. $(y - 1)^2 = 6(x + 5).$ **26.** $(x + 4)^2 = -16(y - 1).$

27. $(y + 3)^2 = 2(x - 7).$ **28.** $(y + 2)^2 = -12(x + 6).$

29. Find the equation of the parabola with vertex at $(-3, -4)$ and focus at $(1, -4)$. (Hint: Draw new axes, respectively parallel to the original axes, with new origin at $(-3, -4)$. Find the equation of the parabola relative to the new axes. Then translate back to the original axes.)

30. Find the equation of the parabola whose vertex is at $(-3, 2)$ and whose focus is $(-3, -1)$.

31. Use the definition 6.2.1 to find the equation of the parabola whose focus is $(2, 1)$ and whose directrix is $4x + 3y + 2 = 0$. (Note: This parabola is not in standard position so neither Theorem 6.2.2 nor 6.2.3 applies.)

32. From the definition 6.2.1 find the equation of the parabola whose focus is $(-2, 2)$ and whose directrix is $3x - 2y - 6 = 0$.

6.3 CENTRAL CONICS $(e \neq 1)$

If $e \neq 1$, the conic is an ellipse or a hyperbola (6.1.2). Each ellipse and each hyperbola has two vertices (6.1.3). The point midway between the vertices is called the **center** of the conic.

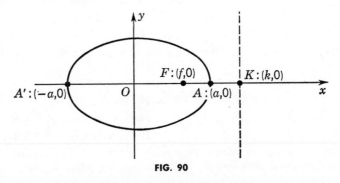

FIG. 90

Since a parabola has only one vertex, it cannot have a center. Ellipses and hyperbolas are called **central conics.**

A central conic is said to be in **standard position** when its center is the origin and its principal axis is one of the coordinate axes.

Place the origin of coordinates at the center of a central conic and the x-axis along the principal axis (Figs. 90 and 91). Call the vertices A' and A, with A' to the left of A. Let $OA = a$, a positive number. Then the coordinates of A are $(a, 0)$ and the coordinates of A' are $(-a, 0)$. We seek the coordinates of the focus, F, and the equation of the directrix, in terms of the known positive numbers a and e.

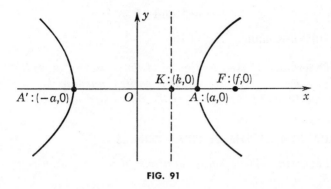

FIG. 91

Indicate by K the point of intersection of the directrix and the x-axis. Temporarily denote the coordinates of F by $(f, 0)$ and the coordinates of K by $(k, 0)$. We seek the values of f and k in terms of a and e.

Since A is on the conic we have, by the definition of a conic (6.1.1),

$$|FA| = e|KA|.$$

But $FA = a - f$ and $KA = a - k$ (2.1.3). Therefore

$$|a - f| = e|a - k|.$$

Squaring both members to remove the absolute value signs (1.4.3), we have

(1) $$a^2 - 2af + f^2 = e^2(a^2 - 2ak + k^2).$$

Again, A' is on the locus, so

$$|FA'| = e|KA'|.$$

But $FA' = -a - f$ and $KA' = -a - k$ (2.1.3). Therefore

$$|-a - f| = e|-a - k|.$$

Squaring both members, we obtain

(2) $$a^2 + 2af + f^2 = e^2(a^2 + 2ak + k^2).$$

Adding equations (1) and (2), member by member, we get

(3) $$a^2 + f^2 = e^2(a^2 + k^2).$$

Subtracting equation (1) from equation (2), member by member, we have

(4) $$f = e^2k.$$

Solving (3) and (4) simultaneously for f and k in terms of a and e, we find

$$f = \pm ae \quad \text{and} \quad k = \pm a/e.$$

By equation (4), f and k have the same sign. We will take them both positive so that the focus and directrix will lie to the right of the origin (Figs. 90 and 91). Then, since a and e are positive,

$$f = ae \quad \text{and} \quad k = \frac{a}{e}.$$

Our results are summarized in the

6.3.1 Theorem. *If the coordinates of the vertices of a central conic with eccentricity e are $(\pm a, 0)$, where a is a positive number, the coordinates of a focus are $(ae, 0)$ and the equation of the corresponding directrix is $x = a/e$.*

6.4   EQUATION OF THE CENTRAL CONICS

6.4.1 Theorem. *The equation of a central conic with focus at $(ae, 0)$ and directrix $x = a/e$ is*

$$\frac{x^2}{a^2} + \frac{y^2}{a^2(1 - e^2)} = 1,$$

where $a > 0$.

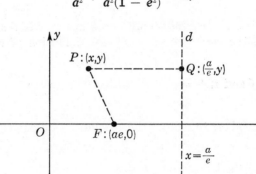

FIG. 92

Proof. Let $P:(x, y)$ be any point on the central conic (Fig. 92). Draw a perpendicular from P to the directrix and call its foot Q. By 2.1.1 and 2.1.2, the coordinates of Q are $(a/e, y)$.

Since P is on the locus,
$$|FP| = e|QP| \qquad \text{(by 6.1.1)}.$$

But $|FP| = \sqrt{(x - ae)^2 + y^2}$ and $QP = x - a/e$ (2.1.3). Therefore,

$$\sqrt{(x - ae)^2 + y^2} = e|x - a/e|.$$

Squaring both members and collecting terms, we get

$$(1 - e^2)x^2 + y^2 = a^2(1 - e^2).$$

Dividing both members by $a^2(1 - e^2)$, we have

$$\frac{x^2}{a^2} + \frac{y^2}{a^2(1 - e^2)} = 1,$$

which completes the proof.

Since the equation in 6.4.1 contains no odd powers of either x or y, the central conic is symmetric with respect to both coordinate axes (by 3.6.6 and 3.6.8). Because of this symmetry it is clear that the ellipse or hyperbola must have a second focus, $F' : (-ae, 0)$, and a second directrix,

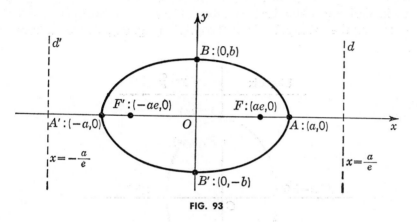

FIG. 93

$x = -a/e$ (Fig. 93). Either focus, along with its corresponding directrix, can be used to construct the whole conic.

6.4.2 Corollary. *The central conic*

$$\frac{x^2}{a^2} + \frac{y^2}{a^2(1 - e^2)} = 1$$

has two foci, $F:(ae, 0)$ and $F':(-ae, 0)$, whose corresponding directrices are $x = a/e$ and $x = -a/e$, respectively.

6.5 THE ELLIPSE $(e < 1)$

For the ellipse, $e < 1$, so that $a^2(1 - e^2)$ is positive and $\sqrt{a^2(1 - e^2)}$ is real. For simplicity of notation, let

$$b = a\sqrt{1 - e^2}.$$

On substituting this in the equation of 6.4.1 we obtain

6.5.1 Theorem. *The standard equation of the ellipse with foci at $F:(ae, 0)$*

and $F':(-ae, 0)$ *and corresponding directrices* $x = a/e$ *and* $x = -a/e$ *is*

$$\frac{x^2}{a^2} + \frac{y^2}{b^2} = 1,$$

where a *and* b *are positive numbers and* $b^2 = a^2(1 - e^2)$.

The segment $\overline{AA'}$ of the principal axis of the ellipse lying between the vertices, $(\pm a, 0)$ is called the **major axis** of the ellipse (Fig. 93). Its length is $2a$.

The segment $\overline{BB'}$ of the y-axis intercepted by the ellipse is the **minor axis** of the ellipse (Fig. 93). Its length is $2b$.

If, in deriving a standard equation of the ellipse, we had placed the y-axis along the principal axis of the ellipse (Fig. 94), we would have the

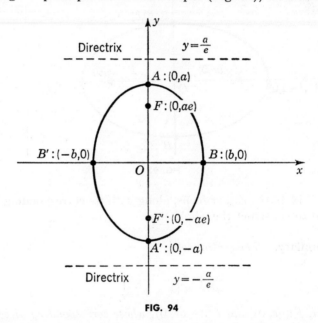

FIG. 94

6.5.2 Theorem. *If the foci of an ellipse are at* $(0, \pm ae)$ *and the directrices are* $y = \pm a/e$, *then the standard equation of the ellipse is*

$$\frac{x^2}{b^2} + \frac{y^2}{a^2} = 1,$$

where a *and* b *are positive numbers and* $b^2 = a^2(1 - e^2)$.

We know that, for the ellipse, $0 < e < 1$ and therefore $1 - e^2$ is a positive number less than 1. From this and from $b^2 = a^2(1 - e^2)$ we see that always $a^2 > b^2$ in the equation of the ellipse. This makes it easy for us to decide in a given numerical equation whether the foci are on the x-axis or the y-axis.   For example, in the ellipse

$$\frac{x^2}{9} + \frac{y^2}{4} = 1$$

we have $9 > 4$ and therefore 9 must be a^2 and 4 must be b^2.   Thus 6.5.1
applies and the foci are on the x-axis.   On the other hand, in

$$\frac{x^2}{6} + \frac{y^2}{16} = 1$$

we have $b^2 = 6$ and $a^2 = 16$, so that 6.5.2 applies and the foci are on the
y-axis.

Example.   Find the vertices, foci, directrices, eccentricity, and the lengths of
the major and minor axes of the ellipse

$$\frac{x^2}{25} + \frac{y^2}{9} = 1.$$

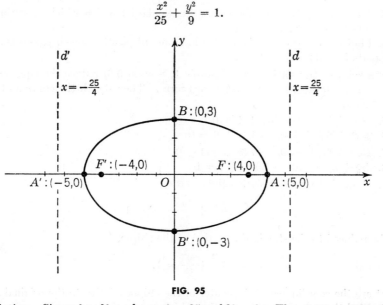

FIG. 95

Solution.   Since $a^2 > b^2$, we have $a^2 = 25$ and $b^2 = 9$.   Thus 6.5.1 applies.   The
vertices are $(\pm 5, 0)$ and the lengths of the major and minor axes are 10 and 6,
respectively.   Now $b^2 = a^2(1 - e^2)$.   Substituting the values of b^2 and a^2, we
have $9 = 25(1 - e^2)$.   Solving for e, we find $e = 4/5$.   Therefore $ae = 4$ and
$a/e = 25/4$, so the coordinates of the foci are $(\pm 4, 0)$ and the equations of the
directrices are $x = \pm 25/4$ (Fig. 95).

EXERCISES

Make a sketch for each exercise.

Find the eccentricity, the coordinates of the foci and of the vertices, the equations of the directrices, and the lengths of the major and minor axes for the ellipses
in Exercises 1 to 6.

1. $\dfrac{x^2}{9} + \dfrac{y^2}{4} = 1.$ **2.** $\dfrac{x^2}{36} + \dfrac{y^2}{25} = 1.$

3. $\dfrac{x^2}{4} + \dfrac{y^2}{16} = 1.$ **4.** $\dfrac{x^2}{10} + \dfrac{y^2}{5} = 1.$

5. $36x^2 + 9y^2 = 324.$ **6.** $9x^2 + 12y^2 = 108.$

In Exercises 7 to 12, find the equation of the ellipse in standard position from the given data.

7. A focus at $(4, 0)$ and eccentricity $1/2$.

8. A focus at $(-3, 0)$ and a vertex at $(6, 0)$.

9. A focus at $(0, 2)$ and length of minor axis 6.

10. A focus at $(0, -5)$ and eccentricity $1/3$.

11. A vertex at $(5, 0)$ and passing through the point $(2, 3)$.

12. A focus at $(0, -2)$ and directrix $y = -6$.

13. Find the equation of the ellipse in standard position which goes through the points $(2, 3)$ and $(3, 1)$.

14. Find the equation of the ellipse in standard position which passes through the points $(-5, 1)$ and $(-4, -2)$.

By a suitable translation (see Example 1, Section 5.6) reduce the equations of ellipses in Exercises 15 to 18 to standard form. Then sketch the curve and both sets of axes.

15. $x^2 + 4y^2 - 2x + 16y + 1 = 0.$

16. $25x^2 + 9y^2 + 150x - 18y + 9 = 0.$

17. $25x^2 + 36y^2 + 50x - 72y - 839 = 0.$

18. $2x^2 + 5y^2 + 20x - 30y + 75 = 0.$

19. Show that by a translation the equation

$$\frac{(x - h)^2}{a^2} + \frac{(y - k)^2}{b^2} = 1$$

can be reduced to the standard equation of the ellipse,

$$\frac{x'^2}{a^2} + \frac{y'^2}{b^2} = 1.$$

What are the coordinates of the center of the ellipse relative to the original axes?

20. Find the equations of translation which reduce the equation

$$\frac{(x - h)^2}{b^2} + \frac{(y - k)^2}{a^2} = 1$$

to the standard equation of the ellipse,

$$\frac{x'^2}{b^2} + \frac{y'^2}{a^2} = 1.$$

What are the coordinates of the center of the ellipse relative to the original axes?

In Exercises 21 to 26, sketch the ellipses whose equations are given. Find the coordinates of the center of each ellipse.

21. $\dfrac{(x - 3)^2}{25} + \dfrac{(y + 1)^2}{16} = 1.$ **22.** $\dfrac{(x + 2)^2}{16} + \dfrac{(y - 5)^2}{9} = 1.$

23. $\dfrac{(x-4)^2}{16} + \dfrac{(y-2)^2}{49} = 1.$ **24.** $\dfrac{(x+6)^2}{4} + \dfrac{y^2}{36} = 1.$

25. $\dfrac{(x-7)^2}{7} + \dfrac{(y+4)^2}{4} = 1.$ **26.** $\dfrac{x^2}{8} + \dfrac{(y-2)^2}{12} = 1.$

27. Use definition 6.1.1 to find the equation of the ellipse with focus at $(1, 3)$ and corresponding directrix $2x + y + 6 = 0$, if its eccentricity is $1/2$. (Note: Since the ellipse is not in standard position, Theorems 6.5.1 and 6.5.2 do not apply.)

28. Use definition 6.1.1 to find the equation of the ellipse with focus $(2, -2)$ and corresponding directrix $2x - 3y + 6 = 0$, if its eccentricity is $2/3$.

6.6   THE HYPERBOLA $(e > 1)$

In the case of the hyperbola, $e > 1$, so that $a^2(e^2 - 1)$ is positive and therefore $\sqrt{a^2(e^2 - 1)}$ is real. For simplicity of notation let

$$b = a\sqrt{e^2 - 1}.$$

On substituting this in the equation of 6.4.1 we obtain

6.6.1 Theorem. *The standard equation of the hyperbola with foci* $F:(ae, 0)$ *and* $F':(-ae, 0)$ *and corresponding directrices* $x = a/e$ *and* $x = -a/e$ *is*

$$\frac{x^2}{a^2} - \frac{y^2}{b^2} = 1,$$

where a and b are positive numbers and $b^2 = a^2(e^2 - 1).$

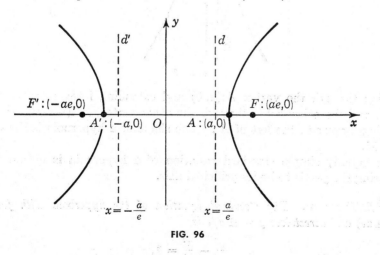

FIG. 96

The segment $\overline{AA'}$ of the principal axis lying between the vertices $(\pm a, 0)$ is called the **transverse axis** of the hyperbola (Fig. 96). Its length is $2a$.

Since the standard equation of the hyperbola contains no odd power of either x or y, the hyperbola is symmetric with respect to both of the co-ordinate axes (by 3.6.6 and 3.6.8).

The hyperbola does not intersect the y-axis; for if we substitute $x = 0$ in the equation of the hyperbola (6.6.1) we get $y = \pm b\sqrt{-1}$, which is imaginary. However, the line segment terminated by the points $(0, \pm b)$ is called the **conjugate axis** of the hyperbola. Its length is $2b$.

Solving the equation of the hyperbola for y in terms of x, we obtain

$$(1) \qquad\qquad y = \pm\frac{b}{a}\sqrt{x^2 - a^2}.$$

If $x^2 < a^2$, the expression $\sqrt{x^2 - a^2}$ is imaginary. Therefore y is imaginary in equation (1) for all values of x between $-a$ and a. Thus the hyperbola fails to exist in the vertical band lying between the lines $x = a$ and $x = -a$.

Moreover, y is real in equation (1) for all other values of x. This means that the hyperbola is not a closed curve but consists of two branches—one

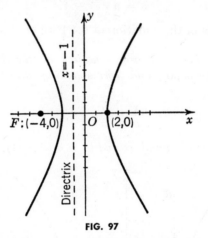

FIG. 97

passing through the vertex $A:(a, 0)$ and extending forever to the right of A, and the other going through the other vertex, $A':(-a, 0)$, and extending forever to the left of A'. The shape of a hyperbola is shown in Fig. 96.

An equally simple standard equation of a hyperbola is obtained by choosing the y-axis to be its principal axis.

6.6.2 Theorem. *The standard equation of the hyperbola with foci at* $(0, \pm ae)$ *and directrices* $y = \pm a/e$ *is*

$$\frac{y^2}{a^2} - \frac{x^2}{b^2} = 1,$$

where a and b are positive numbers and $b^2 = a^2(e^2 - 1)$.

Example. Find the standard equation of the conic with a focus at $(-4, 0)$ and corresponding directrix $x = -1$.

Solution. The x-axis is the principal axis of the conic, since it goes through the given focus and is perpendicular to the given directrix (Fig. 97). Then $(4, 0)$ and $x = 1$ are also a focus and a directrix. Using 6.6.1, we have $ae = 4$ and $a/e = 1$. Hence $a^2 = 4$, $a = 2$, and $e = 2$.

Substituting these results in $b^2 = a^2(e^2 - 1)$, we obtain $b^2 = 12$. Therefore the desired equation (6.6.1) is

$$\frac{x^2}{4} - \frac{y^2}{12} = 1.$$

EXERCISES

Make a sketch for each exercise.

Find the eccentricity, the coordinates of the foci and of the vertices, the equations of the directrices, and the lengths of the transverse and conjugate axes for the hyperbolas in Exercises 1 to 6.

1. $\dfrac{x^2}{9} - \dfrac{y^2}{4} = 1.$ **2.** $\dfrac{x^2}{25} - \dfrac{y^2}{16} = 1.$

3. $4y^2 - 16x^2 = 64.$ **4.** $6x^2 - 15y^2 = 90.$

5. $36y^2 - 10x^2 = 360.$ **6.** $4x^2 - 49y^2 = 196.$

In Exercises 7 to 14, the hyperbolas are in standard position. Find their equations from the given data.

7. A focus is $(3, 0)$ and the eccentricity is 2.

8. A focus is $(5, 0)$ and a vertex is $(4, 0)$.

9. A focus is $(0, 4)$ and the hyperbola goes through the point $(1, 3)$.

10. A focus is $(-\sqrt{17}, 0)$ and the corresponding directrix is $x = -5/\sqrt{17}$.

11. A vertex is $(0, -3)$ and the eccentricity is $3/2$.

12. The y-axis is its principal axis, its eccentricity is $\sqrt{6}/2$ and it passes through the point $(2, 4)$.

13. The x-axis is its principal axis and it passes through the two points $(-3, 2)$ and $(-6, 5)$.

14. A focus is $(0, -5)$ and the hyperbola goes through the point $(3, 4)$.

By a translation (see 5.6), reduce the equations of the hyperbolas in Exercises 15 to 18 to standard form.

15. $9x^2 - 16y^2 + 54x + 64y - 127 = 0.$

16. $9x^2 - 4y^2 - 18x - 8y - 31 = 0.$

17. $6x^2 - 10y^2 + 48x - 100y - 94 = 0.$

18. $25x^2 - 4y^2 - 350x + 24y + 1289 = 0.$

19. Show that by a translation the equation

$$\frac{(x - h)^2}{a^2} - \frac{(y - k)^2}{b^2} = 1$$

can be reduced to

$$\frac{x'^2}{a^2} - \frac{y'^2}{b^2} = 1.$$

What are the original coordinates of the center of the hyperbola?

20. What are the equations of translation which reduce the equation

$$\frac{(y - k)^2}{a^2} - \frac{(x - h)^2}{b^2} = 1$$

to the standard form

$$\frac{y'^2}{a^2} - \frac{x'^2}{b^2} = 1?$$

What are the original coordinates of the center of the hyperbola?

In Exercises 21 to 26, sketch the hyperbolas whose equations are given. What are the coordinates of the center of each hyperbola?

21. $\dfrac{(x - 5)^2}{4} - \dfrac{(y + 2)^2}{9} = 1.$

22. $\dfrac{(y - 7)^2}{36} - \dfrac{(x - 1)^2}{16} = 1.$

23. $\dfrac{(x + 4)^2}{20} - \dfrac{(y + 11)^2}{4} = 1.$

24. $\dfrac{(y + 3)^2}{49} - \dfrac{(x - 8)^2}{25} = 1.$

25. $\dfrac{x^2}{10} - \dfrac{(y - 6)^2}{5} = 1.$

26. $\dfrac{(x - 2)^2}{64} - \dfrac{(y + 7)^2}{16} = 1.$

27. Use definition 6.1.1 to find the equation of the hyperbola whose focus is $(0, 4)$ and whose corresponding directrix is $x - 2y + 2 = 0$, if its eccentricity is 3.

28. Use definition 6.1.1 to find the equation of the hyperbola with focus at $(-2, -1)$ and corresponding directrix $4x + 3y - 12 = 0$, if its eccentricity is 2.

6.7   ASYMPTOTES OF A HYPERBOLA

Hyperbolas enjoy a property not possessed by either parabolas or ellipses. Through the center of every hyperbola pass two straight lines called

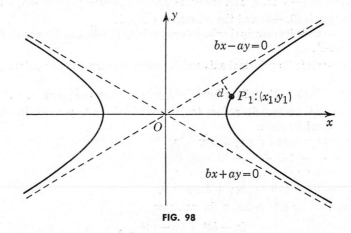

FIG. 98

asymptotes. As the hyperbola extends farther and farther out, it gets closer and closer to the asymptotes. In fact, sufficiently far out the hyperbola will be as close to an asymptote as we please. Yet the hyperbola never actually touches its asymptotes. This situation is sometimes pic-turesquely expressed by saying that a hyperbola is "tangent to its asymp-totes at infinity."

6.7.1 Theorem. *The two lines*

$$\frac{x}{a} - \frac{y}{b} = 0 \quad \text{and} \quad \frac{x}{a} + \frac{y}{b} = 0$$

are asymptotes of the hyperbola

$$\frac{x^2}{a^2} - \frac{y^2}{b^2} = 1.$$

Proof. Let $P_1:(x_1, y_1)$ be any point on that part of the hyperbola which lies in the first quadrant (Fig. 98). Then

$$\frac{x_1^2}{a^2} - \frac{y_1^2}{b^2} = 1 \qquad \text{(by 3.1.2)},$$

or

(1) $$b^2x_1^2 - a^2y_1^2 = a^2b^2.$$

Equation (1) can be rewritten $(bx_1 - ay_1)(bx_1 + ay_1) = a^2b^2$, whence

(2) $$bx_1 - ay_1 = \frac{a^2b^2}{bx_1 + ay_1}.$$

Now the equation of the line

$$\frac{x}{a} - \frac{y}{b} = 0$$

can be written $-bx + ay = 0$, and the directed distance, d, from this line to the point $P_1:(x_1, y_1)$ is

(3) $$d = \frac{-bx_1 + ay_1}{\sqrt{a^2 + b^2}} \qquad \text{(by 4.4.1)}.$$

Substituting (2) in (3), we have

(4) $$d = \left(\frac{-a^2b^2}{\sqrt{a^2 + b^2}} \right) \left(\frac{1}{bx_1 + ay_1} \right).$$

As P_1 is chosen farther and farther out on the hyperbola in the first quad-rant, x_1 and y_1 become larger and larger, and the expression $1/(bx_1 + ay_1)$ approaches zero. Since the expression in the first parentheses of (4) is con-stant, it follows that d approaches zero. That is, the hyperbola gets as close as we please to the line $x/a - y/b = 0$ if we go sufficiently far out, yet the hyperbola never meets this line.

By symmetry, a similar situation prevails in the other quadrants.

Asymptotes are guiding lines and are of great help in sketching a hyperbola. When the equation is given in a standard form, say, 6.6.1, the student should first draw lightly the **fundamental rectangle,** whose vertices are the points (a, b), $(-a, b)$, $(-a, -b)$, and $(a, -b)$ (see Fig. 99). Its diagonals, extended, are the asymptotes, as may be verified. The vertices of the hyperbola are the points of intersection of the x-axis and the fundamental rectangle. A good sketch of the hyperbola can be quickly made without plotting a single point by simply drawing the hyperbola through its vertices, tangent to the vertical sides of the fundamental rectangle, and approaching closer and closer to the asymptotes as it moves farther out.

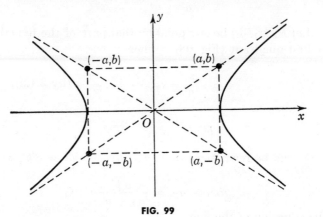

FIG. 99

A hyperbola whose asymptotes are perpendicular to each other is called an equilateral hyperbola.

Example.   Find the asymptotes of the hyperbola $25x^2 - 16y^2 = 400$. Sketch the curve.

Solution.   This equation can be written

$$\frac{x^2}{16} - \frac{y^2}{25} = 1.$$

By 6.7.1, the asymptotes are $\frac{x}{4} - \frac{y}{5} = 0$ and $\frac{x}{4} + \frac{y}{5} = 0$. To draw the hyperbola, we first construct the fundamental rectangle whose vertices are $(\pm 4, \pm 5)$. The asymptotes of the hyperbola are along the diagonals of this rectangle. We draw the hyperbola tangent to the vertical sides of the fundamental rectangle at A and A', and approaching more and more closely to the asymptotes as it goes farther and farther out (Fig. 100).

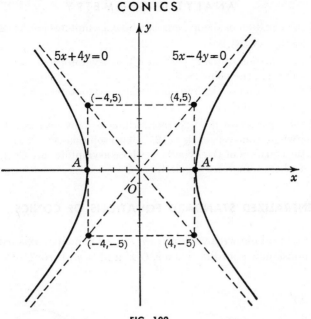

FIG. 100

EXERCISES

Make a sketch for each exercise.

In Exercises 1 to 6, find the equations of the asymptotes of each hyperbola. Then construct the fundamental rectangle, draw the asymptotes and sketch the hyperbola.

1. $4x^2 - 25y^2 = 100$.

2. $49x^2 - 9y^2 = 441$.

3. $25y^2 - 16x^2 = 400$.

4. $98y^2 - 128x^2 = 12544$.

5. $\dfrac{(x-3)^2}{16} - \dfrac{(y+5)^2}{9} = 1$.

6. $\dfrac{(y+2)^2}{10} - \dfrac{(x+4)^2}{36} = 1$.

7. Prove that all hyperbolas having the same asymptotes and the same principal axis have the same eccentricity.

8. Show that the hyperbolas

$$\frac{x^2}{4} - \frac{y^2}{25} = 1 \quad \text{and} \quad \frac{x^2}{4k} - \frac{y^2}{25k} = 1,$$

where k is any non-zero constant, have the same asymptotes. Draw three members of this family of hyperbolas by assigning particular values to k.

9. Find the equation of the hyperbola whose asymptotes are $5x \pm 3y = 0$ and whose vertices are $(\pm 6, 0)$.

10. Find the equation of the hyperbola whose asymptotes are $2x \pm y = 0$ and whose vertices are $(0, \pm 4)$.

11. Find the equation of the hyperbola whose asymptotes are $2x \pm y = 0$ and whose foci are $(\pm 10, 0)$.

12. Find the equation of the hyperbola whose asymptotes are $5x \pm 2y = 0$ and whose foci are $(0, \pm\sqrt{58})$.

13. Find the equation of the hyperbola whose asymptotes are $3x \pm 4y = 0$ and which passes through the point $(8, 3)$.

14. Find the equation of the hyperbola whose asymptotes are $7x \pm 2y = 0$ and which passes through the point $(6, 14\sqrt{3})$.

15. Find the equation of the hyperbola whose asymptotes are $x \pm 3y = 0$ and the length of whose transverse axis is 12. (Two solutions.)

16. Find the equation of the hyperbola whose asymptotes are $6x \pm 5y = 0$ and the length of whose transverse axis is 4.

★6.8 GENERALIZED STANDARD EQUATIONS OF CONICS

Consider a parabola with vertex at (h, k) and principal axis parallel to the x-axis.   Choose new coordinate axes, $O'x'$ and $O'y'$, through (h, k), respec-

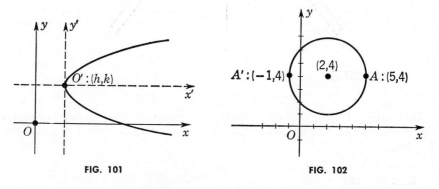

FIG. 101   FIG. 102

tively parallel to the original axes (Fig. 101).   Then the old coordinates, (x, y), of any point in the plane are related to its new coordinates, (x', y'), by means of the formulas of translation (5.5.1),

$$(1) \qquad\qquad x' = x - h,$$
$$y' = y - k.$$

The standard equation of the parabola relative to the new axes is

$$(2) \qquad\qquad y'^2 = 4fx' \qquad\text{(by 6.2.2).}$$

Substituting (1) in (2), we have

$$(y - k)^2 = 4f(x - h),$$

which is the equation of the given parabola in the original coordinates.   It is called a **generalized standard equation** of the parabola.

This proves the

6.8.1 Theorem. *The generalized standard equation of the parabola with vertex at (h, k) and principal axis parallel to the x-axis is*

$$(y - k)^2 = 4f(x - h),$$

where f is the directed distance from the vertex to the focus.

In like manner, it is easy to prove

6.8.2 Theorem. *The generalized standard equation of the ellipse with center at (h, k) and principal axis parallel to the x-axis is*

$$\frac{(x - h)^2}{a^2} + \frac{(y - k)^2}{b^2} = 1.$$

6.8.3 Theorem. *The generalized standard equation of the hyperbola with center at (h, k) and principal axis parallel to the x-axis is*

$$\frac{(x - h)^2}{a^2} - \frac{(y - k)^2}{b^2} = 1.$$

Example 1. Find the generalized standard equation of the ellipse with vertices at $(-1, 4)$ and $(5, 4)$, if its eccentricity is $1/3$. What are the coordinates of the foci and the equations of the directrices?

Solution. The center of the ellipse is midway between the vertices. Thus the coordinates of the center are $(2, 4)$ and $a = 3$ (Fig. 102). Since the principal axis of the ellipse is parallel to the x-axis, the generalized standard equation of the ellipse is

$$\frac{(x - 2)^2}{9} + \frac{(y - 4)^2}{b^2} = 1 \qquad \text{(by 6.8.2)},$$

where b^2 is yet to be determined.

Substituting $a = 3$ and $e = 1/3$ in $b^2 = a^2(1 - e^2)$ (from 6.5.1), we get $b^2 = 8$. Therefore the generalized standard equation of the ellipse is

$$\frac{(x - 2)^2}{9} + \frac{(y - 4)^2}{8} = 1.$$

Since $ae = 1$, the foci are 1 unit to the left and right of the center, $(2, 4)$. That is, the coordinates of the foci are $(1, 4)$ and $(3, 4)$.

Also, $a/e = 9$. Therefore the directrices cut the principal axis 9 units to the left and right of the center, $(2, 4)$. Thus the equations of the directrices are $x = -7$ and $x = 13$.

Example 2. Reduce the equation $9x^2 - 4y^2 + 54x - 8y + 41 = 0$ to generalized standard form and sketch the conic. What is its eccentricity?

Solution. The given equation is in the form $Ax^2 + Cy^2 + Dx + Ey + F = 0$, where $A \neq 0$, $C \neq 0$, and can be reduced to the form $Ax'^2 + Cy'^2 + F' = 0$ by a translation. Using the first method shown in Example 1 of 5.6, we rewrite the given equation as

$$9(x^2 + 6x) - 4(y^2 + 2y) = -41.$$

Completing the squares in the parentheses, we get

$$9(x^2 + 6x + 9) - 4(y^2 + 2y + 1) = 36,$$

or

$$9(x + 3)^2 - 4(y + 1)^2 = 36.$$

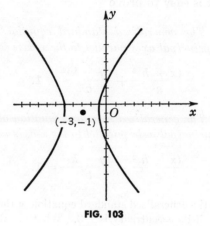

FIG. 103

Dividing both members by 36, we have the generalized standard equation of a hyperbola,

$$\frac{(x + 3)^2}{4} - \frac{(y + 1)^2}{9} = 1.$$

Comparing this equation with 6.8.3, we see that the center of the hyperbola is $(-3, -1)$ and that $a = 2$ and $b = 3$. It is now easy to sketch the locus (Fig. 103).

Substituting $a = 2$ and $b = 3$ in $b^2 = a^2(e^2 - 1)$ (from 6.6.1), we obtain $e = \sqrt{13}/2$.

EXERCISES

Make a sketch for each exercise.

1. Find the generalized standard equation of the parabola whose vertex is the point $(-2, 3)$ and whose focus is $(0, 3)$. What is the equation of its directrix?

2. The vertex of a parabola is $(-3, -3)$ and its directrix is $x - 1 = 0$. Find the generalized standard equation of the parabola.

3. Find the generalized standard equation of the parabola whose principal axis is $y + 3 = 0$, whose vertex is $(4, -3)$, and which goes through the point $(19/4, 0)$.

4. Find the generalized standard equation of the hyperbola whose vertices are $(5, -6)$ and $(-3, -6)$, and whose eccentricity is $5/4$.

5. Find the generalized standard equation of the hyperbola whose foci are $(-5, -3)$ and $(1, -3)$, if the length of its transverse axis is 4. What is its eccentricity?

6. Find the generalized standard equation of the hyperbola whose eccentricity is 2, if its center is $(-5, 4)$ and one focus is $(0, 4)$.

7. Find the generalized standard equation of the ellipse whose eccentricity is $2\sqrt{6}/5$, and whose vertices are $(-2, 6)$ and $(8, 6)$. What are the coordinates of its foci?

8. Find the generalized standard equation of the ellipse whose vertices are $(-2, -3)$ and $(10, -3)$, if one focus is $(8, -3)$. What is its eccentricity?

9. Derive $(x - h)^2 = 4f(y - k)$, the generalized standard equation of a parabola whose principal axis is parallel to the y-axis.

10. Derive $(y - k)^2/a^2 + (x - h)^2/b^2 = 1$, the generalized standard equation of an ellipse whose principal axis is parallel to the y-axis.

11. Derive $(y - k)^2/a^2 - (x - h)^2/b^2 = 1$, the generalized standard equation of a hyperbola whose principal axis is parallel to the y-axis.

12. Find the generalized standard equation of the hyperbola whose vertices are $(-2, 3)$ and $(-2, -2)$ and whose eccentricity is $5/4$. What are the coordinates of its foci and the length of its transverse axis?

13. The focus of a parabola is $(4, 3)$ and its directrix is $y + 1 = 0$. Find the generalized standard equation of the parabola.

14. Find the generalized standard equation of the ellipse whose foci are $(-5, -2)$ and $(-5, -8)$, if the length of its minor axis is 4.

Reduce the equations in Exercises 15–22 to generalized standard form. Sketch the conic and find its eccentricity, the coordinates of its foci, and the equations of its directrices.

15. $y^2 - 4x + 2y + 21 = 0$.   **16.** $y^2 + 8x - 6y + 25 = 0$.

17. $x^2 + 4x + 12y + 64 = 0$.   **18.** $x^2 - 14x - 2y + 55 = 0$.

19. $9x^2 + 25y^2 - 54x - 200y + 256 = 0$.
20. $9x^2 + y^2 - 90x - 2y + 217 = 0$.
21. $4x^2 - 3y^2 - 32x + 6y + 73 = 0$.
22. $16x^2 - 8y^2 + 64x + 32y - 96 = 0$.

6.9 OTHER DEFINITIONS OF CONICS

Ellipses and hyperbolas have other characteristic properties that might have been used for definitions.

Consider any point $P_1:(x_1, y_1)$ on the ellipse

$$\frac{x^2}{a^2} + \frac{y^2}{b^2} = 1.$$

The undirected distances between P_1 and the foci, namely, $|FP_1|$ and $|F'P_1|$, are called the **focal radii** of P_1.

Draw a horizontal line through P_1, intersecting the directrices d' and d in Q' and Q, respectively (Fig. 104).

From the definition of a conic (6.1.1)

$$|F'P_1| = e|Q'P_1| \quad \text{and} \quad |FP_1| = e|QP_1|,$$

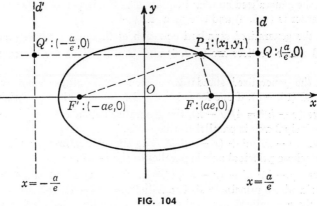

FIG. 104

whence

(1) $$|F'P_1| + |FP_1| = e[|Q'P_1| + |QP_1|].$$

The ellipse lies between its directrices—to the right of d' and to the left of d. Therefore $Q'P_1$ and P_1Q are positive and

$$|Q'P_1| + |QP_1| = Q'P_1 + P_1Q$$
$$= Q'Q \qquad \text{(by 1.2.3).}$$

But

$$Q'Q = \frac{a}{e} - \left(-\frac{a}{e}\right) = \frac{2a}{e}.$$

Therefore

$$|Q'P_1| + |QP_1| = \frac{2a}{e}.$$

Substituting this result in (1), we have

$$|F'P_1| + |FP_1| = 2a.$$

That is, *the sum of the focal radii of any point on an ellipse is constant, and is equal to the length of the major axis.*

This property is characteristic of ellipses. In fact, *an ellipse is often defined as the locus of points, the sum of whose undirected distances from two fixed points is constant.*

It is easy to show, in analogous fashion, that for any point on the hyperbola (6.6.1), the absolute value of the difference of its focal radii is $2a$. This property is characteristic of *the hyperbola, which is often defined as the locus of points, the absolute value of the difference of whose undirected distances from two fixed points is constant.*

The former property suggests a simple method for drawing an ellipse mechanically. Cover a board with a sheet of paper and push thumb tacks halfway in at F and F'. Tie the ends of a piece of string firmly together so as to form a loop of constant length. Place the loop over the tacks and pull taut with a pencil (Fig. 105). The string forms a triangle, PFF'. Move the pencil around the paper, keeping the string taut. The pencil will trace an ellipse with foci at F' and F, for $|FP| + |PF'| + |F'F|$ is constant for all positions of the pencil point, P, since this is the total length

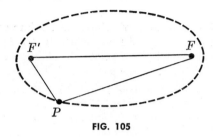

FIG. 105

of the string. But $|F'F|$ is constant in length. Therefore $|FP| + |PF'|$ is constant for all positions of P, and the curve is an ellipse.

6.9.1 NOTE. In the introduction to Chapter 6 we mentioned that ellipses, parabolas, and hyperbolas are obtained as the intersections of right circular cones and planes. A circle is also the intersection of a right circular cone and a plane perpendicular to the axis of the cone. But our definition of a conic (6.1.1) does not yield a circle for any value of e.

However, if we let the eccentricity approach zero while a remains constant in the standard equation of the ellipse,

(1)
$$\frac{x^2}{a^2} + \frac{y^2}{b^2} = 1,$$

the coordinates of the foci, $(\pm ae, 0)$, approach $(0, 0)$. Moreover, since $b^2 = a^2(1 - e^2)$, the quantity b^2 approaches a^2 as e approaches zero. Thus the equation (1) has the limiting form

$$\frac{x^2}{a^2} + \frac{y^2}{a^2} = 1, \quad \text{or} \quad x^2 + y^2 = a^2,$$

which is the equation of a circle with center at the origin and radius a. *A circle is a limiting form of the ellipse.*

This might have been surmised from the mechanical construction of the ellipse which we discussed above. When F and F' are coincident, the pencil traces a circle whose center is F and whose radius is equal to half the length of the loop of string.

EXERCISES

Make a sketch for each exercise.

1. Find the equation of the locus of points, the sum of whose undirected distances from the two points $(\pm 2, 0)$ is equal to 6. Name the locus.

2. Find the equation of the locus of points, the sum of whose undirected distances from the two points (± 3, 0) is equal to 10.

3. Find the equation of the locus of points, the sum of whose undirected distances from the points (0, ± 5) is equal to 12.

4. Find the equation of the locus of points, the absolute value of the difference of whose undirected distances from the points (± 5, 0) is equal to 4.   Name the locus.

5. Find the equation of the locus of points, the absolute value of the difference of whose undirected distances from the two points (0, ± 4) is equal to 3.

6. Find the equation of the locus of points, the absolute value of the difference of whose undirected distances from the points (± 6, 0) is equal to 5.

7. Find the equation of the locus of points, the sum of whose undirected distances from the two points ($\pm ae$, 0) is equal to $2a$.

8. Find the equation of the locus of points, the absolute value of the difference of whose undirected distances from the points ($\pm ae$, 0) is equal to $2a$.

9. Find the equation of the locus of points, the sum of whose undirected distances from the points (3, 6) and (7, 6) is equal to 8.

10. Find the equation of the locus of points, the absolute value of the difference of whose undirected distances from the points (-9, -2) and (1, -2) is equal to 4.

6.10   CONICS NOT IN ANY STANDARD POSITION

The simplicity of the standard equations of the conics is due to their symmetry with respect to the coordinate axes.   It is to be emphasized that the formulas for the coordinates of the foci and the equations of the di-

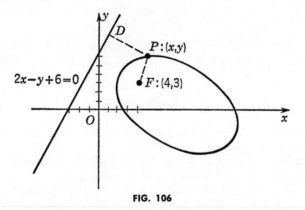

FIG. 106

rectrices and asymptotes, given in 6.2, 6.5, 6.6, and 6.7, apply *only when the conic is in standard position.*

Furthermore, the comparatively simple generalized standard equations of conics are possible only because the principal axis of the conic is parallel to a coordinate axis.

To find the equation of a conic which is not in standard position and whose principal axis is not parallel to a coordinate axis, we start with the definition of a conic (6.1.1) and proceed as in the second fundamental problem (3.7). This is illustrated in the following example.

Example. Find the equation of the ellipse with focus at $(4, 3)$ and corresponding directrix $2x - y + 6 = 0$, if its eccentricity is $2/3$.

Solution. After locating the focus and directrix, sketch the ellipse the way you did in Exercise 2 of Section 6.1.

Let $P: (x, y)$ be any point on the ellipse (Fig. 106). Draw $\overline{PD}$ perpendicular to the directrix. Then P is on the locus if and only if

(1) $$|FP| = e|DP|,$$

(by 6.1.1). But $|FP| = \sqrt{(x - 4)^2 + (y - 3)^2}$ (by 2.2.1) and

$$DP = (-2x + y - 6)/\sqrt{5} \text{ (by 4.4.1)}.$$

Substituting in (1), we have

(2) $$\sqrt{(x - 4)^2 + (y - 3)^2} = \frac{2}{3}\left|\frac{-2x + y - 6}{\sqrt{5}}\right|.$$

Squaring both members and simplifying, we find the equation of the ellipse to be

$$29x^2 + 16xy + 41y^2 - 456x - 222y + 981 = 0.$$

EXERCISES

Make a sketch for each exercise.

1. Find the equation of the parabola whose focus is $(-1, 0)$ and whose directrix is $4x + 3y - 12 = 0$.

2. Find the equation of the parabola whose focus is $(0, 2)$ and whose directrix is $2x - y - 1 = 0$.

3. Find the equation of the parabola with focus at $(3, -2)$ and vertex $(1, -3)$.

4. Find the equation of the parabola with focus $(-1, 4)$ and vertex $(2, 3)$.

5. Find the equation of the ellipse with focus at $(1, 1)$ and corresponding directrix $x + 2y - 6 = 0$, if its eccentricity is $1/3$.

6. Find the equation of the ellipse with focus $(0, 2)$ and corresponding directrix $x + 4y + 4 = 0$, if its eccentricity is $2/5$.

7. Find the equation of the ellipse with focus $(-2, 0)$ and corresponding directrix $x - 2y - 3 = 0$, if its eccentricity is $1/4$.

8. Find the equation of the ellipse with focus $(1, -1)$ and corresponding directrix $2x - y - 8 = 0$, if its eccentricity is $1/5$.

9. Find the equation of the hyperbola with focus at $(-2, 0)$ and corresponding directrix $x + y - 1 = 0$, if its eccentricity is 3.

10. Find the equation of the hyperbola with focus $(2, 2)$ and corresponding directrix $x + 3y + 2 = 0$, if its eccentricity is 2.

11. Find the equation of the hyperbola with focus at $(3, -1)$ and corresponding directrix $2x + y + 2 = 0$, if its eccentricity is $3/2$.

12. Find the equation of the hyperbola with focus $(-3, -2)$ and corresponding directrix $3x + 2y = 0$, if its eccentricity is 4.

6.11 APPLICATIONS OF CONICS

The angle between a conic and a focal radius to some point on it is defined as the angle between the tangent to the conic at that point and the focal radius.   In Fig. 107, FPT is equal to the angle which the focal radius, $\overline{FP}$, makes with the conic.

It will be shown in 8.3.1 that the focal radius to any point on a parabola and the line through that point parallel to the principal axis make equal angles with the parabola.   In Fig. 108, angle FPT is equal to angle GPT',

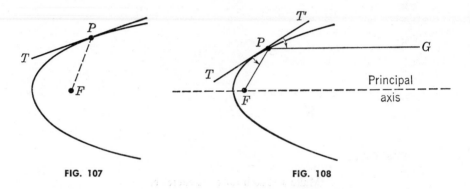

FIG. 107   FIG. 108

where P is any point on the parabola.   Now a law of reflection in physics states that the angle of incidence equals the angle of reflection.   So, if a parabola is revolved about its principal axis to form a hollow, reflecting shell, all light rays from the focus that strike the inside of the shell are reflected outward parallel to the principal axis (Fig. 109).   This property of parabolas is used in designing automobile headlights and searchlights, the light source being placed at the focus.   Of course, incoming rays which are parallel to the principal axis will be reflected to the focus and, since the light rays from a distant star are parallel for all practical purposes, parabolic mirrors are sometimes used in telescopes.   At football games a parabolic microphone is pointed at a distant section of the stadium to pick up cheers or music.

It will also be shown (in 8.5.1) that the two focal radii to any point on an ellipse make equal angles with the ellipse.   In Fig. 110, angle FPT is equal to angle $F'PT'$, where P is any point on the ellipse.   If a hollow shell is formed by revolving an ellipse about its principal axis, all sound waves coming from one focus will strike the inside of the shell and reflect to the other focus.   This explains the phenomenon of whispering galleries; when a dome is elliptical, a person at one focus may hear a distant person at the other focus while people in between may not.

Hyperbolas may be used to locate an enemy battery. Two listening posts record the time at which they hear the gun fire. The difference in these times is proportional to the difference of the distances of the gun from the two listening posts. Since a hyperbola can be defined as the locus of points, the absolute value of the difference of whose undirected distances from two fixed points is constant (see 6.9), the enemy gun lies on a certain

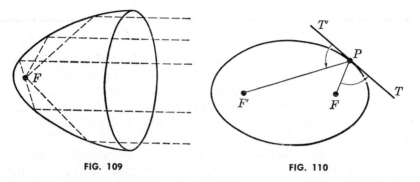

FIG. 109   FIG. 110

hyperbola whose foci are the listening posts. A third listening post along with either of the first two locates the gun on a second hyperbola. The enemy battery is on a point common to both hyperbolas.

A few of the many other applications of conics will be mentioned. The path of a projectile is a parabola if air resistance, etc., are neglected (see 10.2). The cable of an evenly loaded suspension bridge takes the form of a parabola. Arches are often parabolic. Some arches are elliptic. The orbits of the planets are ellipses with one focus at the sun; the earth's orbit is an ellipse whose eccentricity is approximately $\frac{1}{60}$. The paths of meteors are also elliptic before they enter the earth's atmosphere, but the paths of a few comets are parabolic.

7

The Second Degree Equation

We saw in Chapter 6 that the standard equations of the conics are all of the second degree. But in deriving those standard equations, one of the coordinate axes was placed along the principal axis of the conic.

In the present chapter we will prove that no matter where the coordinate axes are located relative to the conic, the Cartesian equation of the conic is always of the second degree.

We will also prove that whenever a second degree equation in x and y has a locus, the locus is a conic (including limiting and degenerate forms).

But first we need another transformation of coordinates.

7.1 THE ROTATION TRANSFORMATION

Consider a pair of coordinate axes, Ox and Oy (Fig. 111). If two new mutually perpendicular lines, Ox' and Oy', through the old origin are chosen

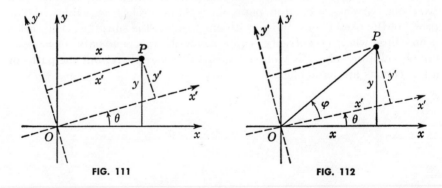

FIG. 111   FIG. 112

for new coordinate axes, then every point P in the plane (except O) will have two sets of coordinates, (x, y) and (x', y'). The original coordinates (x, y) are the directed distances from the original axes, Oy and Ox, to the point P, and the new coordinates (x', y') are the directed distances from the new axes, Oy' and Ox', to the point P. We seek formulas connecting the old and new coordinates of any point P.

7.1.1 Theorem.   *If new coordinate axes are chosen, having the same origin as the original axes and forming an angle θ with the original axes, then the coordinates (x, y) of any point P, relative to the original axes, and its coordinates (x', y'), relative to the new axes, are connected by the equations*

$$x = x' \cos \theta - y' \sin \theta,$$
$$y = x' \sin \theta + y' \cos \theta,$$

or

$$x' = x \cos \theta + y \sin \theta,$$
$$y' = -x \sin \theta + y \cos \theta.$$

Proof.   Let P be any point other than the origin (Fig. 112).   Denote the angle from the original x-axis to the new x'-axis by θ.   Draw $\overline{OP}$ and indicate the angle from the new x'-axis to $\overline{OP}$ by φ.

Then

$$\frac{x}{|OP|} = \cos (\varphi + \theta),$$

or

$$x = |OP| \cos (\varphi + \theta)$$
$$= |OP| (\cos \varphi \cos \theta - \sin \varphi \sin \theta) \qquad \text{(Appendix, 12)}.$$

But

(1) $$\sin \varphi = \frac{y'}{|OP|} \quad \text{and} \quad \cos \varphi = \frac{x'}{|OP|}.$$

Substituting above, we obtain

(2) $$x = x' \cos \theta - y' \sin \theta.$$

Similarly,

$$\frac{y}{|OP|} = \sin (\varphi + \theta).$$

Therefore

$$y = |OP| \sin (\varphi + \theta)$$
$$= |OP| (\sin \varphi \cos \theta + \cos \varphi \sin \theta) \qquad \text{(Appendix, 12)}.$$

By means of (1) this becomes

(3) $$y = x' \sin \theta + y' \cos \theta.$$

If we solve the equations (2) and (3) simultaneously for x' and y' in terms of x and y, we get

(4)
$$x' = x \cos \theta + y \sin \theta,$$
$$y' = -x \sin \theta + y \cos \theta,$$

which completes the proof.

Notice that if we substitute $-\theta$ for θ in the equations (2) and (3) and at the same time interchange x and x' and also y and y', we obtain

$$x' = x \cos (-\theta) - y \sin (-\theta),$$
$$y' = x \sin (-\theta) + y \cos (-\theta).$$

Since $\sin (-\theta) = -\sin \theta$ and $\cos (-\theta) = \cos \theta$ (Appendix, 9), these equations simplify to the equations (4). This is hardly surprising, since the angle from the new coordinate axes back to the original axes is $-\theta$.

The student need memorize only the first set of equations for rotation, since the second set of equations can be obtained so easily from the first set. Incidentally, we use the first set much more than the second set.

NOTE. In 5.5 we discussed a transformation of coordinates in which new axes were chosen respectively parallel to the original axes. That transformation has long been known as a **translation.**

In our present transformation of coordinates we select new coordinate axes through the same origin as the original axes but forming an angle θ with the original axes. This transformation is called a **rotation.**

Despite the terms *translation* and *rotation*, no motion is implied. They are technical terms indicating in each case that a new pair of mutually perpendicular lines is selected for new coordinate axes in the way we have described.

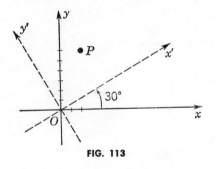

FIG. 113

Example 1. Find the new coordinates of the point $P:(2, 6)$ after a rotation in which the angle is 30° (Fig. 113).

Solution. The second set of equations for rotation in 7.1.1 become

$$x' = x \cos 30° + y \sin 30°,$$
$$y' = -x \sin 30° + y \cos 30°.$$

Substituting $x = 2$, $y = 6$, $\sin 30° = \frac{1}{2}$, and $\cos 30° = \frac{1}{2}\sqrt{3}$ in these equations, we have

$$x' = 2(\tfrac{1}{2}\sqrt{3}) + 6(\tfrac{1}{2}) = \sqrt{3} + 3,$$
$$y' = -2(\tfrac{1}{2}) + 6(\tfrac{1}{2}\sqrt{3}) = -1 + 3\sqrt{3}.$$

Thus the coordinates of P relative to the new axes are

$$(\sqrt{3} + 3, -1 + 3\sqrt{3}).$$

Example 2.   Find the new equation of the locus of $xy = 1$ after a rotation in which the angle is 45°.

Solution.   Since $\sin 45° = \frac{1}{2}\sqrt{2}$ and $\cos 45° = \frac{1}{2}\sqrt{2}$, the first set of equations of rotation (7.1.1) become

$$x = \tfrac{1}{2}\sqrt{2}\,(x' - y'),$$

$$y = \tfrac{1}{2}\sqrt{2}\,(x' + y').$$

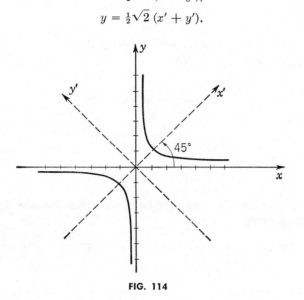

FIG. 114

Substituting these expressions in the given equation, we obtain

$$\tfrac{1}{2}(x' - y')\,(x' + y') = 1,$$

or

$$\frac{x'^2}{2} - \frac{y'^2}{2} = 1,$$

which represents an equilateral hyperbola (6.7) in standard position relative to the new axes, Ox' and Oy' (Fig. 114).

EXERCISES

Make a sketch for each exercise and show both sets of axes.

1. Find the new coordinates of the points $(3, 1)$, $(-2, 2)$, $(0, \sqrt{2})$, and $(2\sqrt{2}, -\sqrt{2})$ after the rotation in which the angle is 45°.

2. Find the new coordinates of the points $(-4, 6)$, $(1, \sqrt{3})$, and $(-2\sqrt{3}, 2)$ after a rotation in which $\theta = 60°$.

3. Solve the first pair of equations in Theorem 7.1.1 for x' and y' in terms of x and y, to obtain the second pair of equations.

4. Find the new equation of the line $x - \sqrt{3}y - 4 = 0$ after a rotation in which the angle is 30°.

5. Find the new equation of the line $4x + 3y - 5 = 0$ after a rotation in which $\tan \theta = 3/4$.

6. Find the new equation of the circle $x^2 + y^2 = 25$ after a rotation in which $\theta = 30°$.

7. Find the new equation of the curve $5x^2 - 6xy + 5y^2 - 36 = 0$ after a rotation in which $\theta = 45°$.

8. Find the new equation of the curve

$$9x^2 - 24xy + 16y^2 - 120x - 90y = 0$$

after a rotation in which $\tan \theta = 3/4$.

9. Find the new equation of the curve

$$69x^2 + 480xy - 407y^2 - 1521 = 0$$

after a rotation in which $\tan \theta = 5/12$.

10. After a rotation in which the angle is 60°, the new equation of a curve is $x'^2 - 2\sqrt{3}x'y' + 3y'^2 + 8\sqrt{3}x' + 8y' = 0$. What was the original equation of the curve?

7.2 SIMPLIFICATION OF THE GENERAL SECOND DEGREE EQUATION BY ROTATION

The most general equation of the second degree in x and y is

(1) $$Ax^2 + Bxy + Cy^2 + Dx + Ey + F = 0,$$

where not all of A, B, and C are zero. As usual, we assume the coefficients to be real numbers.

Every real second degree equation in x and y can be so expressed. For example, in the equation $y = (2x - 3)/(x + 5)$ we have $A = 0$, $B = 1$, $C = 0$, $D = -2$, $E = 5$, and $F = 3$, since this equation can be rewritten $xy - 2x + 5y + 3 = 0$.

Substituting the equations of rotation,

$$x = x' \cos \theta - y' \sin \theta,$$
$$y = x' \sin \theta + y' \cos \theta,$$

in (1), we obtain

$$A(x'^2 \cos^2 \theta - 2x'y' \cos \theta \sin \theta + y'^2 \sin^2 \theta)$$
$$+ B(x'^2 \cos \theta \sin \theta + x'y' \cos^2 \theta - x'y' \sin^2 \theta - y'^2 \sin \theta \cos \theta)$$
$$+ C(x'^2 \sin^2 \theta + 2x'y' \sin \theta \cos \theta + y'^2 \cos^2 \theta)$$
$$+ D(x' \cos \theta - y' \sin \theta) + E(x' \sin \theta + y' \cos \theta) + F = 0.$$

If we collect terms, this becomes

(2) $$A'x'^2 + B'x'y' + C'y'^2 + D'x' + E'y' + F' = 0,$$

wherein

$$
\begin{aligned}
A' &\equiv A \cos^2 \theta + B \sin \theta \cos \theta + C \sin^2 \theta, \\
B' &\equiv B(\cos^2 \theta - \sin^2 \theta) - 2(A - C) \sin \theta \cos \theta, \\
C' &\equiv A \sin^2 \theta - B \sin \theta \cos \theta + C \cos^2 \theta, \\
D' &\equiv D \cos \theta + E \sin \theta, \\
E' &\equiv -D \sin \theta + E \cos \theta, \\
F' &\equiv F.
\end{aligned}
$$

(3)

We will show that if $B \neq 0$ in the equation (1), it is always possible to find a rotation which transforms (1) into an equation of the form (2), in which $B' = 0$. That is, we can always get rid of the $x'y'$-term by means of the proper rotation.

Since $\cos^2 \theta - \sin^2 \theta = \cos 2\theta$ and $2 \sin \theta \cos \theta = \sin 2\theta$ (Appendix, 13), the expression for B' in (3) can be rewritten

(4) $$ B' = B \cos 2\theta - (A - C) \sin 2\theta. $$

If $A = C$ in (4), then $B' = B \cos 2\theta$ and thus B' will be zero when $\cos 2\theta = 0$; that is, B' will be zero if $\theta = 45°$.

If $A \neq C$ in (4), B' will be zero if

$$ B \cos 2\theta - (A - C) \sin 2\theta = 0, $$

or

$$ \tan 2\theta = B/(A - C). $$

This proves the

7.2.1 Theorem.   *The equation*

$$ Ax^2 + Bxy + Cy^2 + Dx + Ey + F = 0 $$

is transformed into

$$ A'x'^2 + C'y'^2 + D'x' + E'y' + F' = 0 $$

by a rotation in which $\theta = 45°$ if $A = C$, and

$$ \tan 2\theta = \frac{B}{A - C} $$

if $A \neq C$.

Example.   By means of a rotation find a new equation of the locus of $41x^2 - 24xy + 34y^2 - 90x + 5y + 25 = 0$ which contains no $x'y'$ term.

Solution.   Since $A \neq C$ we choose θ, the angle of rotation, so that

$$ \tan 2\theta = \frac{B}{A - C} = \frac{-24}{7}. $$

From $\tan 2\theta = -24/7$, we must find $\sin\theta$ and $\cos\theta$. From the sketch (Fig. 115) we read $\cos 2\theta = -7/25$. Using the half-angle formulas from trigonometry (Appendix, 14), we obtain

$$\cos\theta = \sqrt{\frac{1 - \frac{7}{25}}{2}} = \frac{3}{5}, \quad \sin\theta = \frac{4}{5}.$$

Thus the equations of rotation are

$$x = \tfrac{1}{5}(3x' - 4y'), \quad y = \tfrac{1}{5}(4x' + 3y').$$

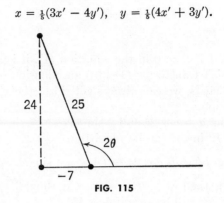

FIG. 115

Substituting in the given equation, we obtain

$$\tfrac{1}{25}[41(9x'^2 - 24x'y' + 16y'^2) - 24(12x'^2 - 7x'y' - 12y'^2)$$
$$+ 34(16x'^2 + 24x'y' + 9y'^2)] + \tfrac{1}{5}[-90(3x' - 4y') + 5(4x' + 3y')] + 25 = 0.$$

If we collect terms, this becomes

$$\tfrac{1}{25}[(369 - 288 + 544)x'^2 + 24(-41 + 7 + 34)x'y' + (656 + 288 + 306)y'^2]$$
$$+ \tfrac{1}{5}[(-270 + 20)x' + (360 + 15)y'] + 25 = 0,$$

or

$$\tfrac{1}{25}(625x'^2 + 1250y'^2) + \tfrac{1}{5}(-250x' + 375y') + 25 = 0,$$

or

$$x'^2 + 2y'^2 - 2x' + 3y' + 1 = 0,$$

which is the desired equation.

Since the equations of rotation,

$$x = x'\cos\theta - y'\sin\theta,$$
$$y = x'\sin\theta + y'\cos\theta,$$

are of the first degree in the variables x, y, x', and y', their substitution in the equation of a locus cannot result in a new equation of higher degree. That is, rotation cannot raise the degree of the equation of a locus.

Nor can rotation result in a new equation of lower degree for the locus. For if it did, the reverse rotation with angle $-\theta$, which restores the original coordinate system, would transform the new, lower degree equation of the locus back into the original, higher degree equation of the locus, which is impossible.

Therefore the degree of the equation of a locus is unchanged by a rotation.

The same reasoning applies to the equations of translation (5.5.1).

This is summarized in the

7.2.2 Theorem.   *The degree of the equation of a locus is invariant under a rotation or a translation.*

EXERCISES

In each of the following exercises transform the coordinates by an appropriate rotation so that the new equation of the locus will contain no xy term.

1. $9x^2 + 4xy + 6y^2 - 5 = 0.$ 2. $8x^2 + 5xy - 4y^2 + 2 = 0.$

3. $12x^2 + 7xy - 12y^2 - 5 = 0.$ 4. $2x^2 + 9xy + 14y^2 + 5 = 0.$

5. $x^2 + 4xy + y^2 + \sqrt{2}x - 3\sqrt{2}y + 6 = 0.$

6. $x^2 + 14xy + 49y^2 + \sqrt{2}y + 1 = 0.$

7. $9x^2 + 6xy + y^2 - \sqrt{10}x + 2 = 0.$

8. $x^2 + 12xy + 6y^2 - 2x + 5y + 1 = 0.$

9. $2x^2 - 24xy - 5y^2 + x + 3y + 9 = 0.$

10. $2x^2 + xy + 2y^2 + 3\sqrt{2}x + 7 = 0.$

7.3   FURTHER SIMPLIFICATION OF THE SECOND DEGREE EQUATION BY TRANSLATION

In the preceding section we proved that any second degree equation in x and y,

$$(1) \qquad Ax^2 + Bxy + Cy^2 + Dx + Ey + F = 0,$$

can be transformed by a suitable rotation into an equation of the form

$$(2) \qquad A'x'^2 + C'y'^2 + D'x' + E'y' + F' = 0.$$

We will now show how this latter equation can be further simplified by translation.

Since the degree of an equation is unchanged by a rotation (7.2.2), and since the equation (1) is of the second degree, the equation (2) is also of the second degree.   That is, the coefficients A' and C' in the equation (2) cannot both be zero.

Two cases will be considered according as both A' and C' are different from zero, or only one of A' and C' is different from zero.

CASE I

If $A' \neq 0$ and $C' \neq 0$, by the method of completing squares we can write (2) in the form

(3) $A'\left(x' + \dfrac{D'}{2A'}\right)^2 + C'\left(y' + \dfrac{E'}{2C'}\right)^2 = \dfrac{D'^2}{4A'} + \dfrac{E'^2}{4C'} - F'.$

If we substitute

$$x'' = x' + \frac{D'}{2A'}, \quad y'' = y' + \frac{E'}{2C'},$$

which is a translation with the new origin at

$$O'' : \left(-\frac{D'}{2A'}, -\frac{E'}{2C'}\right) \qquad \text{(by 5.5.1)},$$

we have

(4) $A'x''^2 + C'y''^2 = F'',$

where

$$F'' = \frac{D'^2}{4A'} + \frac{E'^2}{4C'} - F'.$$

CASE II

If either A' or C' in (2) is zero, say $A' = 0$ and $C' \neq 0$, (2) can be rewritten

(5) $C'\left(y'^2 + \dfrac{E'}{C'}y'\right) + D'x' + F' = 0.$

Completing the square in the parentheses, we obtain

(6) $C'\left(y' + \dfrac{E'}{2C'}\right)^2 + D'x' + F' - \dfrac{E'^2}{4C'} = 0.$

If $D' \neq 0$, (6) can be rewritten

(7) $C'\left(y' + \dfrac{E'}{2C'}\right)^2 + D'\left(x' + \dfrac{F'}{D'} - \dfrac{E'^2}{4C'D'}\right) = 0.$

Substituting

$$y'' = y' + \frac{E'}{2C'}, \quad x'' = x' + \frac{4C'F' - E'^2}{4C'D'},$$

in (7), which is equivalent to a translation with new origin at the point

$$O'' : \left(-\frac{4C'F' - E'^2}{4C'D'}, -\frac{E'}{2C'}\right),$$

we get

(8) $C'y''^2 + D'x'' = 0.$

If $D' = 0$, (6) can be written

(9) $C'\left(y' + \dfrac{E'}{2C'}\right)^2 + F' - \dfrac{E'^2}{4C'} = 0.$

If we substitute

$$y'' = y' + \frac{E'}{2C'}$$

in (9), which is equivalent to a translation in which the new origin is **at** $(0, -E'/2C')$, (9) becomes

(10) $$C'y''^2 + K = 0,$$

where $K = F' - E'^2/4C'$

We have proved the

7.3.1 Theorem.   *By a translation, the equation*

$$A'x'^2 + C'y'^2 + D'x' + E'y' + F' = 0$$

can always be reduced to the form

$$A'x''^2 + C'y''^2 = F'$$

if $A' \neq 0$ and $C' \neq 0$, and to the form

$$C'y''^2 + D'x'' = 0 \quad \text{or} \quad C'y''^2 + K = 0$$

when $A' = 0$ and $C' \neq 0$.

Similarly, if $A' \neq 0$ but $C' = 0$, equation (2) can be reduced to the form $A'x''^2 + E'y'' = 0$ or $A'x''^2 + L = 0$.

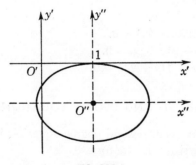

FIG. 116

Example.   Simplify the equation $x'^2 + 2y'^2 - 2x' + 3y' + 1 = 0$ by a translation.

Solution.   The given equation can be rewritten

$$(x'^2 - 2x') + 2\left(y'^2 + \frac{3y'}{2}\right) = -1.$$

Completing the squares in the parentheses by adding 1 and $\frac{9}{8}$ to both members, we obtain

$$(x'^2 - 2x' + 1) + 2\left(y'^2 + \frac{3y'}{2} + \frac{9}{16}\right) = -1 + 1 + \frac{9}{8},$$

or

$$(x' - 1)^2 + 2\left(y' + \frac{3}{4}\right)^2 = \frac{9}{8}.$$

If we substitute x'' for $x' - 1$ and y'' for $y' + \frac{3}{4}$, which is equivalent to a translation with a new origin at $(1, -\frac{3}{4})$ (see 5.5.1), the equation becomes

$$x''^2 + 2y''^2 = \frac{9}{8},$$

or

$$\frac{x''^2}{\frac{9}{8}} + \frac{y''^2}{\frac{9}{16}} = 1,$$

which represents an ellipse in standard position relative to the x''-, y''-axes (6.5.1). The locus is shown in Fig. 116.

EXERCISES

Reduce each of the following equations to standard form. Then draw both sets of axes and sketch the locus.

1. $y^2 - 3x + 8y + 22 = 0.$

2. $25x^2 + 4y^2 + 50x - 16y - 59 = 0.$

3. $x^2 + 6x + 9y = 0.$

4. $9x^2 - 5y^2 - 72x + 10y + 184 = 0.$

5. $9x^2 + 20y^2 + 90x + 40y + 65 = 0.$

6. $y^2 - 7x - 8y + 58 = 0.$

7. $x^2 + 2x - 6y + 49 = 0.$

8. $49x^2 + 16y^2 - 196x - 588 = 0.$

9. $x^2 - 2y^2 + 20x - 24y + 26 = 0.$

10. $5x^2 + 2y^2 + 10x - 44y + 237 = 0.$

7.4   LOCUS OF ANY SECOND DEGREE EQUATION

We have seen that every second degree equation in x and y, with real coefficients, can be written in the form

(1) $Ax^2 + Bxy + Cy^2 + Dx + Ey + F = 0,$

where not all of A, B, and C are zero.

By means of a rotation, (1) can be reduced to the form

(2) $A'x'^2 + C'y'^2 + D'x' + E'y' + F' = 0,$

where not both A' and C' are zero (by 7.2.1).

I. If $A' \neq 0$ and $C' \neq 0$, (2) can be reduced to the form

(3) $A'x''^2 + C'y''^2 = F''$

by a translation (7.3.1).

If A', C', and F'' have the same sign, (3) can be rewritten in the form 6.5.1 or 6.5.2, and its locus is an **ellipse** or a **circle,** which is a limiting form of an ellipse. If A' and C' have the same sign and F'' has the opposite sign, (3) has **no locus.** If A' and C' have the same sign and $F'' = 0$, the locus reduces to a single point. This is a limiting form of an ellipse and is sometimes called a **point-ellipse.**

If A' and C' have opposite signs in (3) and $F'' \neq 0$, the equation (3) can be written in the form 6.6.1 or 6.6.2, and the locus is a **hyperbola.** If A' and C' have opposite signs and $F'' = 0$, the equation (3) can be factored into two linear factors and the locus is two intersecting lines—a **degenerate hyperbola.**

II. If $A' = 0$ and $D' \neq 0$, (2) can be reduced to the form

(4) $$C'y''^2 + D'x'' = 0$$

by a translation (7.3.1). The locus of (4) is a **parabola** (6.2.2).

If $A' = D' = 0$, (2) can be reduced to the form

(5) $$C'y''^2 + K = 0$$

by a translation (7.3.1). If C' and K have the same sign there is **no locus.** If C' and K have opposite signs, equation (5) can be factored into two linear factors whose locus is two parallel lines—a **degenerate parabola.** If $K = 0$, the locus of (5) is two coincident lines—a **degenerate parabola.**

Similar results are obtained if $A' \neq 0$ and $C' = 0$.

All this may be summarized as follows:

CASE I. $A' \neq 0$, $C' \neq 0$.

1. A' and C' have like signs.
    (a) F'' has same sign as A' and C'.   **Ellipse.**
    (b) F'' has opposite sign from A' and C'.   **No locus.**
    (c) $F'' = 0$.   **Point-ellipse.**
2. A' and C' have unlike signs.
    (a) $F'' \neq 0$.   **Hyperbola.**
    (b) $F'' = 0$.   Two intersecting lines—**degenerate hyperbola.**

CASE II. $A' = 0$, $C' \neq 0$.

1. $D' \neq 0$.   **Parabola.**
2. $D' = 0$.
    (a) K has the same sign as C'.   **No locus.**
    (b) K has opposite sign from C'.   Two parallel lines—a **degenerate parabola.**
    (c) $K = 0$.   Two coincident lines—a **degenerate parabola.**

CASE III. $A' \neq 0$, $C' = 0$.   The results are similar to those in Case II.

Now the translation and rotation transformations of the coordinates have no effect on the locus. Its equation is simplified but the locus remains unchanged. We conclude, then, that if (1) has a locus, it is always a conic, or a limiting form of a conic, or a degenerate conic. This is stated in the

7.4.1 Theorem. *The locus, if any, of a second degree equation in plane Cartesian coordinates is always a conic, or a limiting form of a conic, or a degenerate conic.*

Since a translation is sufficient to reduce the equation (2) to a standard form, the principal axis of the conic, represented by (2), is parallel to, or coincident with, one of the coordinate axes. Moreover, since a properly chosen rotation, in which the angle is acute, will remove the xy term in equation (1), it follows that the principal axis of the conic represented by a second degree equation containing a term in xy is never parallel to a coordinate axis.

7.4.2 Corollary. *The xy term is present in a second degree equation if and only if the principal axis of the conic it represents is not parallel to either coordinate axis.*

Example. Reduce to standard form the equation $5x^2 - 3xy + y^2 + 65x - 25y + 203 = 0$. Then sketch the locus, showing all three sets of axes.

Solution. Since $A \neq C$ in the given equation we choose θ, the angle of rotation, so that

$$\tan 2\theta = \frac{B}{A - C} = \frac{-3}{5 - 1} = -\frac{3}{4}.$$

Then $\cos 2\theta = -\frac{4}{5}$, and

$$\sin \theta = \sqrt{\frac{1 - \cos 2\theta}{2}} = \sqrt{\frac{1 + \frac{4}{5}}{2}} = \frac{3}{\sqrt{10}},$$

$$\cos \theta = \frac{1}{\sqrt{10}}.$$

Thus the equations of rotation are

$$x = \tfrac{1}{10}\sqrt{10}(x' - 3y'), \quad y = \tfrac{1}{10}\sqrt{10}(3x' + y').$$

Substituting the equations of rotation in the given equation, we obtain

$$\tfrac{1}{10}[5(x'^2 - 6x'y' + 9y'^2) - 3(3x'^2 - 8x'y' - 3y'^2) + (9x'^2 + 6x'y' + y'^2)]$$

$$+ \tfrac{1}{10}\sqrt{10}[65(x' - 3y') - 25(3x' + y')] + 203 = 0,$$

or, if we collect terms,

$$x'^2 + 11y'^2 - 2\sqrt{10}x' - 44\sqrt{10}y' + 406 = 0.$$

By the method of completing the squares this equation can be rewritten

(1) $$(x' - \sqrt{10})^2 + 11(y' - 2\sqrt{10})^2 = 44.$$

If we substitute

(2) $$x'' = x' - \sqrt{10}, \quad y'' = y' - 2\sqrt{10},$$

in the equation (1), we get

(3) $$\frac{x''^2}{44} + \frac{y''^2}{4} = 1.$$

The substitution (2) is a translation with new origin at $(\sqrt{10}, 2\sqrt{10})$.

The locus of (3) is an ellipse in standard position relative to the x''- and y''-axes. To sketch it, we draw the original x- and y-axes (Fig. 117). Then we draw the

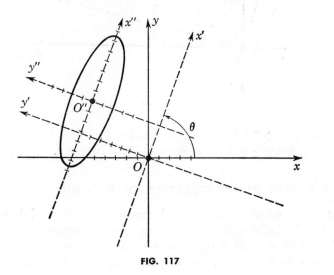

FIG. 117

x'- and y'-axes through the same origin but so that $\theta = $ arc tan 3 (see Example 1, Section 2.3). We now locate the point $(\sqrt{10}, 2\sqrt{10})$ relative to the x'- and y'-axes and draw the x''- and y''-axes through that point parallel to the x'- and y'-axes, respectively. Finally, we sketch the ellipse in standard position on the x''- and y''-axes.

EXERCISES

Reduce the following equations to standard form. Then sketch the curve, showing all three sets of axes.

1. $62x^2 + 168xy + 13y^2 + 380x - 90y - 575 = 0$.
2. $6x^2 + 3xy + 2y^2 + 81x + 17y + 236 = 0$.
3. $16x^2 - 24xy + 9y^2 + 85x + 30y + 175 = 0$.
4. $3x^2 + 2xy + 3y^2 - 12\sqrt{2}x + 4\sqrt{2}y + 24 = 0$.
5. $5x^2 - 6xy - 3y^2 + 168x + 24y + 612 = 0$.
6. $6x^2 - 5xy - 6y^2 + 78x + 52y + 26 = 0$.
7. $x^2 + 2xy + y^2 + 12\sqrt{2}x - 6 = 0$.
8. $4x^2 + 4xy + y^2 + 14x - 18y + 101 = 0$.
9. $1396x^2 - 600xy + 801y^2 + 1768x - 3666y - 1859 = 0$.
10. $7x^2 + 12xy + 2y^2 + 140x + 76y + 548 = 0$.

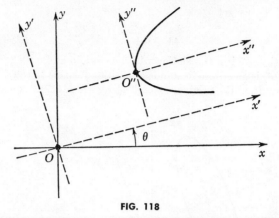

FIG. 118

11. $12x^2 - 12xy + 7y^2 + 60x - 118y + 511 = 0$.
12. $670x^2 + 840xy - 163y^2 + 2340x + 3172y + 2028 = 0$.

7.5   THE DEGREE OF THE EQUATION OF A CONIC

The standard equations of the conics are all of the second degree (Chapter 6).   But in deriving those equations, the coordinate axes were placed in special position relative to the conic.   It will now be proved that no matter where the coordinate axes are, the conic always has a second degree equation.

We recall that a parabola is in standard position, and therefore has a standard equation, if its principal axis is one of the coordinate axes and its vertex is the origin.

A central conic is in standard position, and has a standard equation, if its principal axis is one of the coordinate axes and its center is the origin.

Consider any conic not in standard position (Figs. 118 and 119).   By

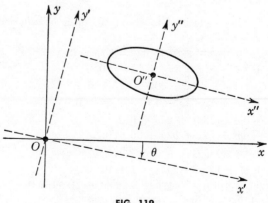

FIG. 119

means of an appropriate rotation and translation we can always select new x''- and y''-axes, with respect to which the conic *is* in standard position. Since the standard equation of the conic is of the second degree, and since the degree of an equation is unchanged by a rotation or a translation (7.2.2), the original equation of the conic must also be of the second degree.

This proves the

7.5.1 Theorem.   *The Cartesian equation of a conic is always of the second degree.*

7.6   THE INDICATOR

It was shown in 7.2 that if the coordinates are subjected to a rotation transformation, the equation

(1) $$Ax^2 + Bxy + Cy^2 + Dx + Ey + F = 0$$

becomes

(2) $$A'x'^2 + B'x'y' + C'y'^2 + D'x' + E'y' + F' = 0,$$

wherein

(3)
$$A' \equiv A \cos^2 \theta + B \sin \theta \cos \theta + C \sin^2 \theta,$$
$$B' \equiv B(\cos^2 \theta - \sin^2 \theta) - 2(A - C) \sin \theta \cos \theta,$$
$$C' \equiv A \sin^2 \theta - B \sin \theta \cos \theta + C \cos^2 \theta.$$

We will now prove that $B^2 - 4AC$ in equation (1) is equal to $B'^2 - 4A'C'$ in equation (2). This does not mean that A, B, and C are respectively equal to A', B', and C', but that the quantity $B^2 - 4AC$ is equal to the quantity $B'^2 - 4A'C'$. The expression $B^2 - 4AC$ in equation (1) is said to be *invariant under a rotation*. The importance of this will soon be apparent.

From (3),

$$
\begin{aligned}
B'^2 - 4A'C' &= [B(\cos^2 \theta - \sin^2 \theta) - 2(A - C) \sin \theta \cos \theta]^2 \\
&\quad - 4(A \cos^2 \theta + B \sin \theta \cos \theta + C \sin^2 \theta) \\
&\quad (A \sin^2 \theta - B \sin \theta \cos \theta + C \cos^2 \theta) \\
&= B^2(\cos^4 \theta - 2 \sin^2 \theta \cos^2 \theta + \sin^4 \theta + 4 \sin^2 \theta \cos^2 \theta) \\
&\quad - 4AB(\sin \theta \cos^3 \theta - \sin^3 \theta \cos \theta - \sin \theta \cos^3 \theta + \sin^3 \theta \cos \theta) \\
&\quad + 4BC(\sin \theta \cos^3 \theta - \sin^3 \theta \cos \theta - \sin \theta \cos^3 \theta + \sin^3 \theta \cos \theta) \\
&\quad + 4A^2(\sin^2 \theta \cos^2 \theta - \sin^2 \theta \cos^2 \theta) \\
&\quad - 4AC(2 \sin^2 \theta \cos^2 \theta + \cos^4 \theta + \sin^4 \theta) \\
&\quad + 4C^2(\sin^2 \theta \cos^2 \theta - \sin^2 \theta \cos^2 \theta)
\end{aligned}
$$

$$= B^2(\sin^2\theta + \cos^2\theta)^2 - 4AC(\sin^2\theta + \cos^2\theta)^2$$
$$= B^2 - 4AC.$$

Therefore,

$$B'^2 - 4A'C' = B^2 - 4AC.$$

We will now show the importance of this result. Suppose that we are given any second degree equation in x and y,

$$(1) \qquad Ax^2 + Bxy + Cy^2 + Dx + Ey + F = 0,$$

and that, by a suitably chosen rotation (7.2.1), this has been transformed into the equation

$$(4) \qquad A'x'^2 + C'y'^2 + D'x' + E'y' + F' = 0,$$

which contains no term in $x'y'$. Since this is an equation of the form (2) in which $B' = 0$, we have

$$B^2 - 4AC = B'^2 - 4A'C' = -4A'C'.$$

But we saw in 7.4 that the locus (if any) of (4) is a hyperbola or an ellipse according as A' and C' have opposite signs or like signs, that is, according as $-4A'C'$ is positive or negative. Moreover, (4) represents a parabola if either A' or C' is zero, that is, if $-4A'C'$ is zero. Thus the locus of (4) is a hyperbola, a parabola, or an ellipse according as $-4A'C'$ is positive, zero, or negative.

Since the locus of (1) is the same as the locus of (4), and since $B^2 - 4AC = -4A'C'$, it follows that the locus, if any, of (1) is a hyperbola, a parabola or an ellipse according as $B^2 - 4AC$ is positive, zero or negative. Of course, the locus may be degenerate.

This proves the

7.6.1 Theorem. *The locus, if any, of*

$$Ax^2 + Bxy + Cy^2 + Dx + Ey + F = 0$$

is a hyperbola, a parabola, or an ellipse (including the point-ellipse) according as $B^2 - 4AC$ is positive, zero, or negative.

For example, the locus of $16x^2 - 24xy + 9y^2 + 60x + 80y - 100 = 0$ is a parabola because $B^2 - 4AC = (-24)^2 - 4(16)(9) = 0$; the locus of $5x^2 - 3xy + y^2 + 65x - 25y + 203 = 0$ is an ellipse since

$$B^2 - 4AC = (-3)^2 - 4(5)(1) = -11;$$

and the locus of $3x^2 - 2y^2 - 24x - 4y + 40 = 0$ is a hyperbola because $B^2 - 4AC = (0)^2 - 4(3)(-2) = 24$.

The quantity $B^2 - 4AC$ is sometimes called the **indicator** of the equation $Ax^2 + Bxy + Cy^2 + Dx + Ey + F = 0$.

EXERCISES

1. Use the indicator to test the equations in the Exercises of Section 7.2.   Tell whether each conic is an ellipse, parabola, or hyperbola.

2. Use the indicator to determine the nature of the conics whose equations are given in the Exercises of Section 7.3.

3. Use the indicator to name the conics in the Exercises of Section 7.4.

★8

Tangents to Conics

8.1 INTRODUCTION

From our experience with lines and circles in plane geometry, we know that a straight line intersects a circle in two points, or is tangent to the circle, or misses the circle completely (Fig. 120). This might tempt us to say that a tangent to a circle is a line which intersects the circle in one and only one point.

But such a description could not serve as a definition for the tangents to most of the other plane curves. For example, the principal axis of a

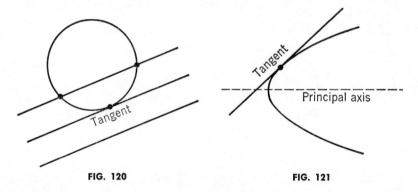

FIG. 120   **FIG. 121**

parabola intersects the parabola in one and only one point (see 6.1.3), yet surely is not what we intuitively think of as a tangent to the parabola (Fig. 121).

A definition which includes not only the tangents to circles but also the tangents to all other plane curves may be framed as follows. Let P_1 and P_2 represent any two neighboring points on a curve (Fig. 122). Think of P_1 as fixed in position and think of P_2 as moving along the curve and approaching P_1. As it does so, the secant through P_1 and P_2 "turns about" P_1. The limiting position of the secant as P_2 approaches P_1 along the curve is the **tangent** to the curve at P_1. By this we mean simply that we can make the angle between the secant and the tangent numerically as small as we please merely by taking P_2 on the curve sufficiently close to P_1.

We are given the coordinates of P_1, so the only additional information we need in order to write the equation of the tangent to the curve at P_1 is the slope of the tangent. In practice we use the

8.1.1 Definition. *Let P_1 and P_2 represent two neighboring points on a plane curve. The **slope of the tangent** to the curve at P_1 is the limit of the slope of the secant through P_1 and P_2 as P_1 remains fixed and P_2 moves along the curve and approaches P_1.*

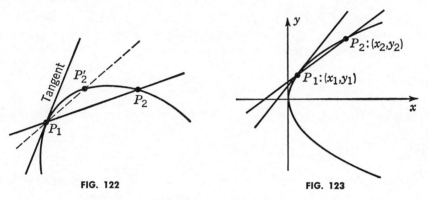

FIG. 122　　　　　　　　　　　　FIG. 123

8.2 TANGENTS TO A PARABOLA

Consider the parabola in standard position

$$y^2 = 4fx,$$

and let $P_1:(x_1, y_1)$ be any point on it other than the vertex (Fig. 123). We seek the equation of the tangent to the parabola at the point P_1.

Let $P_2:(x_2, y_2)$ be any other point on the parabola. The slope of the secant through P_1 and P_2 is

$$(1) \qquad\qquad m = \frac{y_2 - y_1}{x_2 - x_1} \qquad \text{(by 2.4.1).}$$

Since the points P_1 and P_2 are both on the parabola, their coordinates must satisfy the equation of the curve (3.1.2). Thus

$$(2) \qquad\qquad y_1^2 = 4fx_1,$$

and

$$(3) \qquad\qquad y_2^2 = 4fx_2.$$

Subtracting the equation (2) from the equation (3), member by member, we obtain

$$y_2^2 - y_1^2 = 4fx_2 - 4fx_1,$$

or

$$(y_2 - y_1)(y_2 + y_1) = 4f(x_2 - x_1),$$

which may be rewritten

$$\frac{y_2 - y_1}{x_2 - x_1} = \frac{4f}{y_2 + y_1}.$$

If we substitute this result in (1), the slope of the secant through P_1 and P_2 becomes

(4) $$m = \frac{4f}{y_2 + y_1}.$$

Now think of $P_1:(x_1, y_1)$ as fixed in position and $P_2:(x_2, y_2)$ as moving along the curve and approaching P_1. Then the value of y_2 will approach y_1 and the right member of (4) will approach

$$\frac{4f}{2y_1} = \frac{2f}{y_1}.$$

Therefore (by 8.1.1) the slope of the tangent to the parabola at P_1 is

(5) $$m_1 = \frac{2f}{y_1}.$$

Substituting this result in the point-slope form of the equation of a line, we find the equation of the tangent to the parabola at the point $P_1:(x_1, y_1)$ to be

$$y - y_1 = \frac{2f}{y_1}(x - x_1),$$

or

$$y_1 y - y_1{}^2 = 2fx - 2fx_1.$$

If we replace $y_1{}^2$ by its value as given in (2), this becomes

(6) $$y_1 y = 2f(x + x_1).$$

The expression (5) for the slope of the tangent was derived under the assumption that P_1 was not the vertex of the parabola, since in that case the tangent would be vertical (Fig. 123) and would have no slope. But if the coordinates of the vertex, $(0, 0)$, are substituted for x_1 and y_1 in the equation (6), we obtain $x = 0$ which is the equation of the vertical line through the vertex of the parabola. Therefore (6) is the equation of the tangent to the parabola at *any* point on it.

We have proved the

8.2.1 Theorem. *The equation of the tangent to the parabola $y^2 = 4fx$ at any point (x_1, y_1) on it is*

$$y_1 y = 2f(x + x_1).$$

Example 1. Find the equation of the tangent to the parabola $y^2 = 8x$ at the point $(2, -4)$.

Solution. Substituting $x_1 = 2$, $y_1 = -4$, and $f = 2$ in 8.2.1, we obtain

$$-4y = 4(x + 2),$$

or

$$x + y + 2 = 0,$$

which is the desired equation of the tangent at $(2, -4)$ (Fig. 124).

Example 2. Find the equation of the tangent to the parabola $x^2 = -10y$ at the point $(2\sqrt{5}, -2)$.

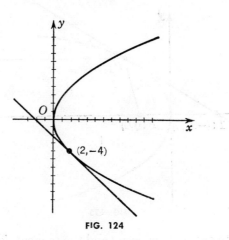

FIG. 124

Solution. By analogy with 8.2.1, the equation of the tangent to the parabola $x^2 = 4fy$ is

$$x_1x = 2f(y + y_1).$$

Substituting $f = -5/2$, $x_1 = 2\sqrt{5}$, and $y_1 = -2$, we get

$$2\sqrt{5}x = -5(y - 2),$$

or

$$2\sqrt{5}x + 5y - 10 = 0.$$

8.3 REFLECTION PROPERTY OF THE PARABOLA

It was stated in Section 6.11 that if a hollow reflecting shell is formed by revolving a parabola about its principal axis, and a light source is placed at the focus, all light rays from the focus which strike the inside of the shell are reflected parallel to the principal axis (Fig. 109). This depends on a geometric property of the parabola which we will now prove.

Let $P_1:(x_1, y_1)$ be any point on the parabola

$$y^2 = 4fx.$$

Then (by 3.1.2),

(1) $$y_1^2 = 4fx_1.$$

As usual (6.2.2), the focus is $F:(f, 0)$.

The tangent to the parabola at P_1 is

$$y_1 y = 2f(x + x_1) \qquad \text{(by 8.2.1)}.$$

This tangent intersects the x-axis in the point $T:(-x_1, 0)$.

Through P_1 draw a line l parallel to the principal axis (Fig. 125). We

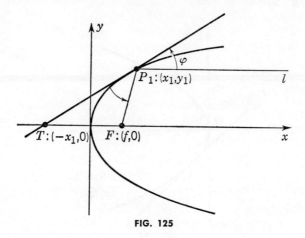

FIG. 125

will prove that the angle φ, between l and the tangent, is equal to the angle TP_1F.

Now

$$|FP_1| = \sqrt{(x_1 - f)^2 + y_1^2} \qquad \text{(by 2.2.1)}.$$

If we replace y_1^2 by its value from (1), this becomes

$$|FP_1| = \sqrt{x_1^2 + 2fx_1 + f^2}$$

$$= |x_1 + f|.$$

Moreover,

$$|TF| = |f + x_1| \qquad \text{(by 2.1.4)}.$$

Therefore

$$|FP_1| = |TF|,$$

and the triangle P_1TF is isosceles. Thus the angle FTP_1 is equal to the angle TP_1F. But angle $FTP_1 = \varphi$ (Appendix, 3). Therefore

$$\text{angle } TP_1F = \varphi.$$

This proves the

8.3.1 Theorem. *The tangent to a parabola at any point P_1 makes equal angles with the focal radius to P_1 and the line through P_1 parallel to the principal axis.*

A law of physics says that when a light ray strikes a reflecting surface, the angle of incidence is equal to the angle of reflection. It follows from this and from the above theorem that light rays from the focus of a parabolic reflector are reflected parallel to the principal axis.

By the same principles light rays from a star, which are for all practical purposes parallel, may be concentrated at the focus of a parabolic mirror.

Since sound obeys the same laws of reflection as light, parabolic microphones are used to pick up and concentrate sounds from a distant part of a football stadium.

Radar and radio telescopes are based on these same principles.

EXERCISES

Make a sketch for each exercise.

The **normal** to a curve at a given point on the curve is the line through that point perpendicular to the tangent there. In Exercises 1 to 8, find the equations of the tangent and the normal to the parabola at the given point.

1. $y^2 = 16x$, $(1, -4)$.　　　　　　　**2.** $x^2 = 4y$, $(4, 4)$.

3. $x^2 = -10y$, $(2\sqrt{5}, -2)$.　　　　**4.** $y^2 = -15x$, $(-3, -3\sqrt{5})$.

5. $x^2 = 2y$, $(2\sqrt{3}, 6)$.　　　　　**6.** $x^2 = -6y$, $(3\sqrt{2}, -3)$.

7. $y^2 = -9x$, $(-1, -3)$.　　　　　**8.** $y^2 = 20x$, $(2, -2\sqrt{10})$.

9. The slope of the tangent to the parabola $y^2 = 5x$ at a certain point on the parabola is $\sqrt{5}/4$. Find the coordinates of that point.

10. The slope of the tangent to the parabola $x^2 = -14y$ at a certain point on the parabola is $-2\sqrt{7}/7$. Find the coordinates of that point.

11. Find the equations of the tangents to the parabola $x^2 = 5y$ whose y-intercepts are -5.

12. Find the equation of the tangent to the parabola $y^2 = -2x$ whose y-intercept is $\sqrt{3}$.

13. Find the equations of the tangents to the parabola $y^2 = 16x$ from the point $(-3, 4)$.

14. Find the equations of the tangents to the parabola $x^2 = -4y$ from the point $(\frac{3}{2}, 1)$.

15. Find the equation of the tangent to the parabola $x^2 = 13y$ which is parallel to the line $4\sqrt{13}x - 13y + 20 = 0$.

16. Find the equation of the tangent to the parabola $y^2 = -18x$ which is parallel to the line $3x - 2y + 4 = 0$.

17. The segment of any line through the focus of a parabola, intercepted by the parabola, is called a **focal chord.** Prove that the tangents to a parabola at the extremities of any focal chord intersect on the directrix.

18. Prove that the tangents to a parabola at the extremities of any focal chord are perpendicular to each other (see Ex. 17).

19. Find the equation of the tangent to the parabola $(y - 1)^2 = 8(x + 5)$ at the point $(-3, 5)$.   (Hint: Use a translation.)

20. Find the equation of the tangent to the parabola $y^2 - 4x + 6y + 1 = 0$ at the point $(7, 3)$.   (Hint: Use a translation.)

8.4 TANGENTS TO ELLIPSES AND HYPERBOLAS

Consider the ellipse in standard position

$$b^2x^2 + a^2y^2 = a^2b^2,$$

and let $P_1:(x_1, y_1)$ be any point on it (Fig. 126).   We wish to find the equation of the tangent to the ellipse at P_1.

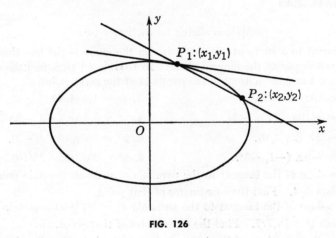

FIG. 126

Let $P_2:(x_2, y_2)$ be any other point on the ellipse.   The slope of the secant through P_1 and P_2 is

(1) $$m = \frac{y_2 - y_1}{x_2 - x_1} \qquad \text{(by 2.4.1).}$$

Since the points P_1 and P_2 are on the ellipse, their coordinates satisfy the equation of the ellipse (3.1.2).   That is,

(2) $$b^2x_1^2 + a^2y_1^2 = a^2b^2 \quad \text{and} \quad b^2x_2^2 + a^2y_2^2 = a^2b^2,$$

or

(3) $$y_1^2 = \frac{b^2(a^2 - x_1^2)}{a^2}$$

and

(4)
$$y_2{}^2 = \frac{b^2(a^2 - x_2{}^2)}{a^2}.$$

If we subtract (3) from (4), member by member, we obtain

$$y_2{}^2 - y_1{}^2 = \frac{b^2(a^2 - x_2{}^2)}{a^2} - \frac{b^2(a^2 - x_1{}^2)}{a^2}$$

$$= \frac{-b^2(x_2{}^2 - x_1{}^2)}{a^2}.$$

This may be rewritten

$$(y_2 - y_1)(y_2 + y_1) = \frac{-b^2(x_2 - x_1)(x_2 + x_1)}{a^2},$$

from which

$$\frac{y_2 - y_1}{x_2 - x_1} = -\frac{b^2(x_2 + x_1)}{a^2(y_2 + y_1)}.$$

Substituting this result in (1), we find the slope of the secant through P_1 and P_2 to be

(5)
$$m = -\frac{b^2(x_2 + x_1)}{a^2(y_2 + y_1)}.$$

Now think of P_1:(x_1, y_1) as fixed in position and P_2:(x_2, y_2) as moving along the curve and approaching P_1. Then the value of x_2 will approach x_1, the value of y_2 will approach y_1, and the right-hand member of (5) will approach

$$-\frac{b^2(2x_1)}{a^2(2y_1)} = -\frac{b^2 x_1}{a^2 y_1}.$$

Therefore (by 8.1.1) the slope of the tangent to the ellipse at P_1 is

$$m_1 = -\frac{b^2 x_1}{a^2 y_1}.$$

The equation of the tangent to the ellipse at P_1:(x_1, y_1) is

$$y - y_1 = -\frac{b^2 x_1}{a^2 y_1}(x - x_1) \qquad \text{(by 4.1.2)},$$

or

$$b^2 x_1 x + a^2 y_1 y = b^2 x_1{}^2 + a^2 y_1{}^2.$$

By means of (2) this may be rewritten

$$b^2 x_1 x + a^2 y_1 y = a^2 b^2,$$

which is the equation of the tangent to the ellipse at the point (x_1, y_1). This proves the

8.4.1 Theorem.　*The equation of the tangent to the ellipse*

$$b^2 x^2 + a^2 y^2 = a^2 b^2$$

at the point (x_1, y_1) *is*

$$b^2x_1x + a^2y_1y = a^2b^2.$$

. In like manner it is easy to prove the

8.4.2 Theorem.   *The equation of the tangent to the hyperbola*

$$b^2x^2 - a^2y^2 = a^2b^2$$

at the point (x_1, y_1) *is*

$$b^2x_1x - a^2y_1y = a^2b^2.$$

Example.   Find the equations of the tangents to the ellipse $3x^2 + 7y^2 - 75 = 0$ which are parallel to the line $2x - 7y - 2 = 0$.

Solution.   By 8.4.1, the equation of the tangent to the given ellipse at the point (x_1, y_1) is

(1) $$3x_1x + 7y_1y - 75 = 0.$$

The slope of this tangent is $-3x_1/7y_1$, and the slope of the given line is $2/7$ (by 4.2.2).   Therefore

$$-\frac{3x_1}{7y_1} = \frac{2}{7},$$

or

(2) $$3x_1 + 2y_1 = 0.$$

Since (x_1, y_1) is on the ellipse,

(3) $$3x_1^2 + 7y_1^2 - 75 = 0   \text{(by 3.1.2).}$$

Solving equations (2) and (3) simultaneously, we get

$$x_1 = \pm 2,   y_1 = \mp 3.$$

By substituting these results in (1), we find the equations of the desired tangents to be

$$6x - 21y \mp 75 = 0,$$

or

$$2x - 7y \mp 25 = 0.$$

8.5   REFLECTION PROPERTY OF THE ELLIPSE

Sound obeys the same reflection law as light.   If an ellipse is revolved about its principal axis to form a hollow shell, sounds coming from either focus and striking any part of the inside of the shell are reflected to the other focus.   This explains how a person standing in a certain spot in a "whispering gallery" may be heard by another person some distance away but not by anyone in between.

We will now establish the geometric property of ellipses on which this is based.

Let $P_1:(x_1, y_1)$ be any point on that portion of the ellipse

$$b^2x^2 + a^2y^2 = a^2b^2$$

which is in the fourth quadrant (Fig. 127). Then (by 3.1.2)

(1) $b^2x_1^2 + a^2y_1^2 = a^2b^2.$

Denote the angle between the tangent and the focal radius $\overline{FP_1}$ by φ, and let θ denote the supplement of the angle between the tangent and the focal radius $\overline{F'P_1}$ (Fig. 127). We wish to prove that $\varphi = \theta$.

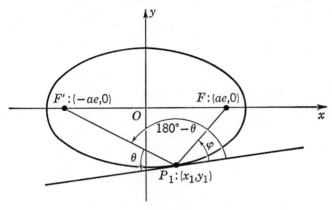

FIG. 127

We saw in the preceding section that the equation of the tangent to the ellipse at P_1 is

(2) $b^2x_1x + a^2y_1y = a^2b^2.$

The slope of this tangent is

$$-\frac{b^2x_1}{a^2y_1} \qquad \text{(by 4.2.2)},$$

and, the slope of the focal radius $\overline{FP_1}$ is

$$\frac{y_1}{x_1 - ae} \qquad \text{(by 2.4.1)}.$$

Therefore (by 2.6.1)

$$\tan \varphi = \frac{\dfrac{y_1}{x_1 - ae} + \dfrac{b^2x_1}{a^2y_1}}{1 - \left(\dfrac{y_1}{x_1 - ae}\right)\left(\dfrac{b^2x_1}{a^2y_1}\right)}$$

$$= \frac{b^2x_1^2 + a^2y_1^2 - b^2aex_1}{(a^2 - b^2)x_1y_1 - a^3ey_1}.$$

But $b^2x_1^2 + a^2y_1^2 = a^2b^2$ and $a^2 - b^2 = a^2e^2$ (by 6.5.1). Substituting above, we obtain

$$\tan \varphi = \frac{a^2 b^2 - b^2 a e x_1}{a^2 e^2 x_1 y_1 - a^3 e y_1}$$

$$= \frac{b^2 (a^2 - a e x_1)}{-a e y_1 (a^2 - a e x_1)}.$$

Therefore

(3) $$\tan \varphi = -\frac{b^2}{a e y_1}.$$

Similarly, since the slope of the focal radius $\overline{F'P_1}$ is

$$\frac{y_1}{x_1 + ae},$$

we have

$$\tan (180° - \theta) = \frac{\dfrac{y_1}{x_1 + ae} + \dfrac{b^2 x_1}{a^2 y_1}}{1 - \left(\dfrac{y_1}{x_1 + ae}\right)\left(\dfrac{b^2}{a^2 y_1}\right)}$$

$$= \frac{b^2 x_1{}^2 + a^2 y_1{}^2 + a e b^2 x_1}{(a^2 - b^2) x_1 y_1 + a^3 e y_1}$$

$$= \frac{b^2 (a^2 + a e x_1)}{a e y_1 (a^2 + a e x_1)}$$

$$= \frac{b^2}{a e y_1}.$$

But $\tan (180° - \theta) = -\tan \theta$ (Appendix, 9).   Therefore

(4) $$\tan \theta = -\frac{b^2}{a e y_1}.$$

From (3) and (4),

$$\tan \varphi = \tan \theta.$$

Since φ and θ are acute angles, it follows that

$$\varphi = \theta.$$

We have proved that $\varphi = \theta$ under the assumption that $P_1:(x_1, y_1)$ is in the fourth quadrant. But because of the symmetry of the ellipse with respect to both coordinate axes, it follows that $\varphi = \theta$ no matter what quadrant P_1 is in.

This proves the

8.5.1 Theorem.   *The focal radii to any point on an ellipse make equal angles with the tangent to the ellipse at that point.*

EXERCISES

Make a sketch for each exercise.

In Exercises 1 to 8, find the equations of the tangent and the normal to the given conic at the given point.

1. $4x^2 + 9y^2 - 72 = 0$, $(3, 2)$.

2. $25x^2 + 16y^2 - 356 = 0$, $(-2, 4)$.

3. $8x^2 + 5y^2 - 133 = 0$, $(1, -5)$.

4. $2x^2 + 6y^2 - 24 = 0$, $(-3, -1)$.

5. $16x^2 - 9y^2 - 31 = 0$, $(4, 5)$.

6. $4x^2 - 25y^2 - 96 = 0$, $(-7, 2)$.

7. $9x^2 - 4y^2 + 36 = 0$, $(3, -3\sqrt{13}/2)$.

8. $5x^2 - 12y^2 + 60 = 0$, $(4\sqrt{165}/5, 7)$.

9. The slope of the tangent to the ellipse $5x^2 + 3y^2 - 17 = 0$ at a certain point on the ellipse is $5/6$. What are the coordinates of the point of tangency? (Two solutions.)

10. The slope of the tangent to the hyperbola $2x^2 - 7y^2 - 35 = 0$ at a certain point on the hyperbola is $-2/3$. What are the coordinates of the point of tangency? (Two solutions.)

11. Find the equation of the tangent to the hyperbola $5x^2 - 6y^2 - 30 = 0$ which is parallel to the line $2x + \sqrt{3}y + 1 = 0$.

12. Find the equation of the tangent to the ellipse $x^2 + 2y^2 - 2 = 0$ which is parallel to the line $3x - 3\sqrt{2}y - 7 = 0$.

13. Find the equations of the tangents to the ellipse $4x^2 + y^2 - 20 = 0$ whose y-intercepts are 5.

14. Find the equations of the tangents to the hyperbola $2x^2 - 3y^2 - 6 = 0$ whose x-intercepts are 1.

15. Find the equations of the tangents to the hyperbola $12x^2 - 5y^2 - 28 = 0$ from the point $(\frac{7}{3}, \frac{14}{5})$.

16. Find the equations of the tangents to the ellipse $3x^2 + 8y^2 - 35 = 0$ from the point $(\frac{7}{3}, \frac{7}{4})$.

17. Prove that the product of the distances from the foci of an ellipse to any tangent is constant.

18. Prove that the point of contact of any tangent to a hyperbola is midway between the points in which the tangent intersects the asymptotes.

19. By means of a translation, find the equation of the tangent to the ellipse $(x - 3)^2 + 4(y - 4)^2 = 8$ at the point $(5, 5)$.

20. Find the equation of the tangent to the hyperbola $3x^2 - y^2 - 12x + 2y = 0$ at the point $(4, 2)$.

9

Curve Sketching

~~~~~~

9.1 INTRODUCTION

We saw in Chapter 3 that the two problems underlying a first course in analytic geometry are sketching the locus of an equation and finding the equation of a locus. We had considerable practice with the latter problem while finding the equations of lines and conics. It is now time to turn our attention again to curve sketching.

The first thing to notice in sketching the locus of an equation is whether it is algebraic or transcendental. If the given equation can be reduced to polynomial form (3.4), it is **algebraic**; otherwise, it is **transcendental**. For example, $y = 3/\sqrt{x^2 - 1}$ is algebraic because the squaring of both members and cross multiplication reduces the given equation to $x^2y^2 - y^2 - 9 = 0$. On the other hand, equations involving trigonometric, inverse trigonometric, exponential, or logarithmic functions are transcendental. The equations $y = \sin x$, $y = \tan 3x$, $y = \text{arc cos } x$, $y = 2^x$ (notice the variable exponent), and $y = \log_{10} x$ are all transcendental. Transcendental equations will be discussed in (9.8).

If the given equation is algebraic, we next ask its degree (3.4.5). A first degree equation in x and y always represents a straight line and is easily sketched from its intercepts or from one intercept and its slope.

A second degree equation, if it has any locus at all, represents a conic or a limiting form of a conic. If the equation is in standard form it is easy to draw the conic (Chapter 6). If the second degree equation is not in standard form, its indicator (7.6) tells whether it represents a hyperbola, parabola, or ellipse, and a half dozen points on the curve usually suffice to make a sketch.

All plane curves other than lines and conics are called **higher plane curves**. In the next few sections we will develop an orderly procedure for sketching those higher plane curves which are algebraic.

The labor involved in sketching the locus of an algebraic equation can often be considerably reduced by certain preliminary tests. Before any

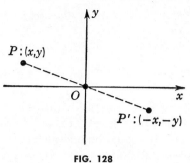

FIG. 128

points are plotted we should analyze the curve for *symmetry, intercepts, tangents at the origin, asymptotes,* and *excluded regions.*

9.2 SYMMETRY AND INTERCEPTS

We learned in 3.6.6 that *the locus of an equation in polynomial form is symmetric with respect to the x-axis if the equation contains no odd power of y.*

Also, *the locus of an equation in polynomial form is symmetric with respect to the y-axis if the equation contains no odd power of x* (3.6.8).

Now two points, P and P', are said to form a **symmetric pair** with respect to the origin if the line segment $\overline{PP'}$ is bisected by the origin (Fig. 128). Each of the points, P and P', is the **symmetric partner** of the other with respect to the origin. The origin is its own symmetric partner.

Clearly the coordinates of either point in a symmetric pair are the negatives of the coordinates of the other point (Fig. 128). For example, the points $(-2, 3)$ and $(2, -3)$ form a symmetric pair with respect to the origin. So do $(-4, -1)$ and $(4, 1)$.

- A plane curve is said to be **symmetric with respect to the origin** if the symmetric partner (with respect to the origin) of every point on the curve also lies on the curve (Fig. 129). From this we have the

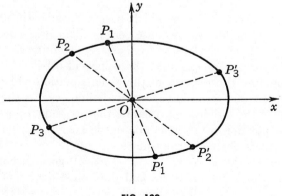

FIG. 129

9.2.1 Theorem.   *The locus of an equation in polynomial form in x and y is symmetric with respect to the origin if substitution of $-x$ for x and $-y$ for y throughout the equation leaves the equation essentially unchanged* (3.6).

For example, the locus of $y = x^3$ is symmetric with respect to the origin because $(-y) = (-x)^3$ is equivalent to $y = x^3$ (Fig. 137). On the other hand, the locus of $y^2 = x^3$ is symmetric with respect to the x-axis but not with respect to the y-axis or the origin (Fig. 138).

Usually the easiest points to find on a curve are its intersections (if any) with the coordinate axes.   *To find the x-intercepts of a plane curve, substitute zero for y in the given equation and solve for x* (3.5).   Similarly, *to find the y-intercepts substitute zero for x in the given equation and solve for y.*

For example, the x-intercepts of the locus of $x^4 - xy^3 - 6x^2 + 2y + 5 = 0$ are $x = \pm\sqrt{5}$ and $x = \pm 1$, while its y-intercept is $-\frac{5}{2}$.

EXERCISES

Test the following equations for symmetry with respect to the coordinate axes and symmetry with respect to the origin.   Find the intercepts.

1. $xy = 1$.
2. $xy - x - 2 = 0$.
3. $4x^2 + 9y^2 - 36 = 0$.
4. $y^2 - 4x + 12 = 0$.
5. $x^2 + y^2 - 2x + y = 0$.
6. $2x^2 - y^2 - 10 = 0$.
7. $x = y^3$.
8. $3x^3 - xy^2 - 3 = 0$.
9. $y = x^3 - 4x$.
10. $x^3 + 3x^2 + y^2 - 4x = 0$.
11. $2x^3 - xy^2 + 3x^2y - 4x - 7y = 0$.
12. $x^3 + y^3 + xy^2 + x^2y - x - y = 0$.
13. $x^4 + y^3 - 2y^2 + y = 0$.
14. $x^4 - x^2y^2 - 4x^2 + y^2 = 0$.
15. $x^4 - xy^3 + 2y^4 - x^2 + 4y^2 - 6 = 0$.
16. $x^2y^2 + x^2 + 2y^2 + 5y - 3 = 0$.

9.3 TANGENTS AT THE ORIGIN

Consider any algebraic curve which passes through the origin (3.5.1). The coordinates of points on the curve very near the origin are numerically small numbers. Their squares and cubes are also numerically small and much closer to zero. For example, the square of 0.1 is 0.01 and its cube is 0.001. Therefore those terms in the given equation which contain the higher powers of x and y can have very little influence on the shape of the curve very near the origin. It follows that a good approximation to the shape and position of an algebraic curve near the origin is given by the terms of lowest degree in the equation.

For example, the locus of $x^2y^2 - 4x^2 + y^2 = 0$ goes through the origin since it contains no constant term, and the lowest degree of any term in the equation is 2. After discarding all terms of degree greater than 2, we have $-4x^2 + y^2 = 0$, or $(2x - y)(2x + y) = 0$. Thus the two lines, $2x - y = 0$ and $2x + y = 0$, approximate the shape and position of the curve very near the origin (Fig. 130).

By means of the calculus it can be proved that this method gives the equations of the tangents (if any) to an algebraic curve at the origin. The

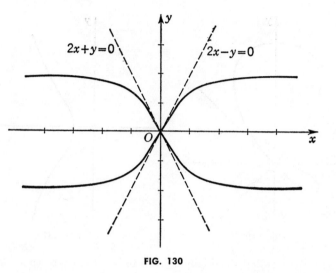

FIG. 130

direction of a curve at any point on it is the direction of the tangent to the curve at that point.

To summarize: *if an algebraic plane curve goes through the origin, the equations of its tangents (if any) at the origin may be found by reducing the given equation to polynomial form and then discarding all terms except those of lowest degree.*

Example 1. Find the equations of the tangents to the curve

$$x^4 + y^4 + 5x^2y - 5y^3 = 0$$

at the origin.

Solution. The lowest degree of any term in the given equation is 3. Discarding all terms of higher degree than 3, we have

$$5x^2y - 5y^3 = 0.$$

If we factor the left member of this equation we obtain

$$y(x - y)(x + y) = 0.$$

Therefore the equations of the tangents to the given curve at the origin are

$$y = 0 \text{ (the x-axis)}, \ x - y = 0, \quad \text{and} \quad x + y = 0 \text{ (Fig. 131)}.$$

Example 2. Find the equations of the tangents (if any) to the curve $y^2 = x^3 - x^2$ at the origin.

Solution. The lowest degree of any term in this equation is 2. So we discard all terms of degree greater than 2. This leaves $y^2 = -x^2$, or

$$x^2 + y^2 = 0.$$

Since the left member of this equation cannot be factored into *real* linear factors, there are no tangents to the given curve at the origin.

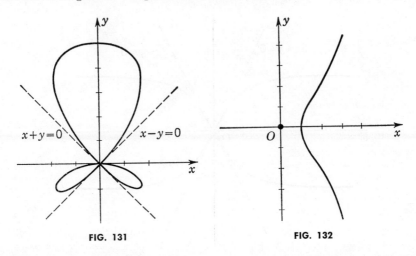

FIG. 131   FIG. 132

The trouble here is that the origin happens to be what is known as an **isolated point** on the given curve (Fig. 132). The coordinates of the origin satisfy the equation of the curve and therefore the origin is a point on the locus (3.1.1). But there are no other points on the curve which are less than one unit from the isolated point.

A line is never tangent to a curve at an isolated point.

EXERCISES

Find the equations of the tangents to each of the following curves at the origin.

1. $y = x^3$.
2. $x^4 - 3x^3y + 2y^2 - 5x + y = 0$.
3. $x^2y - y^3 + 4x^2 - 16y^2 = 0$.
4. $x^5 + x^2y^3 + 2x^3 - 6x^2y + 6xy^2 + 2y^3 = 0$.
5. $y^3 - x^2 + y^2 = 0$.
6. $y^3 + x^2 + y^2 = 0$.
7. $x^3 + 3y^3 - 2x^2 - xy = 0$.
8. $3x^4 - y^3 + xy = 0$.
9. $x^3 + 2x^2 - xy + y^2 = 0$.
10. $x^5y^2 - 3x^6 + 4xy^4 - x^3 - 8y^3 = 0$.
11. $x^4 + 6x^2y^2 - xy^2 + 3x^2 - 4xy + 5y^2 = 0$.
12. $xy^2 + y^3 + 4x^2 + 23xy + 15y^2 = 0$.
13. $x^2y^2 + 3x^2y - 17xy^2 - 6y^3 = 0$.

14. $x^3 - 3x^2y + 3xy^2 + y^3 + 1 = 0$.
15. $7y^5 + 81x^4 + 16y^4 = 0$.
16. $19y^6 + 81x^5 - 16xy^4 = 0$.

9.4 HORIZONTAL AND VERTICAL ASYMPTOTES

We recall that every hyperbola has two asymptotes—lines which the hyperbola approaches more and more closely as it goes farther and farther out (6.7). This situation is sometimes described by saying that a hyperbola is tangent to its asymptotes at infinity.

Higher plane curves may also have asymptotes. Although the calculus is needed for a complete discussion of this subject, it is easy to state rules for finding the horizontal and vertical asymptotes (if any) of a plane algebraic curve.

Consider the equation

$$(1) \qquad x^2y - x^2 - 1 = 0.$$

Solving for y in terms of x, we obtain

$$y = \frac{x^2 + 1}{x^2},$$

or

$$(2) \qquad y = 1 + \frac{1}{x^2}.$$

As x takes on the values ± 1, ± 2, ± 5, ± 10, ± 100, $\cdots$, y takes on the corresponding values 2, 1.25, 1.04, 1.01, 1.0001, $\cdots$, respectively. Plot-

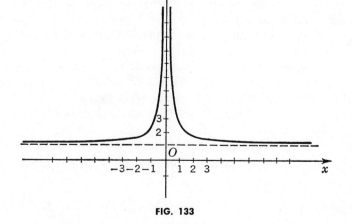

FIG. 133

ting these points (Fig. 133), we see that the curve gets closer and closer to the horizontal line $y = 1$ as the curve goes farther and farther out to the right or left.　In fact, sufficiently far out to the right or left, the curve gets as close as we please to the line $y = 1$.

We say that the straight line $y = 1$ is an asymptote of the curve (1).

9.4.1 Definition.　*If, in the equation of an algebraic plane curve, y approaches a constant k as x or $-x$ increases indefinitely, the line $y = k$ is a* **horizontal asymptote** *of the curve.*

As $|x|$ increases indefinitely in equation (2), $1/x^2$ approaches zero and y approaches 1.　Therefore $y = 1$, or

$$(3) \qquad\qquad y - 1 = 0,$$

is a horizontal asymptote of the curve (1).

The above definition leads to a simple method for finding the horizontal asymptotes of a plane algebraic curve.　Returning to the equation (1), we note that the highest power of x in that equation is x^2.　If we collect the terms involving x^2, equation (1) becomes

$$(4) \qquad\qquad (y - 1)x^2 - 1 = 0.$$

But the left-hand member of (3) is the coefficient of x^2 in (4).　Thus the horizontal asymptote of the curve may be found by equating to zero the coefficient of the highest power of x in (4).

This was to be expected.　For if we divide both members of (4) by x^2, we have

$$(5) \qquad\qquad (y - 1) - \frac{1}{x^2} = 0.$$

As $|x|$ becomes indefinitely great, $1/x^2$ will approach zero and the left member of (5) will approach in form the left member of (3).　Thus the locus of (5) approximates more and more closely the line $y - 1 = 0$, as it extends farther and farther out to the right and left.

It can be proved that this method is perfectly general.

To find the **horizontal asymptotes** *of a plane curve whose equation is in polynomial form, denote by x^k the highest power of x in the given equation and collect all terms involving x^k.　The real linear factors of the coefficient of x^k, set equal to zero, give the horizontal asymptotes of the curve.*

If the coefficient of x^k has no real linear factors in y, the curve has no horizontal asymptotes.

Similarly, *to find the* **vertical asymptotes** *of a plane curve whose equation is in polynomial form, equate to zero the real linear factors of the coefficient of the highest power of y.*

Example 1.　Find the vertical asymptotes of the curve $x^2y - x^2 - 1 = 0$.

Solution.　The coefficient of the highest power of y in the given equation is x^2. Setting equal to zero the real linear factors of x^2, we find the vertical asymptote of the curve to be $x = 0$ (see Fig. 133).

Example 2.   Find the horizontal and vertical asymptotes of the curve $xy^2 - y^2 - x = 0$.

Solution.   The highest power of x in the given equation is x.   If we collect the terms in x, the given equation becomes

$$(y^2 - 1)x - y^2 = 0.$$

Setting equal to zero the coefficient of x, we have

$$y^2 - 1 = 0,$$

or

$$y - 1 = 0 \quad \text{and} \quad y + 1 = 0.$$

Therefore the horizontal asymptotes of the curve are $y = 1$ and $y = -1$ (see Fig. 134).

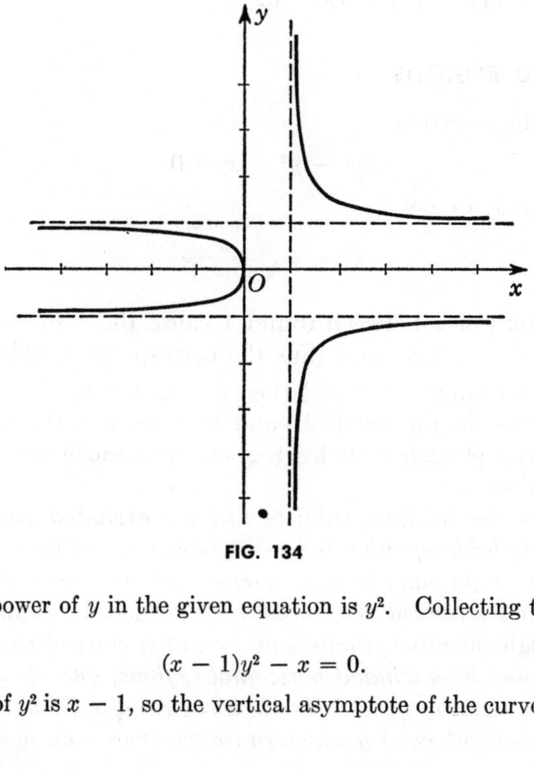

FIG. 134

The highest power of y in the given equation is y^2.   Collecting the terms in y^2, we get

$$(x - 1)y^2 - x = 0.$$

The coefficient of y^2 is $x - 1$, so the vertical asymptote of the curve is $x = 1$ (Fig. 134).

EXERCISES

Find the horizontal asymptotes and the vertical asymptotes of the following curves.

1. $xy = 1$.
2. $x^3 + x^2y - 4y + 6 = 0$.
3. $xy^2 - 2y^2 - 9x = 0$.

4. $x^2y^2 + 2x^2 + 5y^2 = 0$.

5. $x^2y^2 + 2x^2y + 2x^2 + 4y - 7 = 0$.

6. $x^2y^2 - 16x^2 + y^2 + 1 = 0$.

7. $3x^3 - y^3 + x^2y - 2x + 4y + 5 = 0$.

8. $x^2y + y - 10 = 0$.

9. $x^2y + xy^2 - 3x^2 + y + 4 = 0$.

10. $x^2y^2 - 25x^2 - 2y^2 - 1 = 0$.

11. $x^2y^2 - 2x^2 - 5y^2 = 0$.

12. $x^2y^2 - 3x^2 - 4y^2 = 0$.

13. $xy^2 + 2x^2 - y^2 - 3x + y + 1 = 0$.

14. $x^2y^2 + 11x^2 - 36y^2 = 0$.

15. $x^2y^2 + xy^3 + 5x^2y - 7y^3 + 4x^2 = 0$.

16. $y^3 - 7xy - 14y^2 - 49y + 686 = 0$.

9.5   EXCLUDED REGIONS

If we solve the equation

(1) $$xy^2 - y^2 - x = 0$$

for y in terms of x, we get

(2) $$y = \pm\sqrt{\frac{x}{x - 1}}.$$

Clearly, all values of x between 0 and 1 cause the expression under the radical sign to be negative and thus the corresponding values of y to be imaginary. For example, if $x = \frac{1}{2}$ then $y = \pm\sqrt{-1}$. Consequently the curve cannot exist in the vertical band between $x = 0$ and $x = 1$ (Fig. 134). Knowledge of such excluded regions saves much unnecessary labor in curve sketching.

This suggests the working rule: *to find the **excluded vertical regions,** solve the given algebraic equation for y in terms of x. If there is a radical of even degree in the right hand member, exclude all values of x which cause the expression under the radical to be negative. If there is no radical of even degree in the right member, there is no excluded vertical region.*

Similarly, *to find the **excluded horizontal regions,** solve the given algebraic equation for x in terms of y. If there is a radical of even degree in the right member, exclude all values of y which cause the expression under the radical to be negative.*

For example, if we solve the equation $x^2y^2 - 4x^2 + y^2 = 0$ for x in terms of y, we obtain

$$x = \frac{\pm y}{\sqrt{4 - y^2}}.$$

All values of y greater than 2 or less than -2 cause the expression under the radical to be negative and must be excluded. Thus the horizontal excluded regions are $y < -2$ and $2 < y$ (Fig. 130).   Solving for y in terms of x, we have

$$y = \frac{\pm 2x}{\sqrt{x^2 + 1}}.$$

Since no value of x, positive, negative, or zero, causes the expression under the radical to be negative, there is no vertical excluded region (Fig. 130).

EXERCISES

Find the excluded regions for each of the following loci.

1. $x^2 - y^2 + 3x - 4 = 0.$
2. $4x^3 - y^2 = 0.$
3. $x^4 - x^2 + y^2 = 0.$
4. $x^4 - 3xy^2 + 2x^2 - 3 = 0.$
5. $x^2y^2 - x^2 - y^2 - 1 = 0.$
6. $xy^2 - x^2 + 4 = 0.$
7. $x^2y + 3x^2 - 2y + 5 = 0.$
8. $y^3 - x^2 + 9y^2 + 27y + 27 = 0.$
9. $x^2y^2 - 2x + 1 = 0.$
10. $x^4 + 16y^4 - 81 = 0.$
11. $x^4 + y^4 - 16 = 0.$
12. $x^3 - 5x^2 - y^2 + 6x - 2y - 1 = 0.$
13. $xy^2 - x^2 - 4 = 0.$
14. $x^2y^2 - 6xy^2 + 8y^2 - 1 = 0.$

9.6   EXAMPLES OF CURVE SKETCHING

We will now show, by means of two examples, a systematic procedure for sketching algebraic plane curves.

Example 1.   Sketch the locus of $x^2y - 4x + 2y = 0.$

Solution.   The equation is algebraic and of degree greater than 2.   We therefore make a preliminary analysis, testing for symmetry, intercepts, tangents at the origin, horizontal and vertical asymptotes, and excluded regions.

Symmetry.   Substitution of $-x$ for x throughout the given equation yields $(-x)^2y - 4(-x) + 2y = 0$, or $x^2y + 4x + 2y = 0$, which is not equivalent to the original equation.   Therefore the curve is not symmetric with respect to the y-axis (3.6.7).

Similarly, we find that the curve is not symmetric with respect to the x-axis. But substitution of $-x$ for x and $-y$ for y throughout gives

$$(-x)^2(-y) - 4(-x) + 2(-y) = 0, \quad \text{or} \quad -x^2y + 4x - 2y = 0$$

which becomes the original equation when both members are multiplied by -1. Therefore the curve is symmetric with respect to the origin (9.2.1).

Intercepts. Substitution of zero for y in the given equation yields $-4x = 0$. Therefore the only x-intercept is zero (9.2). Substituting zero for x in the given equation, we get $2y = 0$. Thus the only intersection with the y-axis is at the origin.

Tangent at the Origin. Since the curve goes through the origin we note that the lowest degree of any term is 1. Discarding all terms of higher degree we have $-4x + 2y = 0$ or $2x - y = 0$, which is the equation of the tangent to the curve at the origin (9.3).

Horizontal and Vertical Asymptotes. The highest power of x in the given equation is 2. There is only one term involving x^2 and its coefficient is y. Therefore $y = 0$, the x-axis, is the only horizontal asymptote.

The highest power of y in the given equation is 1. If we collect the terms involving y to the first power, the equation becomes $(x^2 + 2)y - 4x = 0$. The coefficient of y is $x^2 + 2$ which has no real linear factors. Therefore there are no vertical asymptotes.

Excluded Regions. Solving the given equation for y in terms of x, we obtain

$$y = \frac{4x}{x^2 + 2}.$$

Since no even radical appears in the right member, there is no vertical excluded region.

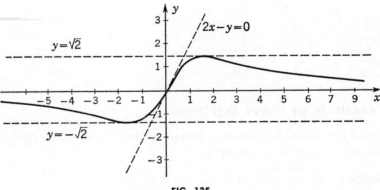

FIG. 135

The given equation is quadratic in x. Using the quadratic formula (Appendix, 1), we solve the equation for x in terms of y, getting

$$x = \frac{2 \pm \sqrt{4 - 2y^2}}{y}.$$

The expression under the radical is $2(2 - y^2)$, so we must exclude all values of y which make $2 - y^2$ negative. That is, we must exclude $y > \sqrt{2}$ and $y < -\sqrt{2}$. Therefore there can be no curve above the line $y = \sqrt{2}$ and no curve below the line $y = -\sqrt{2}$.

We now draw the coordinate axes, the tangent at the origin $2x - y = 0$, the horizontal asymptote $y = 0$, and the boundary lines $y = \sqrt{2}$ and $y = -\sqrt{2}$ of the excluded regions.　Recalling that the curve is symmetric with respect to the origin, we need calculate the approximate coordinates of only a few points.

x	.5	1	1.5	2	3	4	5	10
y	.9	1.3	1.4	1.3	1.1	.9	.7	.4

The curve is now easily drawn (Fig. 135).

Example 2.　Sketch the locus of $x^4 - 2x^3 + y^2 = 0$.

Solution.　We first analyze the curve.

Symmetry.　The curve is symmetric with respect to the x-axis.

Intercepts.　It crosses the x-axis at $(0, 0)$ and at $(2, 0)$. Its only intersection with the y-axis is at the origin.

Tangents at the Origin.　The curve is tangent to $y = 0$ (the x-axis) at the origin.

Horizontal or Vertical Asymptotes.　None.

Excluded Regions.　Exclude $x < 0$ and $x > 2$.

After computing values of y for $x = .5, 1, 1.5$ and 1.8, the shape of the curve is fairly evident.　But it would be helpful to know the tangent to the curve at $(2, 0)$.

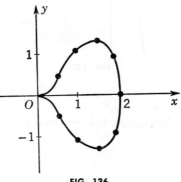

FIG. 136

If we translate the coordinate system to a new origin at $(2, 0)$ by means of the substitutions $x = x' + 2$, $y = y'$ (5.5.1), our equation becomes $x'^4 + 6x'^3 + 12x'^2 + y'^2 + 8x' = 0$. The lowest degree of any term in the new equation is 1.　Thus the tangent to the curve at the new origin is $x' = 0$.　This is a vertical line and therefore the tangent to our curve at the point whose original coordinates were $(2, 0)$ is the vertical line $x = 2$ (Fig. 136).

EXERCISES

Write out an analysis of each of the following equations and then sketch its locus.

1. $x^3 + xy^2 - 4y^2 = 0$.

2. $x^2y - 4x + y = 0$.

3. $x^4 + y^4 - 16 = 0$.

4. $x^3 + xy^2 - 6x^2 + 2y^2 = 0$.

  5. $x^2y^2 + 4x^2 - 4y^2 = 0.$ **6.** $xy^2 - 3x - 9 = 0.$

  7. $y^3 - x = 0.$ **8.** $x^4 - y^4 - 16 = 0.$

  9. $x^3 - y^2 - 4x = 0.$ **10.** $x^2y^2 - 4x^2 - 4y^2 = 0.$

  11. $x^2y + 4y - 8 = 0.$ **12.** $x^3 + 4x^2 - y^2 + 4x = 0.$

  13. $y^4 - 4y^3 + 4x^2 = 0.$ **14.** $x^2y^2 - x^2 + y^2 + 1 = 0.$

  15. $xy^2 + x - 8y = 0.$ **16.** $y^3 - x^2 - 9y = 0.$

9.7   SOME CUBIC CURVES

If we recall that the loci of first degree equations were discussed in a few paragraphs (4.2) while the second degree equation required a full

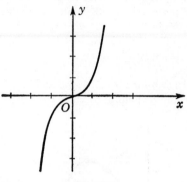

FIG. 137

chapter, it may not be so surprising that a whole book can be devoted to the loci of third degree equations.*

In this section we will discuss briefly the loci of some common cubic equations.

The locus of

(1) $$y = kx^3,$$

where k is any non-zero constant, is called a **cubical parabola.** Fig. 137 shows the curve when $k = 1$. It is symmetric with respect to the origin. The curve is tangent to the x-axis at the origin and crosses the x-axis there. A point of tangency at which the curve crosses the tangent line is called a **point of inflection** of the curve. Thus the origin is a point of inflection of the cubical parabola (1).

The locus of

(2) $$y^2 = kx^3,$$

a **cuspidal cubic,** is shown in Fig. 138. It is symmetric with respect to

* H. S. White, *Plane Curves of the Third Order* (Cambridge, Harvard Univ. Press, 1925).

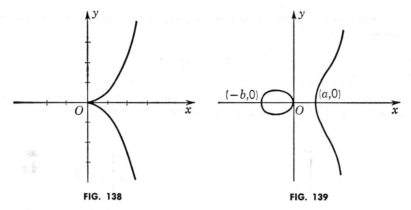

FIG. 138   FIG. 139

the x-axis and is tangent to that axis at the origin.

The graph of

$$(3) \qquad y^2 = k(x - a)x(x + b),$$

where a and b are positive constants, is given in Fig. 139. It is called a **bipartite cubic.** The oval is not an ellipse. The curve is not degenerate but consists of two parts which together constitute the locus of the equation.

The equation

$$(4) \qquad y^2 = k(x - a)x^2,$$

where $a > 0$, has for its locus an **acnodal cubic** (Fig. 140). It consists of a curve and an isolated point, the origin. The coordinates of the origin satisfy the equation, yet no other point near the origin is on the curve.

The locus of

$$(5) \qquad y^2 = kx^2(x + b),$$

in which $b > 0$, is called a **nodal cubic** (Fig. 141). Since two branches of the curve go through the origin, the origin is called a **double point** of the curve.

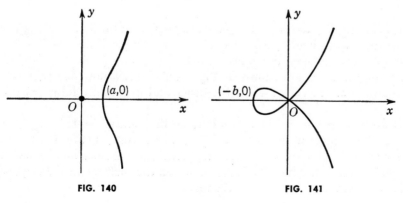

FIG. 140   FIG. 141

Now the four preceding equations are all special cases of the more general equation

$$(6) \qquad y^2 = k(x - a)x(x + b),$$

where a and b are any real numbers. The equation (6) takes on the form (2) when $a = b = 0$, the form (3) when $a > 0$ and $b > 0$, the form (4) when $a > 0$ and $b = 0$, and the form (5) when $a = 0, b > 0$.

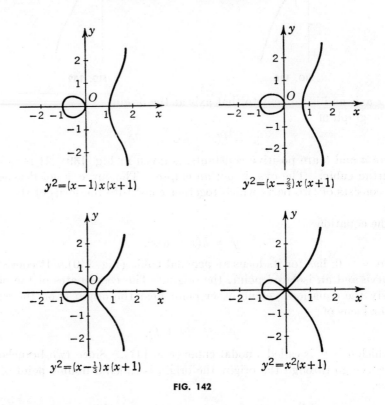

$$y^2 = (x-1)x(x+1)$$

$$y^2 = (x-\tfrac{2}{3})x(x+1)$$

$$y^2 = (x-\tfrac{1}{3})x(x+1)$$

$$y^2 = x^2(x+1)$$

FIG. 142

It is instructive to sketch the loci of the equation (6) for several different values of a, while holding b and k fixed. For example, if we keep $k = b = 1$ and allow a to take on the values $a = 1$, $a = \tfrac{2}{3}$, $a = \tfrac{1}{3}$, $a = 0$, the various forms of the locus are shown in Fig. 142. Notice how one part of the bipartite cubic reaches toward the other and eventually forms with it a nodal cubic.

If we keep $k = a = 1$ and let b take on the values $b = 1$, $b = \tfrac{2}{3}$, $b = \tfrac{1}{3}$, $b = 0$, the changes in the locus of $y^2 = k(x - a)x(x + b)$ are shown in Fig. 143. Observe how the oval of the bipartite cubic shrinks and becomes an isolated point. In general, a small change in the coefficients of an equation brings about a small change in the locus.

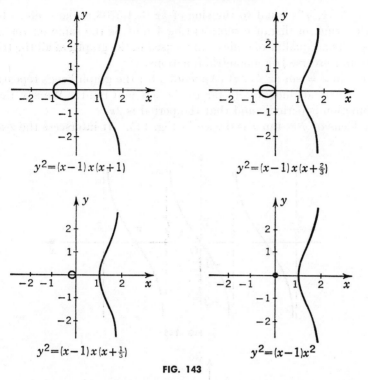

$$y^2 = (x-1)\,x\,(x+1)$$

$$y^2 = (x-1)\,x\,(x+\tfrac{2}{3})$$

$$y^2 = (x-1)\,x\,(x+\tfrac{1}{3})$$

$$y^2 = (x-1)x^2$$

FIG. 143

9.8 TRIGONOMETRIC AND INVERSE TRIGONOMETRIC FUNCTIONS

For further work in mathematics or the physical sciences, some familiarity with the trigonometric and the inverse trigonometric functions is desirable, and the ability to sketch their graphs quickly is useful. All these curves can be sketched quickly without the use of tables provided we remember the shape of the sine and tangent curves.

The graph of $y = \sin x$ is shown in Fig. 144, where x is expressed in radians; that is, x, like y, is a number. To compute the value of y for a given value of x, we compute the sine of the angle whose radian measure is the number x. Thus, when $x = 1$, y is equal to the sine of one radian;

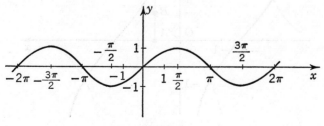

FIG. 144

when $x = \frac{1}{2}\pi$, y is equal to the sine of $\frac{1}{2}\pi \doteq 1.5708$ radians, etc. In Fig. 144, the scale, or distance representing 1 unit, is the same on the x- and y-axes. This equality of scales will be used in the graphs of all the trigonometric and inverse trigonometric functions.

Since $\sin x = \sin (x + 2\pi)$ (Appendix, 8), the graph keeps repeating itself as it extends indefinitely far to the left and right. We say that the sine function is periodic and that the period is 2π.

The locus of $y = \tan x$ is drawn in Fig. 145. It intersects the x-axis in

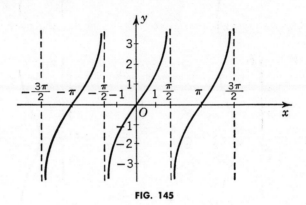

FIG. 145

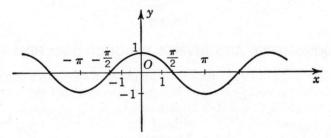

FIG. 146

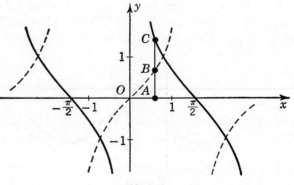

FIG. 147

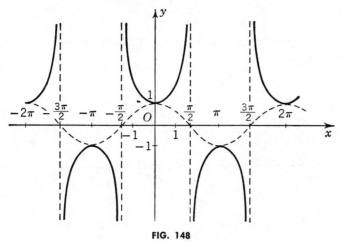

FIG. 148

the points $(n\pi, 0)$, where n is any integer, and has for asymptotes the vertical lines $x = \frac{1}{2}n\pi$. The period of this tangent function is π.

Since we have $\cos x = \sin (x + \frac{1}{2}\pi)$ (Appendix, 9), $y = \cos x$ may be sketched by drawing $y = \sin x$ and then choosing a new y-axis $\frac{1}{2}\pi$ units to the right of the old y-axis (Fig. 146). This curve is easily sketched by recalling that the sine and cosine curves have exactly the same over-all shape and period but that $\sin 0 = 0$ while $\cos 0 = 1$.

A simple way to draw the graph of $y = \cot x$ is to rewrite the equation as $y = 1/\tan x$. Then sketch lightly from memory the graph of $y = \tan x$ and find the reciprocal of $\tan x$ for a sufficient number of values of x. For example, in Fig. 147 the graph of $y = \tan x$ is dotted. Choose any point A on the x-axis and draw a vertical line through A intersecting $y = \tan x$ in some point B. Estimate the directed length AB. In the diagram this

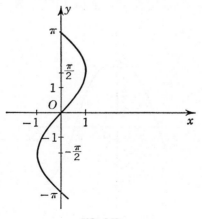

FIG. 149

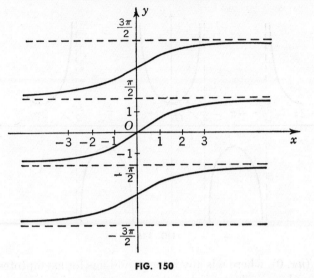

FIG. 150

seems to be about $\frac{3}{5}$. Since $AB = \tan x$, $1/AB = \cot x$. We therefore mark C on the vertical line so that $AC = \frac{5}{3}$. After finding a number of points in this manner we draw a smooth curve through them. This is the locus of $y = \cot x$.

Notice that the graphs of $y = \tan x$ and $y = \cot x$ intersect on the lines $y = 1$ and $y = -1$. This is because the reciprocal of 1 is 1 and the reciprocal of -1 is -1. Since $y = \tan x$ crosses the x-axis at the origin, the curve $y = \cot x$ has the y-axis as an asymptote.

This method can also be used to sketch $y = \sec x$, since $y = \sec x$ can be rewritten $y = 1/\cos x$ (Fig. 148).

The sketching of $y = \csc x$ as $y = 1/\sin x$ is left for the student.

To graph the inverse trigonometric function, $y = \text{arc sin } x$, or, as it is sometimes written, $y = \sin^{-1} x$, we recall that this is equivalent to $x = \sin y$.

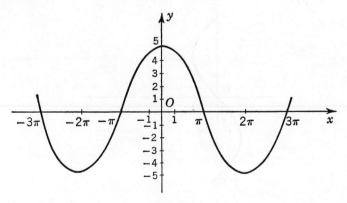

FIG. 151

The latter can be graphed from our memory of $y = \sin x$ by interchanging the roles of the x- and y-axes (Fig. 149).

The graph of $y = \text{arc tan } x$ is found by drawing $x = \tan y$ (Fig. 150). Similarly, for the other inverse trigonometric functions.

Example. Sketch the locus of $y = 5 \cos \frac{1}{2}x$.

Solution. Since the period of $\cos x$ is 2π, and since $\frac{1}{2}x$ increases by 2π only when x increases by 4π, the period of $\cos \frac{1}{2}x$ is 4π. Similarly, the periods of $\cos kx$ and $\sin kx$ are $2\pi/k$. The graph of $y = 5 \cos \frac{1}{2}x$ crosses the x-axis when $\cos \frac{1}{2}x$ is zero; that is, when $x = \pm\pi, \pm3\pi, \pm5\pi$, etc. Moreover, y takes on its maximum value, 5, when $x = 0, \pm4\pi, \pm8\pi$, etc., and its minimum value, -5, when $x = \pm2\pi, \pm6\pi$, etc. The curve is shown in Fig. 151.

9.9 EXPONENTIAL AND LOGARITHMIC FUNCTIONS

· The exponential and the logarithmic functions are just as important as the trigonometric functions.

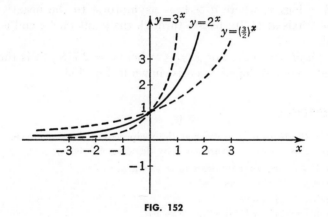

FIG. 152

The exponential curve $y = a^x$, where $a > 1$, is asymptotic to the negative x-axis, crosses the y-axis at $(0, 1)$, and rises more and more steeply as it extends to the right in the first quadrant. The greater the value of a, the steeper the curve is at $(0, 1)$.

A table of values for $y = 2^x$ follows:

x	-3	-2	-1	0	1	2	3	4
y	$\frac{1}{8}$	$\frac{1}{4}$	$\frac{1}{2}$	1	2	4	8	16

In Fig. 152 the graph of $y = 2^x$ is drawn as a solid line, and the graphs of $y = 3^x$ and $y = (\frac{3}{2})^x$ are shown as dotted lines.

In sketching the locus of $y = \log_a x$, where $a > 1$, we make use of the definition of a logarithm (Appendix, 2) to rewrite the given equation as $x = a^y$. The graph of the latter is the same as the graph of the exponential curve discussed above, but with the coordinate axes interchanged. The

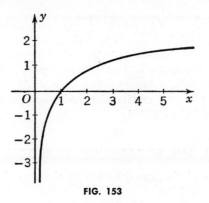

FIG. 153

locus of $y = \log_a x$, where $a > 1$, is asymptotic to the negative y-axis, crosses the x-axis at $(1, 0)$, passes through the point $(a, 1)$, and is concave downward.

The graph of $y = \log_e x$, or $x = e^y$ (where $e = 2.718 \ldots$ is the base of the natural system of logarithms) is shown in Fig. 153.

EXERCISES

1. Sketch the locus of $y = \csc x$ as the reciprocal of the sine curve.
2. Sketch the locus of $y = \arccos x$ by drawing $x = \cos y$.
3. Sketch $y = \text{arc cot } x$ by drawing $x = \cot y$.
4. Sketch $y = \text{arc sec } x$ as $x = \sec y$.
5. Sketch $y = \text{arc csc } x$.
6. Sketch $y = \log_{10} x$ by drawing $x = 10^y$.

Draw the graph of each of the following equations, using radian measure for x.

7. $y = 3 \sin 2x$.
8. $y = 2 \tan 2x$.
9. $y = 2 \sin \frac{1}{2}x$.
10. $y = 3 \cos (x - \frac{1}{4}\pi)$.
11. $y = \frac{1}{2} \sec \frac{1}{4}x$.
12. $y = 4 \tan \frac{1}{2}x$.
13. $y = 2 \sin \pi x$.
14. $y = -3 \cos \frac{1}{3}x$.
15. $y = 2 \sin^2 2x$.
16. $y = \sin^2 \frac{1}{2}x$.
17. $y = \tan (x + \frac{1}{6}\pi)$.
18. $y = 2 \tan \frac{1}{2}x$.
19. $y = \csc \frac{1}{2}x$.
20. $y = 2 \arccos 2x$.
21. $y = \frac{1}{2} \arcsin 2x$.
22. $y = 3 \arctan \frac{1}{2}x$.
23. $y = 3e^x$.
24. $y = 2^{x^2}$.
25. $y = 2e^{x-2}$.
26. $y = 2^{-x}$.
27. $y = \log_{10} x^2$.
28. $y = \log_e (x - 4)$.

29. $y = \log_e \tfrac{1}{2}x$.

30. $y = \log_{10} (-x)$.

31. $y = \log_e \sin x$.

32. $y = \log_e \cos x$.

9.10 ADDITION OF ORDINATES

A device which often proves useful in rapid curve sketching is explained in the following example.

Example.   Draw the graph of $y = \tfrac{1}{3}x^2 + \cos 2x$.

Solution.   Draw lightly the locus of $y = \tfrac{1}{3}x^2$ which is a parabola in standard position opening upward (Fig. 154).   On the same set of coordinate axes sketch lightly the locus of $y = \cos 2x$, a cosine curve with period π.   Radian measure should be used for the latter curve.

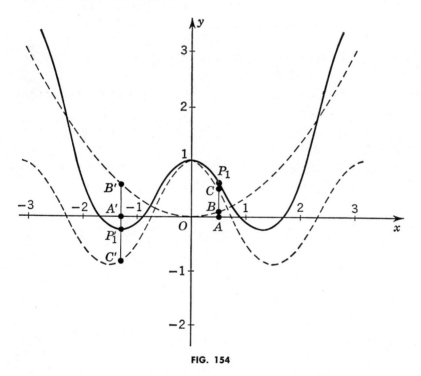

FIG. 154

For each value of x in the given equation, it is obvious that the ordinate (or y-coordinate) $y = \tfrac{1}{3}x^2 + \cos 2x$ is the sum of the ordinates $y = \tfrac{1}{3}x^2$ and $y = \cos 2x$.

Choose any point $A:(x_1, 0)$ on the x-axis and draw a vertical line through A, intersecting the locus of $y = \tfrac{1}{3}x^2$ in B and the locus of $y = \cos 2x$ in C (Fig. 154). The ordinate of the point B on the first locus is the directed length $AB = \tfrac{1}{3}x_1^2$, and the ordinate of the point C on the second locus is $AC = \cos 2x_1$.   Therefore the ordinate of the point $P_1:(x_1, y_1)$ in which the vertical line intersects the desired curve $y = \tfrac{1}{3}x^2 + \cos 2x$ is $\tfrac{1}{3}x_1^2 + \cos 2x_1 = AB + AC$.

This addition of ordinates can be done graphically by using a pair of dividers or the edge of a sheet of paper. No numbers need be computed.

After finding a number of points in this way, we draw the desired locus of $y = \frac{1}{3}x^2 + \cos 2x$ through them.

This method of graphing a function which is the sum (or difference) of two or more functions is known as the **method of addition of ordinates.**

EXERCISES

Graph the following equations by the method of addition (or subtraction) of ordinates. Use radian measure for x.

1. $y = 2x^2 + 4x - 1$.   **2.** $y = x^3 + 3x^2 + 5$.

3. $y = \frac{1}{4}x^4 - x^2$.   **4.** $y = \frac{1}{3}x + \tan x$.

5. $y = \sin x + \cos x$.   **6.** $y = 2 \sin x + 3 \cos x$.

7. $y = 2 \sin x - 3 \cos 3x$.   **8.** $y = 3 \sin \frac{1}{3}x + 2 \cos \frac{1}{2}x$.

9. $y = \sin 2x - e^x$.   **10.** $y = 2^x + \sin \frac{1}{2}x - 6$.

11. $y = \frac{1}{2}(e^x - e^{-x})$ **(hyperbolic sine).**

12. $y = \frac{1}{2}(e^x + e^{-x})$ **(hyperbolic cosine).**

13. $y = \dfrac{a}{2}(e^{\frac{x}{a}} + e^{-\frac{x}{a}})$, $a > 0$ **(catenary).** A perfectly flexible cable, which does not stretch, hangs in the form of a catenary when suspended between two points.

14. $y = \sin x + \frac{1}{3} \sin 3x$.   **15.** $y = \sin x + \frac{1}{3} \sin 3x + \frac{1}{5} \sin 5x$.

16. $y = \sin x - \frac{1}{2} \sin 2x$.   **17.** $y = \sin x - \frac{1}{2} \sin 2x + \frac{1}{3} \sin 3x$.

18. $y = \cos x + \frac{1}{9} \cos 3x$.   **19.** $y = \cos x + \frac{1}{9} \cos 3x + \frac{1}{25} \cos 5x$.

20. $y = \cos x + \frac{1}{9} \cos 3x + \frac{1}{25} \cos 5x + \frac{1}{49} \cos 7x$.

10

Parametric Equations

~~~~~~

10.1 INTRODUCTION

In what we have done so far, a plane curve has always been represented by a single equation in x and y. But there is another way of representing curves which is often useful.

Consider a line l with angle of inclination α and passing through a fixed point $P_1:(x_1, y_1)$ (Fig. 155). Let $P:(x, y)$ be any other point on the line and denote the directed distance P_1P by d.

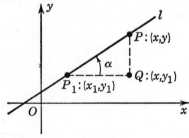

FIG. 155

Since $\cos \alpha = P_1Q/d$ and $P_1Q = x - x_1$, we have $\cos \alpha = (x - x_1)/d$ or $x = x_1 + d \cos \alpha$.

Similarly, $\sin \alpha = (y - y_1)/d$ or $y = y_1 + d \sin \alpha$.

The equations

(1) $$x = x_1 + d \cos \alpha, \quad y = y_1 + d \sin \alpha,$$

are called **parametric equations** of the line and d is the **parameter**. They were derived under the assumption that P and P_1 were distinct but are also valid if P and P_1 are identical, since in that case $d = 0$, $x = x_1$, and $y = y_1$.

Notice that x_1, y_1, $\sin \alpha$, and $\cos \alpha$ are constants while d is variable. For every real value of the parameter d the equations (1) give the coordinates of a unique point P on the line. Moreover, every point P on the given line gives rise to a unique value of d because d is the directed distance P_1P. Thus there is a one-to-one correspondence between the real values of the parameter d and the points of the line.

We first used the word *parameter* in discussing families of straight lines (4.5). In that connection, different values of the parameter corresponded to different lines of the system. Here, different values of the parameter correspond to different points on the *same* straight line.

The line can be drawn by assigning various values to the parameter d and computing the coordinates of the corresponding points on the line from (1).

We can also find the x,y equation of the line by eliminating the parameter d between the equations (1). Solving the first of these equations for d, we have $d = (x - x_1)/\cos \alpha$. Substituting this result in the second equation, we obtain

$$y = y_1 + (x - x_1) \frac{\sin \alpha}{\cos \alpha},$$

or

$$y - y_1 = \tan \alpha \, (x - x_1),$$

which is the point-slope form of the equation of the line.

Example 1. Draw the line whose parametric equations are $x = 3 - \frac{1}{2}d$, $y = -1 + \frac{1}{2}\sqrt{3}d$, and then find its x,y equation.

Solution. By assigning the values $-2, -1, 0, 1$, and 2 to d in the given equations, we find the coordinates of the corresponding points to be approximately $(4, -2.7)$, $(3.5, -1.9)$, $(3, -1)$, $(2.5, -0.1)$, and $(2, 0.7)$, respectively. After plotting these points we draw the desired curve through them (Fig. 156).

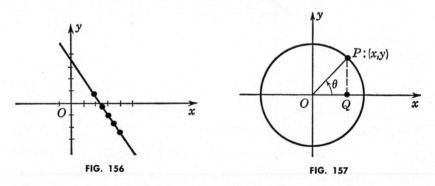

FIG. 156   FIG. 157

To find its x,y equation we solve the first of the given equations for d, obtaining $d = 6 - 2x$. Substituting this in the second equation and simplifying, we get $\sqrt{3}x + y + 1 - 3\sqrt{3} = 0$.

Now consider a circle, with center at the origin and radius r (Fig. 157). Let $P:(x, y)$ be any point on the circle. Then

$$\cos \theta = \frac{x}{r} \quad \text{and} \quad \sin \theta = \frac{y}{r}.$$

Thus

(2) $x = r \cos \theta, \quad y = r \sin \theta$

are parametric equations of the circle. As the parameter θ takes on values from $0°$ to $360°$, the equations (2) give the Cartesian coordinates of all points on the circle.

To eliminate the parameter and thus obtain the x,y equation of the curve, we rewrite the equations (2) as $\cos \theta = x/r$ and $\sin \theta = y/r$. Squaring both members and substituting in the trigonometric identity $\sin^2 \theta + \cos^2 \theta = 1$, we obtain

$$\frac{x^2}{r^2} + \frac{y^2}{r^2} = 1, \quad \text{or} \quad x^2 + y^2 = r^2.$$

Example 2. Plot the locus of the parametric equations $x = a \sec \varphi$ and $y = b \tan \varphi$. Afterwards find its x,y equation by eliminating the parameter φ.

Solution. To take a specific case, we will let $a = 3$ and $b = 2$.
A table of approximate values follows:

φ	0°	30°	60°	90°	120°	150°	180°	210°	240°	270°	300°	330°	360°
x	3	3.5	6	—	−6	−3.5	−3	−3.5	−6	—	6	3.5	3
y	0	1.2	3.5	—	−3.5	−1.2	0	1.2	3.5	—	−3.5	−1.2	0

The curve is shown in Fig. 158.

To eliminate the parameter we obtain $\sec^2 \varphi = x^2/9$ and $\tan^2 \varphi = y^2/4$ from the

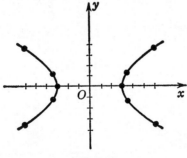

FIG. 158

given equations and substitute these results in the familiar trigonometric identity, $1 + \tan^2 \varphi = \sec^2 \varphi$ (Appendix, 11). This gives $1 + \frac{1}{4}y^2 = \frac{1}{9}x^2$, or

$$\frac{x^2}{9} - \frac{y^2}{4} = 1,$$

which represents a hyperbola in standard position.

EXERCISES

Graph each of the following curves by assigning values to the parameter.　Then eliminate the parameter and obtain the x,y equation.

1. $x = 2t$, $y = 3t$.

2. $x = 4t - 1$, $y = 2t$.

3. $x = 4t^2$, $y = 4t$.

4. $x = t - 4$, $y = \sqrt{t}$.

5. $x = t$, $y = 1/t$.

6. $x = t^2$, $y = t^3$.

7. $x = t/2$, $y = t^3$.

8. $x = 3\sqrt{t - 3}$, $y = 2\sqrt{4 - t}$.

9. $x = \dfrac{3t}{1 + t^3}$, $y = \dfrac{3t^2}{1 + t^3}$.

10. $x = 3 \sin \theta$, $y = 5 \cos \theta$.

11. $x = 4 \sec \theta$, $y = 3 \tan \theta$.

12. $x = \cot \theta$, $y = 5 \csc \theta$.

13. $x = 3 \sin \theta - 1$, $y = 2 \cos \theta + 2$.

14. $x = 5 \sec \theta - 5$, $y = 4 \tan \theta + 4$.

15. $x = 4 \sin^4 \theta$, $y = 4 \cos^4 \theta$.

16. $x = 2 \cos \theta$, $y = 2 \cos \frac{1}{2}\theta$.

17. $x = a \sin^3 \theta$, $y = a \cos^3 \theta$.

18. $x = 2 \tan \theta$, $y = 3 \sin \theta$.

19. $x = \tan \theta$, $y = \tan 2\theta$.

20. $x = \sin 3\theta$, $y = \sin \theta$.

10.2　USES OF PARAMETRIC EQUATIONS

In the physical sciences, parametric equations, where the parameter t represents time, are very convenient for dealing with problems of motion.

For example, it is shown in physics that if air resistance is neglected, the position of a projectile at the end of t seconds, fired with an initial velocity of v_0 feet per second and at an angle θ with the horizontal, is given by the parametric equations

$$(1) \qquad x = (v_0 \cos \theta)t, \quad y = (v_0 \sin \theta)t - 16t^2,$$

where x and y are measured in feet.　Here x, y, and t are variables; all other symbols represent constants.

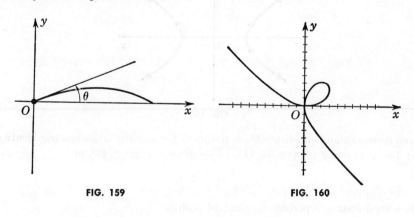

FIG. 159　　　　　　　FIG. 160

The x,y equation of the path of the projectile can be found by eliminating the parameter t between the equations (1). From the first equation we obtain $t = x/(v_0 \cos \theta)$. Substituting this in the second equation and simplifying, we have

$$(2) \qquad y = (\tan \theta)x - \frac{16}{(v_0 \cos \theta)^2} x^2,$$

which (by 7.6.1) represents a parabola (Fig. 159).

Another use of parametric equations is to simplify the task of curve sketching. The student may have concluded from the examples in 10.1 that it is more tedious to sketch a locus from parametric equations than from its x,y equation. Sometimes the contrary is true.

For example, in attempting to sketch the locus of $x^3 + y^3 - 6xy = 0$, we find that a preliminary analysis gives very little information. All that it tells us is that the curve goes through the origin and is tangent to both coordinate axes there.

We must therefore fall back on the plotting of many points. But every time we substitute a value for one variable, we are faced with the task of solving (approximately) a cubic equation in the other variable. For example, if $y = 2$, then x is given by the real roots of $x^3 - 12x + 8 = 0$.

This very tedious task can be greatly simplified by finding parametric equations of the curve. If we substitute $y = mx$ in the given equation, we obtain

$$x^2[(1 + m^3)x - 6m] = 0.$$

Equating the factor in brackets to zero we have $x = 6m/(1 + m^3)$. Substituting this latter result in $y = mx$ we obtain $y = 6m^2/(1 + m^3)$. Thus parametric equations of the curve are

$$(3) \qquad x = \frac{6m}{1 + m^3}, \quad y = \frac{6m^2}{1 + m^3}.$$

By assigning values to the parameter m in these equations we can easily compute the coordinates of as many points on the curve as we wish (Fig. 160).

Before leaving this example it is worth noticing that $y = mx$ represents a line through the origin with slope m. Such a line intersects the curve twice at the origin and in one further point, P, which varies with m. For any particular value of m the equations (2) give the Cartesian coordinates of the latter point, P.

A third reason for studying parametric equations is that they sometimes furnish additional information about familiar loci. For example, consider the two concentric circles, $x^2 + y^2 = a^2$ and $x^2 + y^2 = b^2$, where $a > b$ (Fig. 161). Let Q be any point on the outer circle and denote the intersection of $\overline{OQ}$ with the inner circle by R. Draw $\overline{RS}$ and $\overline{QT}$ perpendicular to the

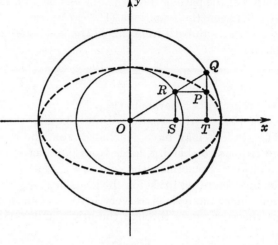

FIG. 161

x-axis.   Drop a perpendicular from R to $\overline{QT}$ and call its foot P.   We seek the locus of P as Q moves around the outer circle.

Let the coordinates of P be (x, y) and indicate by θ the angle of inclination of $\overline{OQ}$.   Then $\sin \theta = SR/|OR|$ and $\cos \theta = OT/|OQ|$.   But $OT = x$, $SR = TP = y$, $|OR| = b$, and $|OQ| = a$.   Therefore

(4) $$\sin \theta = \frac{y}{b}, \quad \cos \theta = \frac{x}{a},$$

or

(5) $$x = a \cos \theta, \quad y = b \sin \theta.$$

Equations (5) are parametric equations of the locus of P, and θ is the parameter.

Squaring the equations (4) and adding them member by member, we have

$$\sin^2 \theta + \cos^2 \theta = \frac{y^2}{b^2} + \frac{x^2}{a^2}, \quad \text{or} \quad \frac{x^2}{a^2} + \frac{y^2}{b^2} = 1.$$

Thus the locus is an ellipse in standard position (Fig. 161).   The circle $x_2 + y_2 = a_2$ is circumscribed about the ellipse and is called its **major auxiliary circle.**   The other circle, $x_2 + y_2 = b_2$, is inscribed in the ellipse and is its **minor auxiliary circle.**

Example.   A football is kicked with an initial velocity of 64 feet per second, at an angle of 30° with the horizontal.   Neglecting air resistance, find parametric equations of the path of the football.   How far away will the ball first hit the ground?   How high will it go?

Solution.   Substituting $v_0 = 64$ and $\theta = 30°$ in (1), we find the parametric equations of the path of the football to be

$$x = 32\sqrt{3}t, \quad y = 32t - 16t^2.$$

The football is on the ground when $y = 0$. We obtain the time of flight by substituting $y = 0$ in the second parametric equation, getting $t = 2$ seconds.

The range of the football is found by substituting $t = 2$ in the first parametric equation. This gives $x = 64\sqrt{3} \doteq 108.8$ feet. Thus the football strikes the ground approximately 108.8 feet away from the kicking position.

The flight of the football takes 2 seconds. From the symmetry of the parabolic path (Fig. 159), it follows that the football reaches its greatest height in half that time, that is, in 1 second. Substituting $t = 1$ in the second parametric equation, we find $y = 16$ feet. Thus the greatest height attained by the football is 16 feet.

EXERCISES

In Exercises 1 to 6, neglect air resistance.

1. A golfer drives his ball with an initial velocity of 160 feet per second, and at an angle whose sine is $\frac{3}{5}$ with the horizontal. Find parametric equations of the path of the golf ball. If the ground is level, how far away will the ball first strike the ground? How high will it go?

2. A pitcher throws a baseball horizontally with an initial velocity of 92 feet per second. If the ball is 6 feet above the ground when he releases it, how far away will it strike the ground? What is its greatest height?

3. A boy throws a ball directly upward with an initial velocity of 48 feet per second. How long does it take the ball to return to the boy's upstretched hands? How many feet upward did it travel?

4. A stone is thrown from the top of a vertical cliff with an initial velocity of $64\sqrt{2}$ feet per second and at an angle of 45° above the horizontal. If the point of release of the stone is 192 feet above the ocean, how far from the foot of the cliff will the stone strike the ocean?

5. A batter hits a baseball with an initial velocity of 104 feet per second, and at an angle whose tangent is $\frac{5}{12}$ with the horizontal. If the ball is 3 feet above the ground when hit, at what height will it strike a wall 192 feet away?

6. A bomb is dropped from an airplane which is moving horizontally at 720 miles per hour. If the plane is 6400 feet above level ground and the target is on the ground, how far from the point directly above the target should the bomb be released?

In Exercises 7 to 12, proceed as in the text (Fig. 160) to find parametric equations for the loci of each of the given equations. Make a sketch.

7. $x^2 + y^2 - 4y = 0$.

8. $4x^2 - 25y^2 - 40x = 0$.

9. $y^2 - 16x = 0$.

10. $4x^2 + 9y^2 + 24x = 0$.

11. $16x^3 - y = 0$.

12. $x^3 - y^2 = 0$.

11

Polar Coordinates

11.1   INTRODUCTION

The student will recall that Descartes' invention of analytic geometry was based on a correspondence between the points of geometry and the numbers of algebra.   He accomplished this by what are now called Cartesian coordinates.   There are, however, many other ways of establishing such a correspondence.   Although each is useful in simplifying some particular class of problems, the only other coordinates we need consider here are **polar coordinates.**

We start with a fixed point, O, called the **pole,** and a fixed "half line," Ox, called the **polar axis** (Fig. 162).   The polar axis starts at the origin

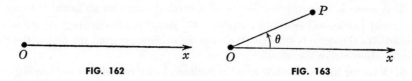

FIG. 162   **FIG. 163**

and extends indefinitely far in one direction, which we will take horizontally to the right.

Let P be any point in the plane.   Draw the line segment $\overline{OP}$ (Fig. 163). Denote by θ an angle xOP having the polar axis for initial side and $\overline{OP}$ for terminal side.   Indicate the undirected distance between O and P by ρ; that is, let $|OP| = \rho$.   Then (ρ, θ), always written in that order, are one set of polar coordinates of P.

For example, to locate the point P whose polar coordinates are $(5, 120°)$, we construct the positive angle $120°$ which has the polar axis for initial side and the pole for vertex [Fig. 164(a)]. P is on the terminal side of this angle, 5 units from the origin.

But this same point, P, as many other sets of polar coordinates—among them $(5, 480°)$ and $(5, -240°)$ [Figs. 164(b) and (c)].

Thus, while a given set of polar coordinates determines just one point,

174

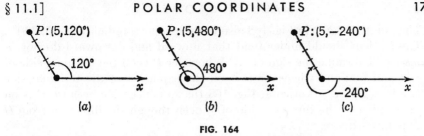

FIG. 164

a given point has indefinitely many sets of polar coordinates. Unlike Cartesian coordinates, the polar coordinate system fails to establish a one-to-one correspondence between the points of the plane and ordered pairs of real numbers. This failure introduces certain difficulties not encountered in Cartesian coordinates, but the student will be alerted to them at the proper time.

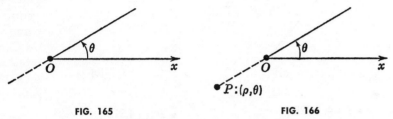

FIG. 165　　　　　　　　　　FIG. 166

In what we have said so far, ρ has been positive or zero. Other polar coordinates in which ρ is negative are defined as follows.

The terminal side of θ was a half line issuing from the pole. By the **extension of the terminal side** of θ we mean the half line issuing from the pole in the opposite direction to the terminal side of θ (Fig. 165). In our diagrams the extension of the terminal side of θ is indicated by a dotted line.

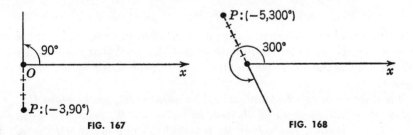

FIG. 167　　　　　　　　　FIG. 168

Let P be any point in the plane. Construct an angle θ so that P is on the extension of its terminal side (Fig. 166). Let $\rho = -|OP|$. Then (ρ, θ) are defined to be a set of polar coordinates of P.

For example, to locate the point $P:(-3, 90°)$ we construct the positive angle 90° which has Ox as initial side (Fig. 167). Because ρ is negative we locate P on the extension of the terminal side of θ, 3 units from the pole.

The point (5, 120°) in Fig. 168 also has the polar coordinates (−5, 300°).

The student should understand that upward and downward do not *in themselves* determine the sign of ρ. Whenever P is on the terminal side of θ, ρ is positive; and whenever P is on the extension of the terminal side of θ, ρ is negative. Notice in Fig. 168 that ρ is negative because P is on the extension of the terminal side of θ, even though the direction from O to P is upward.

Polar coordinate paper has equally spaced circles concentric with the pole, and half lines radiating from the pole. It is useful for plotting points and graphing equations in polar coordinates.

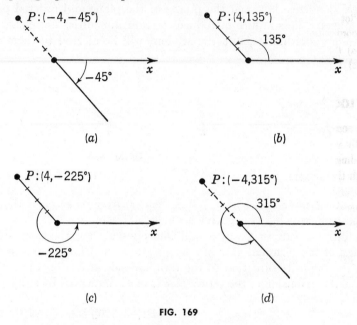

FIG. 169

In numerical examples, when no degree, minute, or second symbol appears in the second polar coordinate, it is understood that θ is measured in radians. Thus the polar coordinates (−2, 3) mean that $\rho = -2$ and $\theta = 3$ *radians*.

This discussion can be summarized as follows: *to plot the point* $P:(\rho, \theta)$, *first construct the angle θ with the pole as vertex and the polar axis as initial side. If ρ is positive, locate P on the terminal side of θ so that $|OP| = \rho$. If ρ is negative, locate P on the extension of the terminal side of θ so that $|OP| = -\rho$.*

Example. Plot the point whose polar coordinates are (−4, −45°) and find three other sets of polar coordinates for the same point.

Solution. Draw the angle −45° in the clockwise direction from its initial line, the polar axis [Fig. 169(a)]. Locate P on the extension of the terminal side of θ, four units from the pole. Other sets of polar coordinates of this same point are $(4, 135°)$, $(4, -225°)$ and $(-4, 315°)$ [Fig. 169(b), (c), and (d)].

EXERCISES

1. Plot the points whose polar coordinates are $(2, 30°)$, $(5, 45°)$, $(4, 315°)$, $(4, 150°)$, $(3, 120°)$, $(7, 250°)$, $(5, 180°)$, $(4, 60°)$, $(6, 300°)$.

2. Plot the points whose polar coordinates are $(3, 15°)$, $(2, 420°)$, $(6, -30°)$, $(4, -150°)$, $(3, 480°)$, $(5, -670°)$, $(0, 0°)$, $(0, 80°)$, $(3, -180°)$.

3. Plot the points whose polar coordinates are $(-4, 45°)$, $(-2, 210°)$, $(4, 75°)$, $(6, \frac{1}{3}\pi)$, $(-5, \frac{3}{2}\pi)$, $(-3, \frac{1}{6}\pi)$, $(3, \frac{7}{6}\pi)$, $(-2, -135°)$, $(2, \frac{1}{4}\pi)$, $(2, 2)$, $(3, 0)$, $(-2, 1)$.

4. Plot the points whose polar coordinates follow. Then give 4 other sets of polar coordinates, two with positive ρ and two with negative ρ, for each point.

(a) $(3, 15°)$;   (b) $(-5, \frac{2}{3}\pi)$;

(c) $(-4, 45°)$;   (d) $(6, 120°)$.

11.2 LOCUS OF A POLAR EQUATION

It is sometimes easy to sketch the locus of an equation in polar coordinates by simply assigning a series of values to θ and computing the corresponding values of ρ. We then plot the points and draw a smooth curve through them.

For example, consider the equation $\rho = 8 \cos \theta$. If we substitute $0°$ for θ in this equation we obtain $\rho = 8$. Thus the point whose polar coordinates are $(8, 0°)$ is on the locus of $\rho = 8 \cos \theta$. Again, if we substitute $30°$ for θ in the given equation we obtain $\rho = 4\sqrt{3}$ and thus the point $(4\sqrt{3}, 30°)$ is on the locus. Continuing this process, our results are shown in the accompanying table of approximate values. After plotting all of

θ	0°	30°	45°	60°	90°	120°	135°	150°	180°
ρ	8	6.8	5.6	4	0	−4	−5.6	−6.8	−8

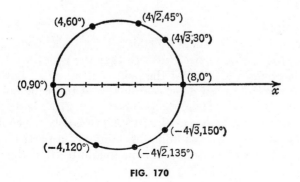

FIG. 170

these points we draw a smooth curve through them, proceeding from one point to the next in the order of their appearance as θ increases from $0°$ to $180°$ (Fig. 170).

The locus seems to be a circle passing through the pole and symmetric with respect to the polar axis. That this is indeed the case will be shown in 11.7.

Now consider the equation

(1)
$$\rho = \frac{2}{1 - \cos \theta}.$$

As before, we construct a table of approximate values by substituting a series of increasing values for θ in (1) and computing the corresponding

θ	$0°$	$45°$	$90°$	$135°$	$180°$	$225°$	$270°$	$315°$
ρ	—	6.8	2	1.2	1	1.2	2	6.8

values of ρ. It will be proved in 11.8 that the locus of (1) is a parabola with focus at the pole (Fig. 171).

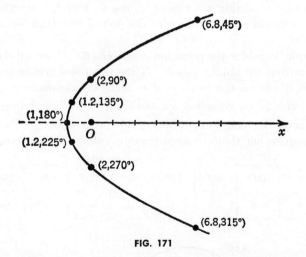

FIG. 171

All this is reminiscent of curve sketching in Cartesian coordinates. But there is one essential difference. Notice that the coordinates $(-2, 270°)$ do not satisfy equation (1). But the point $P:(-2, 270°)$ must be on the curve because another set of polar coordinates of the same point, $(2, 90°)$, do satisfy equation (1). Thus, the point $P:(-2, 270°)$ is on the locus of (1) even though its coordinates $(-2, 270°)$ fail to satisfy the equation. We must conclude that in polar coordinates, failure of a particular set of coordinates to satisfy a given equation is no guarantee that the point is not on the locus of that equation.

11.2.1 Definition.   *A point is on the locus of a polar equation if and only if at least one set of polar coordinates of the point satisfy the given equation.*

EXERCISES

Sketch the locus of each of the following equations.

1. $\rho = 4 \sin \theta$.

2. $\rho = -6 \cos \theta$.

3. $\rho \cos \theta - 5 = 0$.

4. $\rho \sin \theta - 3 = 0$.

5. $\rho = 3$.

6. $\theta = 30°$.

7. $\theta = 2$.

8. $\theta(\theta - 1) = 0$.

9. $\rho = \dfrac{3}{1 + \cos \theta}$.

10. $\rho = \dfrac{4}{1 + \sin \theta}$.

11. $\rho = \dfrac{2}{2 - \cos \theta}$.

12. $\rho = \dfrac{3}{3 - \sin \theta}$.

11.3   RELATIONS BETWEEN CARTESIAN AND POLAR COORDINATES

When a new coordinate system is introduced, it is desirable to have formulas for finding the coordinates of a point in either system if its coordinates in the other system are known.

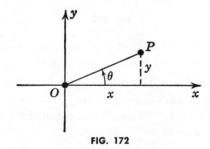

FIG. 172

Let the pole of a polar coordinate system be the same point as the origin of a rectangular Cartesian system, and let the polar axis coincide with the positive x-axis (Fig. 172).   Then any point P in the plane has polar coordinates (ρ, θ) and also Cartesian coordinates (x, y), really two labels for the same point.

If P is on the terminal side of θ (Fig. 172), ρ is positive and $\rho = |OP|$. Then

$$\cos \theta = \frac{x}{|OP|} = \frac{x}{\rho}, \quad \sin \theta = \frac{y}{|OP|} = \frac{y}{\rho},$$

or

(1) $x = \rho \cos \theta, \quad y = \rho \sin \theta$.

If P is on the extension of the terminal side of θ (Fig. 173), ρ is negative and $\rho = -|OP|$ (by 11.1). Let P' be the symmetric partner of P with respect to the origin. Since the Cartesian coordinates of P are (x, y), those of P' are $(-x, -y)$ (by 9.2) and $|OP| = |OP'|$. Now

$$\cos\theta = \frac{-x}{|OP'|} = \frac{-x}{|OP|} = \frac{-x}{-\rho} = \frac{x}{\rho},$$

$$\sin\theta = \frac{-y}{|OP'|} = \frac{-y}{|OP|} = \frac{-y}{-\rho} = \frac{y}{\rho},$$

or

$$x = \rho\cos\theta, \quad y = \rho\sin\theta,$$

which are the same as the equations (1). Thus the formulas (1) are valid in every case.

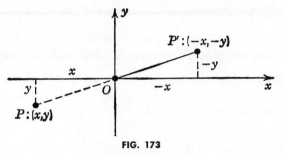

FIG. 173

These formulas enable us to find the Cartesian coordinates of a point whose polar coordinates are known. For example, the Cartesian coordinates of $P:(10, 30°)$ are $x = 10\cos 30° = 5\sqrt{3}$ and $y = 10\sin 30° = 5$. That is, the Cartesian coordinates of P are $(5\sqrt{3}, 5)$.

If we square equations (1) and add them, member by member, we obtain $x^2 + y^2 = \rho^2(\sin^2\theta + \cos^2\theta)$ or

(2) $$\rho = \pm\sqrt{x^2 + y^2}.$$

If we divide the second formula of (1) by the first, member by member, we have

$$\frac{y}{x} = \tan\theta, \quad \text{or} \quad \theta = \text{arc}\tan\frac{y}{x}.$$

Finally, by substituting (2) in (1) we obtain

$$\sin\theta = \frac{y}{\pm\sqrt{x^2 + y^2}}, \quad \cos\theta = \frac{x}{\pm\sqrt{x^2 + y^2}}.$$

This proves the

11.3.1 Theorem. *If the origin and positive x-axis of a rectangular Cartesian coordinate system are the pole and polar axis, respectively, of a polar*

*coordinate system, then the Cartesian and the polar coordinates of any point P
are related by the formulas*

$$x = \rho \cos \theta, \qquad y = \rho \sin \theta;$$

$$\rho = \pm\sqrt{x^2 + y^2}, \quad \theta = \arctan \frac{y}{x};$$

and

$$\sin \theta = \frac{y}{\pm\sqrt{x^2 + y^2}}, \quad \cos \theta = \frac{x}{\pm\sqrt{x^2 + y^2}};$$

*where the sign before the radical is positive if P is on the terminal side of θ
and negative if P is on the extension of the terminal side of θ.*

Example 1. Find polar coordinates of the point P whose rectangular Cartesian
coordinates are $(-1, -1)$.

Solution. By 11.3.1, $\rho = \pm\sqrt{(-1)^2 + (-1)^2} = \pm\sqrt{2}$ and $\theta = \arctan 1$. One
such value of θ is $45°$. From Fig. 174 it is clear that if $\theta = 45°$, P is on the exten-

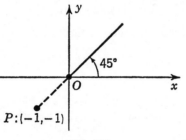

FIG. 174

sion of the terminal side of θ and $\rho = -\sqrt{2}$. Therefore polar coordinates of P are
$(-\sqrt{2}, 45°)$. Other polar coordinates of the same point are $(\sqrt{2}, 225°)$.

Example 2. Find the polar equation of an ellipse in standard position.*

Solution. The Cartesian equation of an ellipse in standard position is

$$\frac{x^2}{a^2} + \frac{y^2}{b^2} = 1.$$

Using the substitutions $x = \rho \cos \theta$, $y = \rho \sin \theta$ (from 11.3.1), we obtain

$$\frac{\rho^2 \cos^2 \theta}{a^2} + \frac{\rho^2 \sin^2 \theta}{b^2} = 1,$$

$$\rho^2(b^2 \cos^2 \theta + a^2 \sin^2 \theta) = a^2b^2.$$

Example 3. Find the general equation of a straight line in polar coordinates.

* Although a locus has many equivalent equations, we will speak of "the" equation
of a locus for simplicity.

Solution. The general equation of a straight line in Cartesian coordinates is

$$Ax + By + C = 0.$$

Substituting $x = \rho \cos \theta$, $y = \rho \sin \theta$ (11.3.1) in this equation we obtain

$$A\rho \cos \theta + B\rho \sin \theta + C = 0,$$

or

$$\rho(A \cos \theta + B \sin \theta) + C = 0.$$

Example 4. Find the Cartesian equation of the locus of

$$\rho = \frac{4}{1 - \cos \theta}.$$

Solution. The given equation can be rewritten $\rho - \rho \cos \theta = 4$. By means of the substitutions $\rho = \pm\sqrt{x^2 + y^2}$ and $x = \rho \cos \theta$ (from 11.3.1), our equation becomes

$$\pm\sqrt{x^2 + y^2} - x = 4.$$

Transposing the term in x and squaring both members, we have

$$x^2 + y^2 = x^2 + 8x + 16,$$

or

$$y^2 = 8x + 16.$$

Its locus is a parabola (7.6.1) which is symmetric with respect to the x-axis (3.6.6).

EXERCISES

Make a sketch for each exercise.

1. Find the Cartesian coordinates of the points whose polar coordinates are: $(3, 45°)$, $(5, 270°)$, $(2, \frac{1}{6}\pi)$, $(-6, \pi)$, and $(4, 120°)$.

2. Find the Cartesian coordinates of the points whose polar coordinates are: $(-2, 225°)$, $(8, 540°)$, $(-5, 0)$, $(8, -60°)$, and $(0, 32°)$.

3. Find polar coordinates of the points whose Cartesian coordinates are: $(\sqrt{3}, 1)$, $(3, -3\sqrt{3})$, $(-3, 0)$, $(-5, 5)$, and $(-2\sqrt{3}, -2)$.

4. Find polar coordinates of the points whose Cartesian coordinates are: $(5, -5\sqrt{3})$, $(0, -4)$, $(0, 2)$, $(-3\sqrt{3}, 3)$, and $(2\sqrt{3}, -2)$.

5. Find the Cartesian equation of the locus of each of the polar equations given in the odd numbered exercises of Section 11.2.

6. Find the Cartesian equation of the locus of each of the polar equations given in the even numbered exercises of Section 11.2.

In Exercises 7 to 16, find the polar equation of the locus of the given Cartesian equation.

7. $2x - 3y + 4 = 0$.　　　　　　**8.** $x - 8 = 0$.

9. $y = 0$.　　　　　　　　　　　**10.** $x^2 + y^2 = 9$.

11. $x^2 + y^2 + 4x - 6y - 3 = 0$.　**12.** $y^2 = x^3$.

13. $y^2 = 2kx$.　　　　　　　　　**14.** $x^2 = 2ky$.

15. $b^2x^2 + a^2y^2 = a^2b^2$.　　　**16.** $b^2x^2 - a^2y^2 = a^2b^2$.

11.4 DISTANCE FORMULA IN POLAR COORDINATES

A basic tool in polar coordinates, as in Cartesian coordinates, is a formula for the undirected distance between two points in terms of the known coordinates of the points.

11.4.1 Theorem.　*The undirected distance between the points $P_1:(\rho_1, \theta_1)$ and $P_2:(\rho_2, \theta_2)$ is*

$$d = \sqrt{\rho_1{}^2 + \rho_2{}^2 - 2\rho_1\rho_2 \cos (\theta_1 - \theta_2)}.$$

Proof.　Let $P_1:(\rho_1, \theta_1)$ and $P_2:(\rho_2, \theta_2)$ be any two points, and d the undirected distance between them (Fig. 175).

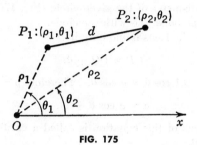

FIG. 175

Applying the law of cosines (Appendix, 15) to the triangle OP_1P_2, we have

$$d^2 = \rho_1{}^2 + \rho_2{}^2 - 2\rho_1\rho_2 \cos (\theta_1 - \theta_2),$$

or

$$d = \sqrt{\rho_1{}^2 + \rho_2{}^2 - 2\rho_1\rho_2 \cos (\theta_1 - \theta_2)},$$

which completes the proof.

Example.　What is the undirected distance between the points $(8, 225°)$ and $(5, 165°)$?

Solution.　Let the first of the given points be $P_1:(\rho_1, \theta_1)$ and the second $P_2:(\rho_2, \theta_2)$. Substituting in the formula of 11.4.1, we get

$$d = \sqrt{64 + 25 - 2(8)(5) \cos 60°} = 7.$$

11.5 POLAR EQUATION OF A LOCUS

One of the fundamental problems of analytic geometry is to find the equation of a locus from its geometric description.　The procedure in polar coordinates is very similar to that in Cartesian coordinates:

1. Select a general point $P:(\rho, \theta)$ on the locus.

2. From the verbal description of the locus, write a geometric statement in-

volving P which is true for all points on the locus and for no points off the locus.

3. Translate the geometric statement in step (2) into an equation involving the coordinates of ρ and θ of P, and simplify.   This is the desired polar equation of the locus.

Polar coordinates are often useful in locus problems where the distance of a general point on the curve from some fixed point varies according to some simple rule.   Usually the given fixed point is chosen for the pole of the polar coordinate system.

Example 1.   Let O be a fixed point on a circle of diameter a.   From O draw any chord $\overline{OQ}$, and continue $\overline{OQ}$ to a point P so that $QP = a$.   Find the equation of the locus of P.

Solution.   Place the pole of a polar coordinate system at the fixed point O, and the polar axis along a diameter of the given circle (Fig. 176).   Denote by A the second intersection of the polar axis with the circle.

A point $P:(\rho, \theta)$ is on the locus if and only if

$$OP = OQ + a.$$

But $OP = \rho$ and $OQ = OA \cos \theta = a \cos \theta$.   Therefore $\rho = a \cos \theta + a$, or

$$\rho = a(\cos \theta + 1).$$

The heart-shaped locus of this equation is called a **cardioid**; it is shown as a dotted curve in Fig. 176.

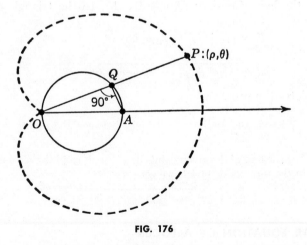

FIG. 176

Example 2.   Find the polar equation of the circle with center at the point $C:(c, \gamma)$ and radius equal to r (Fig. 177).

Solution.   By the definition of a circle, a point $P:(\rho, \theta)$ is on the circle if and only if

$$|CP| = r.$$

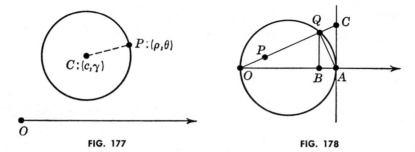

FIG. 177   FIG. 178

But $|CP| = \sqrt{c^2 + \rho^2 - 2c\rho \cos (\theta - \gamma)}$ (by 11.4.1). Therefore

$$\sqrt{c^2 + \rho^2 - 2c\rho \cos (\theta - \gamma)} = r,$$

or

$$\rho^2 - 2c\rho \cos (\theta - \gamma) + (c^2 - r^2) = 0,$$

which is the desired equation.

EXERCISES

1. Find the polar equation of the straight line through the point $(a, 0)$ and perpendicular to the polar axis. Make a sketch.

2. Find the polar equation of the straight line through the point $(a, \frac{1}{2}\pi)$, parallel to the polar axis. Make a sketch.

3. Find the polar equation of the circle with center at the point $(a, 0)$ and passing through the pole. Make a sketch.

4. Find the polar equation of the circle with center at the point $(a, \frac{1}{2}\pi)$ and passing through the pole. Make a sketch.

Exercises 5 to 7 refer to Fig. 176.

5. Find the polar equation of the locus of P if, for all positions of Q on the circle, $|QP|$ is constant and equal to b, where $b > a$. Sketch the locus from its equation. The curve is called a **limaçon**.

6. Find the polar equation of the locus of P if $|QP| = b$, where $b < a$. Then sketch the locus. It is a **limaçon**.

7. Find the polar equation of the locus of P if always $|QP| = |QA|$. Then sketch the locus. It is a **circle**.

Exercises 8 and 9 refer to Fig. 178. Here $\overline{OA}$ is a diameter of the circle, Q is any point on the circle, and C is the point of intersection of the tangent at A with the line through O and Q. The point B is the foot of the perpendicular from Q to the polar axis.

8. Find the polar equation of the locus of points P such that $OP = OB - BA$. Then sketch the locus, which is called a **four-leaved rose**.

9. Find the equation of the locus of points P such that $|OP| = |QC|$. Sketch the locus from its equation. The curve is called a **cissoid**.

10. Find the polar equation of the locus of points P such that the product of the distances of P from the points $(a, 0)$ and (a, π) is always equal to the constant a^2. Then sketch the locus, which is called a **lemniscate**.

11.6   THE STRAIGHT LINE

The polar equation of a line in general position is cumbersome and is less often used than the polar equations of certain special lines.

Consider a line through the point $A:(a, 0°)$, perpendicular to the polar axis (or its extension). Its Cartesian equation is $x = a$. Therefore (by 11.3.1)

$$(1) \qquad\qquad \rho \cos \theta = a$$

is the polar equation of any line perpendicular to the polar axis. When a is positive the line is to the right of the pole (Fig. 179), and when a is negative the line is to the left of the pole.

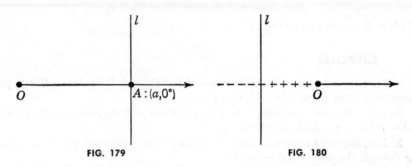

FIG. 179   FIG. 180

For example, the locus of $\rho \cos \theta = -5$ is a straight line perpendicular to the polar axis and five units to the left of the pole. Solving the equation for ρ, we obtain

$$\rho = \frac{-5}{\cos \theta}.$$

When $\theta = 0°$, $\cos \theta = 1$, and $\rho = -5$. Thus the point $(-5, 0°)$ is on the locus. Similarly, the points whose polar coordinates are $(-10, 60°)$ and $(10, 120°)$ are also on the locus (Fig. 180).

Now consider a line l through the point $A:(a, 90°)$ and parallel to the polar axis (Fig. 181). Its Cartesian equation is $y = a$. Therefore (by 11.3.1) its polar equation is

$$(2) \qquad\qquad \rho \sin \theta = a.$$

Thus (2) is *the polar equation of any line parallel to the polar axis.* If a is positive the line is above the polar axis and if a is negative the line is below the polar axis.

Any *line through the pole* has the very simple polar equation

$$(3) \qquad\qquad \theta = k,$$

where the constant k is an angle which the line makes with the polar axis. For, a point lies on such a line if and only if one value of its second polar coordinate is k.

For example, the polar equation of the line through the pole, making a 45° angle with the polar axis is $\theta = 45°$ or $\theta = \frac{1}{4}\pi$ (Fig. 182). But notice that this line has other polar equations, among them $\theta = 405°$ and

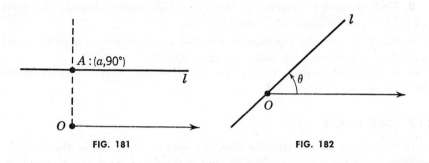

FIG. 181   FIG. 182

$\theta = -135°$. This is because each point has indefinitely many sets of polar coordinates and if any one of these sets satisfies a given equation the point lies on the locus of that equation.

EXERCISES

1. Without using Cartesian coordinates, write the polar equation of the line which is

 (a) perpendicular to the polar axis and 8 units to the right of the pole;
 (b) parallel to the polar axis and 3 units below it;
 (c) through the pole with angle of inclination 60°;
 (d) the polar axis.

2. Without using Cartesian coordinates, write the polar equation of the line which is

 (a) parallel to the polar axis and 10 units above it;
 (b) through the pole with slope 1;
 (c) perpendicular to the polar axis and 2 units to the left of the pole;
 (d) the 90° axis.

3. Without using Cartesian coordinates, find the polar equation of the line through the point (4, 60°) and perpendicular to the polar axis.

4. Without using Cartesian coordinates, find the polar equation of the line through the point $(8, \frac{5}{4}\pi)$, parallel to the polar axis.

5. Sketch the locus of

 (a) $\rho \cos \theta = -7$;   (b) $\rho \sin \theta = 4$;
 (c) $\theta = 126°$;   (d) $\theta = -13°$.

6. Sketch the locus of

(a) $\rho \sin \theta = -10$;   (b) $\rho \cos = 3$;
(c) $\theta = -\frac{1}{3}\pi$;   (d) $\theta = 0$.

7. Write the polar equation of the line which passes through the point $(4, -60°)$ and has slope 5.   (Hint: First find the Cartesian equation and then transform to polar coordinates.)

8. Find the polar equation of the line which passes through the point $(4\sqrt{2}, 135°)$ and has slope -3.   (See hint, above.)

9. What is the polar equation of the line which passes through the point $(3\sqrt{2}, 45°)$ and intersects the polar axis at $(1, 0°)$?

10. Find the polar equation of the line which has slope 4 and intersects the extension of the polar axis in $(3, 180°)$.

11.7 THE CIRCLE

As in the case of the straight line, the general equation of the circle in polar coordinates is so complicated that it is seldom used (see Example 2, Section 11.5).   However, when the circle is in certain special positions its polar equation is simple and useful.

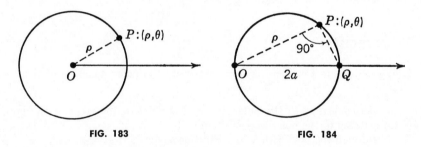

FIG. 183   FIG. 184

Consider a circle with center at the pole and radius r (Fig. 183).   Then a point $P:(\rho, \theta)$ is on the circle if and only if

$$|OP| = r.$$

But $|OP| = \pm\rho$.   Therefore

(1) $$\rho = \pm r$$

are *the polar equations of the circle with center at the pole and radius equal to r.*

We next turn our attention to a circle with center at the point $A:(a, 0°)$ and radius equal to $|a|$.   Denote its second intersection with the polar axis by Q (Fig. 184).

Let $P:(\rho, \theta)$ be any point on the circle.   Then OPQ is a right angle since it is inscribed in a semicircle.   Therefore

$$\cos \theta = \frac{\rho}{2a},$$

or

(2) $$\rho = 2a \cos \theta,$$

is *the polar equation of the circle with radius* $|a|$, *having its center on the polar axis or its extension, and passing through the pole.*

When a is positive in equation (2), the circle is to the right of the pole. When a is negative, the circle is to the left of the pole.

Similarly,

(3) $$\rho = 2a \sin \theta$$

is *the polar equation of the circle with radius* $|a|$ *and center on the* 90° *axis or its extension, and passing through the pole.*

EXERCISES

Make a sketch for each exercise.

1. Find the polar equation of the circle

(a) with center at the pole and radius 8;
(b) with center $(5, 0°)$ and radius 5;
(c) with center $(6, 90°)$ and radius 6;
(d) with center $(4, \pi)$ and radius 4;
(e) with radius 3 and tangent to the polar axis at the pole.

2. Find the polar equation of the circle

(a) with center $(-7, 0°)$ and radius 7;
(b) with center $(-3, 180°)$ and radius 3;
(c) with center $(2, -\frac{1}{2}\pi)$ and radius 2;
(d) with center $(-6, \frac{3}{2}\pi)$ and radius 6;
(e) with radius 5 and tangent to the 90° axis at the pole.

3. Find the center and radius of each of the following circles:

(a) $\rho = 5$;   (b) $\rho = 6 \cos \theta$;
(c) $\rho = -7 \sin \theta$;   (d) $\rho = -2 \cos \theta$.

4. Find the center and radius of each of the following circles:

(a) $\rho = -4$;   (b) $\rho = -12 \sin \theta$;
(c) $\rho = 5 \cos \theta$;   (d) $\rho = 2 \sin \theta$.

5. Find the polar equation of the circle with center $(3, 135°)$ and radius 8.

6. Find the polar equation of the circle with center $(-4, 60°)$ and passing through the point $(-2, 120°)$.

7. Find the polar equation of the circle passing through the pole and with center at $(5, -\frac{1}{6}\pi)$.

8. Find the polar equation of the circle passing through the pole and with center at $(6, 135°)$.

9. Find the polar equation of the circle whose Cartesian equation is $x^2 + y^2 - 2x + 4y + 1 = 0$.

10. Find the polar equation of the circle whose Cartesian equation is $x^2 + y^2 + 8x - 6y + 9 = 0$.

11.8 POLAR EQUATIONS OF CONICS

Very simple polar equations of conics are obtained by placing a focus at the pole and making the corresponding directrix perpendicular to the polar axis (Fig. 185).

Let the directrix be to the left of the focus and denote its intersection with the extension of the polar axis by D. Call the undirected distance between the focus and the directrix d; that is, $|DO| = d$.

Let $P:(\rho, \theta)$ be any point on the conic and drop perpendiculars $\overline{PQ}$ and $\overline{PR}$ to the polar axis (or its extension) and to the directrix, respectively. By 6.1.1, P is on the conic if and only if

(1) $$|OP| = e|RP|,$$

where e is the eccentricity.

Assume for the moment that P is to the right of the directrix and on the

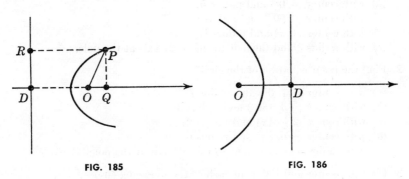

FIG. 185   FIG. 186

terminal side of θ. Then RP and ρ are both positive and so $|RP| = RP$ and $|OP| = \rho$. Substituting in (1) we have

(2) $$\rho = e(RP).$$

But $RP = DQ$ and $DO + OQ = DQ$ (1.2.3). Also,

$$DO = d \quad \text{and} \quad OQ = \rho \cos \theta.$$

Therefore $RP = d + \rho \cos \theta$. Substituting in (2) we obtain

$$\rho = e(d + \rho \cos \theta)$$

or, upon solving for ρ,

(3) $$\rho = \frac{ed}{1 - e \cos \theta}.$$

The locus of (3) is a parabola if $e = 1$ and an ellipse if $0 < e < 1$.   Both of these curves lie entirely to the right of the given directrix.   But under our assumption that P is to the right of the directrix and that ρ is positive, the locus of (3) for $e > 1$ is only one branch of a hyperbola.   It can be shown, however, that by allowing ρ to take on negative as well as positive values, the locus of (3) for $e > 1$ is the whole hyperbola (see Example below).

Similarly, if the directrix is to the right of the corresponding focus (Fig. 186), a polar equation of the conic is

$$\rho = \frac{ed}{1 + e \cos \theta}.$$

All this is summarized in the

11.8.1 Theorem.   *The polar equation of a conic with focus at the pole and corresponding directrix perpendicular to the polar axis is*

$$\rho = \frac{ed}{1 \pm e \cos \theta},$$

where d is the undirected distance between the focus and the corresponding directrix.   The positive sign applies when the given directrix is to the right of the corresponding focus, and the negative sign when the given directrix is to the left of the focus.

Equally simple polar equations of conics are obtained if a focus is at the pole and the directrix is parallel to the polar axis.

11.8.2 Theorem.   *The polar equation of a conic having a focus at the pole and corresponding directrix parallel to the polar axis is*

$$\rho = \frac{ed}{1 \pm e \sin \theta},$$

where d is the undirected distance between the focus and the corresponding directrix.   The positive sign is used when the given directrix is above the polar axis and the negative sign when below.

Example.   Name and sketch the locus of

$$\rho = \frac{30}{5 - 10 \cos \theta}.$$

Solution.   In order to compare the given equation with 11.8.1, we must make the first term in the denominator of the right member equal to unity.   Accordingly, we divide both numerator and denominator of the right member by 5 and obtain

$$\rho = \frac{6}{1 - 2 \cos \theta}.$$

Comparing this with 11.8.1, we see that $e = 2$ and $d = 3$. Therefore the locus is a hyperbola with a focus at the pole and corresponding directrix 3 units to the left of the pole (Fig. 187).

From the table of approximate values it is clear that as θ increases from 0° and approaches 60°, the point $P:(\rho, \theta)$ starts from $(-6, 0°)$, the left vertex of the hy-

θ	0°	20°	40°	60°	80°	100°	120°	140°	160°	180°	200°	220°	240°	260°	280°	300°	320°	340°
ρ	−6	−6.8	−11.1	—	9.1	4.4	3	2.4	2.1	2	2.1	2.4	3	4.4	9.1	—	−11.1	−6.8

perbola, and moves indefinitely far away along the lower half of the left branch. For $\theta = 60°$ there is no value of ρ because the denominator, $1 - 2 \cos 60°$, would be zero. The line $\theta = 60°$ is parallel to an asymptote. As θ increases, taking on

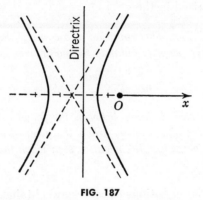

FIG. 187

values between 60° and 300°, the point traces the entire right branch of the hyperbola from top to bottom. For $\theta = 300°$ there is no corresponding ρ. As θ continues to increase, taking on values between 300° and 360°, the point moves in along the upper half of the left branch, completing the curve.

The center is 4 units to the left of the pole and the asymptotes go through the center, making angles of ±60° with the axis.

EXERCISES

Name and draw the conics whose equations are given in Exercises 1 to 10.

1. $\rho = \dfrac{6}{1 - \cos \theta}$.

2. $\rho = \dfrac{4}{2 - \cos \theta}$.

3. $\rho = \dfrac{3}{1 - \sin \theta}$.

4. $\rho = \dfrac{15}{2 + 3 \cos \theta}$.

5. $\rho = \dfrac{10}{7 - 2 \sin \theta}$.

6. $\rho = \dfrac{72}{4 + 9 \sin \theta}$.

7. $\rho = \dfrac{13}{4 + 4 \cos \theta}$.

8. $\rho = \dfrac{26}{7 + 5 \cos \theta}$.

9. $\rho = \dfrac{10}{7 - 7 \sin \theta}.$ 　　　　　　**10.** $\rho = \dfrac{7}{3 + 4 \sin \theta}.$

11. For the parabolas in Exercises 1 to 10, find the polar coordinates of the vertex and the polar equation of the directrix.

12. For the ellipses in Exercises 1 to 10, find the polar coordinates of the vertices and of the center, and the polar equations of the directrices.

13. For the hyperbolas in Exercises 1 to 10, find the polar coordinates of the vertices and of the center, and the polar equations of the directrices.

14. Write the Cartesian equation of each of the conics in

(*a*) Exercises 1, 3, 5, 7, 9;

(*b*) Exercises 2, 4, 6, 8, 10.

11.9 CURVE SKETCHING IN POLAR COORDINATES

In Cartesian coordinates it was often helpful to make a preliminary analysis of an equation before attempting to sketch its locus. We tested it for symmetry, intercepts, asymptotes, etc. Unfortunately, such tests are usually less rewarding in polar coordinates. The trouble is that a point has indefinitely many sets of polar coordinates, and even though one set may not satisfy an equation another set may. But despite this, a few preliminary tests are worth knowing.

Of course, if the given polar equation happens to be one of those derived in 11.6, 11.7 or 11.8, the student should be able to sketch it directly without difficulty.

Should we not recognize the polar equation, it is sometimes profitable to transform it into a Cartesian equation by means of the substitutions 11.3.1. This will not in any way affect the locus, and the Cartesian equation may be familiar to us. For example, the polar equation $\rho^2 \sin 2\theta = 2$ can be rewritten $\rho^2 \sin \theta \cos \theta = 1$ (Appendix, 13). Using the formulas of 11.3.1, the latter equation becomes $xy = 1$. Thus the locus of the original polar equation is the familiar equilateral hyperbola (Example 2, Section 7.1).

If he does not recognize either the polar or the Cartesian equation, the student should try some or all of the following tests before any points are plotted.

1. *Intercepts.* If $\theta = 0$, or $\pm\pi$, or $\pm 2\pi$, or $\pm 3\pi$, etc., the point $P\!:\!(\rho, \theta)$ is on the polar axis or its extension. Therefore, *if we substitute 0 or $\pm\pi$ or $\pm 2\pi$, etc., for θ in the given polar equation, the real solutions (if any) of the resulting equation in ρ are intercepts on the polar axis or its extension.*

For example, the polar intercept of the parabola $\rho = 6/(1 + \cos \theta)$ is found by substituting $0°$ for θ in the equation, obtaining $\rho = 3$. Thus the parabola intersects the polar axis in the point $(3, 0°)$.

Similarly, *to find the intercepts on the $90°$ axis or its extension, substitute $\pm\pi/2$ or $\pm 3\pi/2$ or $\pm 5\pi/2$, etc., for θ in the given polar equation and solve for real values of ρ.*

Sometimes the above tests fail to disclose that a curve goes through the pole. This is because polar coordinates of the pole are $(0, \theta)$, where θ is any angle whatever. Therefore, *to determine whether a curve goes through the pole substitute zero for ρ in the polar equation of the curve. If the resulting equation in θ has any real solution, the curve goes through the pole.*

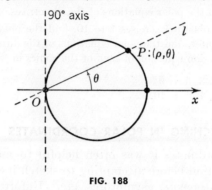

FIG. 188

For example, the first of the above tests only shows that the circle $\rho = 4 \cos \theta$ crosses the polar axis at $(4, 0°)$ (Fig. 188). But substitution of zero for ρ in the equation gives $\cos \theta = 0$ or $\theta = 90°$. Since the coordinates $(0, 90°)$ satisfy the equation, the circle goes through the pole.

2. *Tangents at the Pole.* Consider the circle $\rho = 4 \cos \theta$ (Fig. 188). Let $P:(\rho, \theta)$ be any point on the upper half of the circle. As θ increases and approaches $90°$, the point P moves along the upper half of the circle and approaches 0. At the same time the line l, through O and P, revolves in the counterclockwise direction about 0 and approaches the $90°$ axis as a limiting position.

11.9.1 Definition. *The limiting position of the line through O and P, as O remains fixed and P approaches O along the curve, is a **tangent** to the curve at O.*

In the case of the circle $\rho = 4 \cos \theta$, the limiting position of l as θ increases and P approaches O along the circle is the $90°$ axis. That is, the tangent

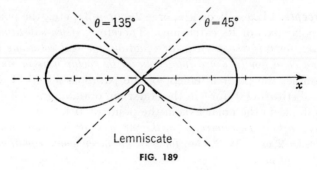

Lemniscate

FIG. 189

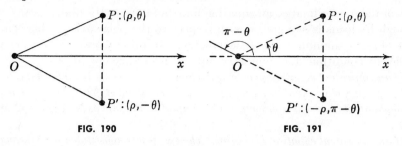

FIG. 190   FIG. 191

to the circle $\rho = 4 \cos \theta$ at the pole is the 90° axis (and its extension). Its equation is $\theta = 90°$.

Notice that the equation of the tangent to the above circle at the pole can be found by substituting zero for ρ in the given equation and solving for θ. We obtain $\cos \theta = 0$, whence $\theta = 90°$.

Thus, *if a curve goes through the pole, the equation of the tangent to the curve at the pole is obtained by substituting zero for ρ in the polar equation of the curve and solving for real values of θ.*

For example, substitution of zero for ρ in the equation of the **lemniscate,** $\rho^2 = 8 \cos 2\theta$, gives $\cos 2\theta = 0$; whence $2\theta = 90°$ or $270°$ and $\theta = 45°$ or $135°$. The coordinates $(0, 45°)$ and $(0, 135°)$ satisfy the given equation and the lemniscate goes through the pole twice (Fig. 189). The equations of the tangent lines at the pole are $\theta = 45°$ and $\theta = 135°$.

3. **Symmetry.** The points $P:(\rho, \theta)$ and $P':(\rho, -\theta)$ are symmetric with respect to the polar axis (Fig. 190). Therefore, *if an equivalent equation is obtained when $-\theta$ is substituted for θ throughout a given polar equation, its locus is symmetric with respect to the polar axis.*

For example, the conic $\rho = ed/(1 + e \cos \theta)$ is symmetric with respect to the polar axis (Fig. 186) because substitution of $-\theta$ for θ gives $\rho = ed/(1 + e \cos (-\theta))$ and, since $\cos (-\theta) = \cos \theta$, the original equation is unchanged.

Again, the points $P:(\rho, \theta)$ and $P':(-\rho, \pi - \theta)$ are symmetric with respect to the polar axis (Fig. 191), and therefore *if an equivalent equation is obtained when $-\rho$ is substituted for ρ and $\pi - \theta$ for θ throughout a given polar equation, its locus is symmetric with respect to the polar axis.*

The student is warned that because of the fact that each point has many

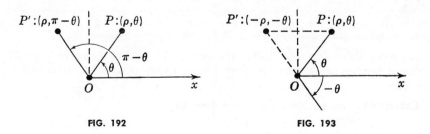

FIG. 192   FIG. 193

sets of polar coordinates, an equation may fail both of the above tests even though its locus is symmetric with respect to the polar axis. This is also true of our remaining tests for symmetry. In other words, these tests are sufficient conditions for symmetry but not necessary conditions.

If an equivalent equation is obtained when $\pi - \theta$ *is substituted for* θ *throughout a given polar equation, or when* $-\rho$ *is substituted for* ρ *and* $-\theta$ *for* θ *throughout, its locus is symmetric with respect to the* 90° *axis* (Figs. 192 and 193).

If an equivalent equation is obtained when $\pi + \theta$ *is substituted for* θ *throughout a given polar equation, or when* $-\rho$ *is substituted for* ρ *throughout, its locus is symmetric with respect to the pole* (Figs. 194 and 195).

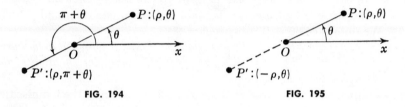

FIG. 194   FIG. 195

Example 1. Sketch the locus of $\rho = 4 \cos \theta + 2$.

Solution. Before plotting any points we will test for intercepts and symmetry. If the curve goes through the pole we will find the tangents to the curve at the pole.

If $\theta = 0°$ in the given equation, $\rho = 6$. Therefore the curve cuts the polar axis at the point $(6, 0°)$. If $\theta = 180°$, $\rho = -2$ and the curve cuts the polar axis again at the point $(-2, 180°)$.

Similarly, the curve cuts the 90° axis in the point $(2, 90°)$ and the extension of the 90° axis in the point $(2, 270°)$.

By substituting zero for ρ in the given equation we obtain $\theta = 120°$ or 240°. The curve goes through the pole twice, and the tangents to the curve at the pole are the lines $\theta = 120°$ and $\theta = 240°$.

Our tests for symmetry with respect to the 90° axis fail. Thus we do not know whether the curve is symmetric with respect to the 90° axis or not. Nor do our tests for symmetry with respect to the pole give us any information.

We now mark on the polar axis and the 90° axis the intercepts we have found, and draw the tangents to the curve at the pole (Fig. 196). After computing a table of

θ	0°	30°	60°	90°	105°	120°	135°	150°	165°	180°
ρ	6	5.5	4	2	1	0	−.8	−1.5	−1.9	−2

approximate values, we draw half of the curve. The rest of the curve is quickly sketched because of its symmetry with respect to the polar axis. It is called a **limaçon.**

Example 2. Sketch the locus of $\rho = 4 \cos 3\theta$.

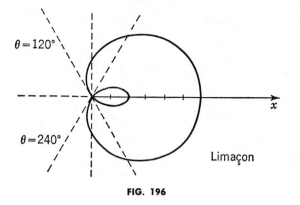

$\theta = 120°$

$\theta = 240°$

Limaçon

FIG. 196

Solution. If $\theta = 0°$, then $\rho = 4$. Therefore the curve cuts the polar axis at $(4, 0°)$. When $\theta = 90°$, $\rho = 0$, so the curve goes through the pole.

To find the tangents to the curve at the pole, we substitute $\rho = 0$ in the given equation, obtaining $\cos 3\theta = 0$. Thus the equations of the tangents at the pole are $\theta = 30°$, $\theta = 90°$, and $\theta = 150°$.

Substituting $-\theta$ for θ in the given equation, we have $\rho = 4 \cos 3(-\theta) = 4 \cos 3\theta$. Since the equation remains essentially unchanged when $-\theta$ is substituted for θ, its locus is symmetric with respect to the polar axis.

After this preliminary analysis, we need plot only a comparatively small number of points. The curve is called a **three-leaved rose** (Fig. 197). Starting at $(4, 0°)$, the arrowheads indicate the continuous path traced by the point $P:(\rho, \theta)$ as θ increases from $0°$ to $180°$.

Example 3. Draw the locus of $\rho = \theta$.

Solution. The curve crosses the polar axis or its extension whenever $\theta = n\pi$ (n any integer). It crosses the $90°$ axis or its extension when $\theta = \frac{1}{2}n\pi$ (n any odd integer).

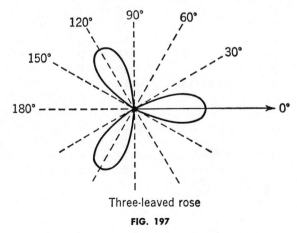

Three-leaved rose

FIG. 197

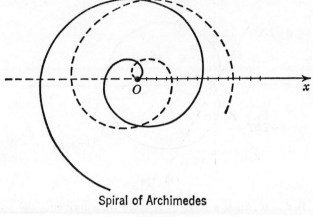

Spiral of Archimedes

FIG. 198

If $\rho = 0$, then $\theta = 0$, and thus the tangent to the curve at the pole is the polar axis.

In plotting points for this curve, it is convenient to use radian measure for θ. Thus when $\theta = 0$, $\rho = 0$; when $\theta = 1$ (radian), $\rho = 1$; when $\theta = \frac{1}{2}\pi$, $\rho = \frac{1}{2}\pi$; when $\theta = -\pi$, $\rho = -\pi$; etc., etc.

The curve is called a **spiral of Archimedes** (Fig. 198). The dotted part of the curve corresponds to negative values of θ.

EXERCISES

Sketch the loci of the following equations.

1. $\rho = 8(3 + 2\cos\theta)$.
2. $\rho = 3\sec\theta$.
3. $\rho = 4 - 4\cos\theta$ (cardioid).
4. $\rho = 7 - 7\sin\theta$ (cardioid).
5. $\rho = 3 + 3\cos\theta$ (cardioid).
6. $\rho = 5 - 2\cos\theta$ (limaçon).
7. $\rho = 3 - 6\sin\theta$ (limaçon).
8. $\rho = 4 - 3\sin\theta$ (limaçon).
9. $\rho = 1 - 5\cos\theta$ (limaçon).
10. $\rho^2 = 9\cos 2\theta$ (lemniscate).
11. $\rho^2 = 4\sin 2\theta$ (lemniscate).
12. $\rho^2 = 5\cos 2\theta$ (lemniscate).
13. $\rho^2 = -16\sin 2\theta$ (lemniscate).
14. $\rho = 3\cos 2\theta$ (four-leaved rose).
15. $\rho = 4\sin 2\theta$ (four-leaved rose).
16. $\rho = 6\cos 3\theta$ (three-leaved rose).
17. $\rho = 2\sin 3\theta$ (three-leaved rose).
18. $\rho = 5\cos 4\theta$ (eight-leaved rose).
19. $\rho = 4\sin 4\theta$ (eight-leaved rose).
20. $\rho = 6\sin 5\theta$ (five-leaved rose).
21. $\rho = 3\cos 5\theta$ (five-leaved rose).
22. $\rho = 2\theta$ (spiral of Archimedes).
23. $\rho = \frac{1}{2}\theta$ (spiral of Archimedes).
24. $\rho = e^\theta$ (logarithmic spiral).
26. $\rho = 3/\theta$ (reciprocal spiral).
25. $\rho = e^{\frac{\theta}{2}}$ (logarithmic spiral).
28. $\rho = 4\tan\theta\sin\theta$ (cissoid).
27. $\rho = 1/\theta$ (reciprocal spiral).
30. $\rho = 2\csc\theta + 4$ (conchoid).
29. $\rho = 3\sec\theta + 1$ (conchoid).

12

The Basic Tools in Space

12.1 RECTANGULAR CARTESIAN COORDINATES

The position of a point in plane analytic geometry was established by means of its directed distances from two mutually perpendicular lines. In three-dimensional space, the position of a point is fixed by its directed distances from each of three mutually perpendicular planes.

For example, any point P in this room can be located if we know its (perpendicular) distances from two adjacent walls and from the floor (Fig. 199).

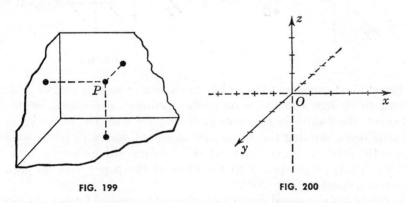

FIG. 199   FIG. 200

Let Ox, Oy, and Oz be three mutually perpendicular directed lines in space (Fig. 200). They are called the **x-axis, y-axis,** and **z-axis,** respectively, and O is the **origin.** All lines parallel to a coordinate axis have the same positive direction as that axis.

Taken in pairs, the coordinate axes determine three coordinate planes—the yz-plane, the zx-plane, and the xy-plane.

Let P be any point in space (Fig. 201). Drop perpendiculars from P to the yz-plane, the zx-plane and the xy-plane, indicating their feet by A, B and C, respectively. Then the coordinates of P are $x = AP$, $y = BP$ and $z = CP$.

12.1.1 Definition.   *The **x-coordinate** of any point in space is its directed distance from the yz-plane; the **y-coordinate** is its directed distance from the zx-plane; and its **z-coordinate** is its directed distance from the xy-plane.*

The x-coordinate of a point is measured perpendicular to the yz-plane, that is, parallel to the x-axis.   The y-coordinate is measured parallel to the y-axis, and the z-coordinate parallel to the z-axis.   In writing the coordinates of a point, *the x-coordinate always appears first, then the y-coordinate, and finally the z-coordinate.*

For example, in plotting the point whose coordinates are $(2, -3, -4)$ we start from the origin and count 2 units to the right along the positive x-axis, then 3 units away from us parallel to the negative y-axis, and then 4 units down, parallel to the negative z-axis (Fig. 202).

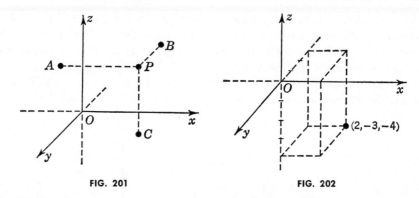

FIG. 201   FIG. 202

The student can orient the coordinate axes any way he pleases without having to change a single word in the theorems, corollaries, or proofs. However, the figures in this book will conform with the usage in many calculus texts, showing the x-axis as a horizontal line with positive direction to the right, the z-axis as a vertical line with positive direction upward, and the y-axis perpendicular to the plane of the paper with its positive direction toward us (Fig. 200).

In our two-dimensional diagrams of three-dimensional figures, the x- and z-axes are drawn perpendicular to each other, since we think of them as lying in the plane of the paper.   To make the y-axis seem to come toward us, we draw it so that angle xOy is about $-135°$ (Fig. 200).

Although the units on the three coordinate axes are actually all of the same length, we draw the units on the y-axis about $\frac{2}{3}$ as long as those on the x- and z-axes so as to further the illusion of three-dimensional space. Of course this is not true perspective drawing, since the units on the y-axis do not appear larger as they come toward us.   But it is simple to execute and gives a surprisingly good illusion of three-dimensional space.

The beginning student is advised to *"complete the box"* when plotting a point, as shown in Fig. 202.   This will help him in making the transition from two-dimensional to three-dimensional visualization.   The box is easy to draw, since all of its edges are parallel to, or segments of, the coordinate axes.

From 12.1.1 and the fact that a line parallel to the yz-plane is everywhere equidistant from that plane (Fig. 203), we have the

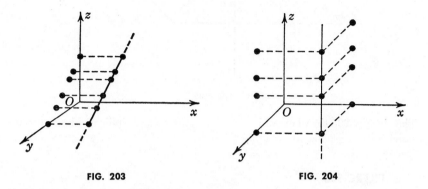

FIG. 203   FIG. 204

12.1.2 Corollary.   *All points on a line parallel to the yz-plane have equal x-coordinates, and conversely.*

Similarly,

12.1.3 Corollary.   *All points on a line parallel to the zx-plane have equal y-coordinates, and conversely.*

12.1.4 Corollary.   *All points on a line parallel to the xy-plane have the same z-coordinate, and conversely.*

Any line parallel to the z-axis is parallel to both the yz- and zx-planes (Fig. 204) or else lies in one of them and is parallel to the other.   Therefore, from 12.1.2 and 12.1.3 we have the

12.1.5 Corollary.   *If a line is parallel to the z-axis all points on it have the same x-coordinates and also the same y-coordinates, and conversely.*

Similar corollaries hold for a line parallel to the x- or y-axis.

Example.   Sketch the locus of points for which $z = 3$.

Solution.   The totality of points whose z-coordinates are equal to 3 form a plane parallel to the xy-plane and 3 units above it.

We of course cannot draw a whole plane since it extends indefinitely.   Throughout this book we- have been representing lines by line-segments.   We will now represent a plane by a finite portion of the plane.

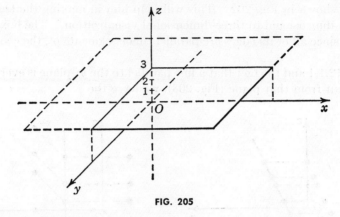

FIG. 205

Thus in Fig. 205 the plane which is the locus of $z = 3$ is indicated by a rectangle, parallel to the xy-plane and 3 units above it.

EXERCISES

1. Plot the points whose coordinates are: $(1, 4, 2)$, $(0, 3, 5)$, $(4, 0, 6)$, $(-3, 1, 5)$, $(-2, 2, 0)$, $(1, 1, 1)$, $(5, 0, 0)$, $(2, -4, -1)$ and $(-6, 2, -7)$.   Complete the "box" in each case.

2. What is peculiar to the coordinates of all points in the yz-plane?

3. What is the locus of points for which $x = 0$?

4. What is the locus of points for which $y = 0$?

5. What is the locus of points for which $x = 0$ and $y = 0$ simultaneously?

6. What is the locus of points for which $z = 5$?   Sketch it.

7. What is the locus of points for which $y = -2$?   Make a sketch.

8. What is the locus of points for which $z = 3$ and $y = 6$ simultaneously? Sketch the locus.

9. What is the locus of points for which $x = y$?   Make a sketch.

10. What is the locus of points for which $x = -y$?   Make a sketch.

12.2 DISTANCE FORMULAS

As in plane analytic geometry, we need certain basic tools in order to apply the analytic method to geometry in three-dimensional space.   The remainder of this chapter will be devoted to the development of such tools. The first is a set of distance formulas.

12.2.1 Theorem.   *If P_1:(x_1, y_1, z_1) and P_2:(x_2, y_2, z_2) are two points on a line parallel to the x-axis, then the directed distance from P_1 to P_2 is*

$$P_1P_2 = x_2 - x_1.$$

Proof.   Denote by Q the intersection of the line through P_1 and P_2 with

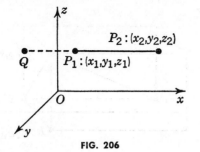

FIG. 206

the yz-plane (Fig. 206).   Since Q, P_1 and P_2 are three points on a directed line,

$$QP_1 + P_1P_2 = QP_2 \qquad \text{(by 1.2.3)},$$

or

$$P_1P_2 = QP_2 - QP_1.$$

But $\qquad\qquad QP_2 = x_2 \quad \text{and} \quad QP_1 = x_1 \qquad \text{(by 12.1.1)}.$

Therefore

$$P_1P_2 = x_2 - x_1.$$

Similarly

12.2.2 Theorem.   *If P_1:(x_1, y_1, z_1) and P_2:(x_2, y_2, z_2) are two points on a line parallel to the y-axis, then*

$$P_1P_2 = y_2 - y_1.$$

12.2.3 Theorem.   *If P_1:(x_1, y_1, z_1) and P_2:(x_2, y_2, z_2) are any two points on a line parallel to the z-axis, then*

$$P_1P_2 = z_2 - z_1.$$

At this time the student should reread 2.1.5.   All that was said there applies equally here, and for the same reasons.   Theorems 12.2.1, 12.2.2, and 12.2.3 are valid no matter what the relative positions of the two points, provided only that they lie on a line parallel to an axis.

We next turn our attention to a formula for the undirected distance between any two points in space.

12.2.4 Theorem.   *The undirected distance between any two points,*
P_1:(x_1, y_1, z_1) and P_2:(x_2, y_2, z_2) is

$$|\boldsymbol{P_1P_2}| = \sqrt{(x_2 - x_1)^2 + (y_2 - y_1)^2 + (z_2 - z_1)^2}.$$

Proof.   Complete the box with edges parallel to the coordinate axes and having $\overline{P_1P_2}$ as a diagonal (Fig. 207).   Label the appropriate corners Q and R so that $\overline{P_1Q}$ is parallel to the x-axis and $\overline{P_2R}$ is parallel to the z-axis.

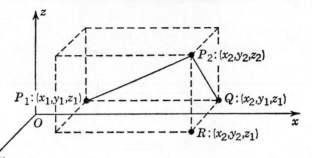

FIG. 207

The coordinates of Q are (x_2, y_1, z_1), and the coordinates of R are (x_2, y_2, z_1) (by 12.1.2 and 12.1.3).

Since $\overline{P_1Q}$ is perpendicular to the plane of Q, R, and P_2, angle P_1QP_2 is a right angle. Therefore

$$(1) \qquad\qquad |P_1P_2|^2 = |P_1Q|^2 + |QP_2|^2.$$

But

$$(2) \qquad\qquad |QP_2|^2 = |QR|^2 + |RP_2|^2.$$

Substituting (2) in (1) we obtain

$$(3) \qquad\qquad |P_1P_2|^2 = |P_1Q|^2 + |QR|^2 + |RP_2|^2.$$

Since $P_1Q = x_2 - x_1$, $QR = y_2 - y_1$, and $RP_2 = z_2 - z_1$ (by 12.2.1, 12.2.2, and 12.2.3), (3) becomes

$$|P_1P_2|^2 = |x_2 - x_1|^2 + |y_2 - y_1|^2 + |z_2 - z_1|^2,$$

whence

$$|P_1P_2| = \sqrt{(x_2 - x_1)^2 + (y_2 - y_1)^2 + (z_2 - z_1)^2}.$$

EXERCISES

Make a sketch for each exercise.

1. Is the line through $P:(4, 2, -1)$ and $Q:(4, 2, 5)$ parallel to one of the coordinate axes? Find PQ.

2. Is the line through $P:(2, 3, -2)$ and $Q:(-2, 3, -2)$ parallel to a coordinate axis? Find PQ.

3. Find the directed distance from the point whose coordinates are $(1, 4, 2)$ to the point whose coordinates are $(1, 4, 5)$.

4. Find the directed distance from the point $(-3, -1, 1)$ to the point $(-3, -7, 1)$.

5. Find the directed distance from the point $(-3, 2, 2)$ to the point $(-3, -5, 2)$.

6. Find the directed distance from the point $(1, 0, -3)$ to the point $(-8, 0, -3)$.

7. Find the undirected distance between each of the following pairs of points:

(a) $(-4, 2, 2)$ and $(1, 3, -5)$;   (b) $(0, 0, 0)$ and $(3, 2, 6)$;

(c) $(2, 7, -3)$ and $(5, 0, 2)$;   (d) $(6, -1, 4)$ and $(-2, -3, -5)$.

8. Find the undirected distance between each of the following pairs of points:

(a) $(-1, 4, 6)$ and $(3, 1, 0)$;   (b) $(6, -3, 9)$ and $(11, 2, -1)$;

(c) $(7, 0, 7)$ and $(-1, -1, -4)$;   (d) $(-4, 2, 5)$ and $(0, 0, 1)$.

9. Express by an equation that the undirected distance between the point P whose coordinates are (x, y, z) and the point $(2, 3, 1)$ is always equal to 5.   Name the locus of P.

10. Express by an equation that the undirected distance between the point $P{:}(x, y, z)$ and the point $C{:}(-1, 2, 0)$ is equal to 4.   What is the locus of all such points P?

11. What is the locus of $(x - 1)^2 + (y + 4)^2 + (z - 2)^2 = 9$?

12. What is the locus of $(x + 2)^2 + y^2 + (z + 3)^2 = 4$?

13. Write an equation of the sphere with center at the origin and radius 7.

14. Write an equation of the sphere with center at $(5, 1, -1)$ and radius 4.

12.3 POSITIVE DIRECTION ON A LINE

We have already seen that lines parallel to a coordinate axis have the same positive direction as that axis.   But what about other lines?

Consider the line-segment $\overline{P_1P_2}$ joining any two points, $P_1{:}(x_1, y_1, z_1)$ and $P_2{:}(x_2, y_2, z_2)$.

12.3.1 Definition.   *The directed distance P_1P_2 is positive if $z_2 > z_1$, and P_1P_2 is negative if $z_2 < z_1$.*

This means that in our diagrams *the positive direction on a line is upward* (Fig. 208).

Since $z_2 > z_1$ if and only if $z_2 - z_1$ is positive, and $z_2 < z_1$ if and only if $z_2 - z_1$ is negative, we have the

12.3.2 Corollary.   *If $\overline{P_1P_2}$ is not parallel to the xy-plane, the sign of P_1P_2 is the same as the sign of $z_2 - z_1$.*

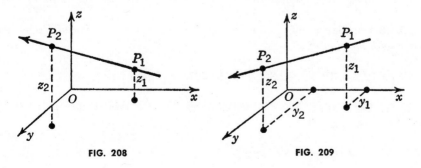

FIG. 208   FIG. 209

If $z_2 - z_1 = 0$, then $z_2 = z_1$ and there is no up or down on the line (Fig. 209). The line is parallel to the xy-plane or lies in it (12.1.4). In agreement with our convention in plane analytic geometry, we state the

12.3.3 Definition. *When* $z_2 - z_1 = 0$, P_1P_2 *is positive if* $y_2 > y_1$ *and negative if* $y_2 < y_1$.

Thus, in our figures *the positive direction on a line lying in, or parallel to, the xy-plane is toward us.*

Since $y_2 > y_1$ if and only if $y_2 - y_1$ is positive, and $y_2 < y_1$ if and only if $y_2 - y_1$ is negative, we have the

12.3.4 Corollary. *If* $z_2 - z_1 = 0$ *and* $\overline{P_1P_2}$ *is not parallel to the x-axis, the sign of P_1P_2 is the same as the sign of* $y_2 - y_1$.

Finally, if both $z_2 - z_1 = 0$ and $y_2 - y_1 = 0$, the line is parallel to the x-axis (by 12.1.5).

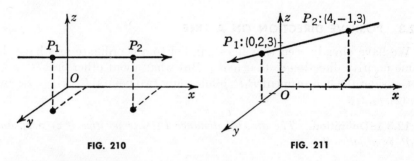

FIG. 210   FIG. 211

12.3.5 Definition. *When* $z_2 - z_1 = 0$ *and* $y_2 - y_1 = 0$, P_1P_2 *is positive if* $x_2 > x_1$ *and negative if* $x_2 < x_1$.

Therefore, in our figures *the positive direction on a line parallel to the x-axis is to the right* (Fig. 210).

Again, $x_2 > x_1$ if and only if $x_2 - x_1$ is positive, and $x_2 < x_1$ if and only if $x_2 - x_1$ is negative. Therefore

12.3.6 Corollary. *If* $z_2 - z_1 = 0$ *and* $y_2 - y_1 = 0$, *the sign of P_1P_2 must agree with the sign of* $x_2 - x_1$.

From 12.2.4, 12.3.2, 12.3.4, and 12.3.6 we obtain the

12.3.7 Corollary. *The directed distance from the point P_1:(x_1, y_1, z_1) to the point P_2:(x_2, y_2, z_2) is*

$$P_1P_2 = \pm\sqrt{(x_2 - x_1)^2 + (y_2 - y_1)^2 + (z_2 - z_1)^2},$$

where the sign before the radical is chosen to agree with the sign of $(z_2 - z_1)$.
If $z_2 - z_1 = 0$, *the sign before the radical must agree with the sign of* $(y_2 - y_1)$.
If $z_2 - z_1 = 0$ *and* $y_2 - y_1 = 0$, *the sign before the radical agrees with that of*
$(x_2 - x_1)$.

Example. Find the directed distance from the point $(0, 2, 3)$ to the point
$(4, -1, 3)$.

Solution. In 12.3.7 let P_1 be the first of the given points and P_2 the second.
Then $P_1P_2 = -\sqrt{(4 - 0)^2 + (-1 - 2)^2 + (3 - 3)^2} = -5$, where, since $(z_2 - z_1)$
$= (3 - 3) = 0$, the sign before the radical was chosen negative to agree with the
sign of $(y_2 - y_1) = (-1 - 2) = -3$ (Fig. 211).

EXERCISES

In Exercises 1 to 8, without making a sketch, determine by inspection the sign
of P_1P_2.

1. P_1:$(3, 4, 1)$, P_2:$(-1, 8, 3)$.   **2.** P_1:$(2, 5, 4)$, P_2:$(-6, 9, 3)$.

3. P_1:$(0, -1, 7)$, P_2:$(-6, 2, 5)$.   **4.** P_1:$(5, -1, 2)$, P_2:$(2, 3, -3)$.

5. P_1:$(-1, 2, 3)$, P_2:$(3, 5, 3)$.   **6.** P_1:$(1, 6, -2)$, P_2:$(-3, 6, -2)$.

7. P_1:$(3, -1, 0)$, P_2:$(6, -1, 4)$.   **8.** P_1:$(0, 4, 1)$, P_2:$(-2, 6, 2)$.

9. Plot the pair of points in Exercises 1, 3, 5, and 7, and in each case find P_1P_2.

10. Plot the pair of points in Exercises 2, 4, 6, and 8, and in each case find P_1P_2.

12.4   DIRECTION ANGLES AND DIRECTION COSINES

While two distinct points always determine a straight line, a line is also
uniquely determined if we know one point on it and the direction of the
line.   The direction of a line is given by its **direction angles.**

12.4.1 Definition.   *The direction angles of a line through the origin are
the angles between each positive coordinate axis and the positive direction on
the line.*

It is customary to denote the three direction angles which a line makes
with the x-, y-, and z-axes by α, β and γ, respectively, and always to write

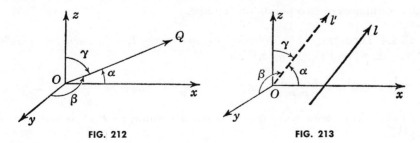

FIG. 212   FIG. 213

them in that order.   Thus, in Fig. 212 $\alpha = xOQ$, $\beta = yOQ$, and $\gamma = zOQ$. A direction angle is never negative and is always less than 180°.

The angle between two lines which fail to intersect is defined, in solid geometry, to be the angle between any two intersecting lines which are respectively parallel to the given lines.   This suggests the

12.4.2 Definition.   *The direction angles of a line not through the origin are the direction angles of the line through the origin which is parallel to the given line* (Fig. 213).

The cosines of the direction angles of a line are called the **direction cosines** of a line.   They are usually more convenient to work with than the angles themselves.   They are always written in the order: cos α, cos β, cos γ.

From 12.4.2 we have the

12.4.3 Corollary.   *Lines having the same direction cosines are parallel, and conversely.*

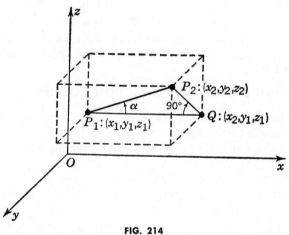

FIG. 214

We need formulas for finding the direction cosines of a line when we know the coordinates of two points on the line.

12.4.4 Theorem.   *The direction cosines of the line through two points, $P_1{:}(x_1, y_1, z_1)$ and $P_2{:}(x_2, y_2, z_2)$, are*

$$\cos \alpha = \frac{x_2 - x_1}{P_1P_2}, \quad \cos \beta = \frac{y_2 - y_1}{P_1P_2}, \quad \cos \gamma = \frac{z_2 - z_1}{P_1P_2}.$$

Proof.   Two cases will be considered according as P_1P_2 is positive or negative.

CASE I. P_1P_2 is positive (Fig. 214).

Through P_1 draw a line parallel to the x-axis and from P_2 draw a perpendicular to this line, intersecting it in Q. Then $\overline{P_2Q}$ is parallel to the yz-plane and the x-coordinate of Q is x_2 (by 12.1.2). Now

(1)
$$\cos \alpha = \frac{P_1Q}{|P_1P_2|}.$$

But $P_1Q = x_2 - x_1$ (by 12.2.1) and, since P_1P_2 is positive in Case I, $|P_1P_2| = P_1P_2$. Substituting in (1),

$$\cos \alpha = \frac{x_2 - x_1}{P_1P_2}.$$

Similarly

$$\cos \beta = \frac{y_2 - y_1}{P_1P_2} \quad \text{and} \quad \cos \gamma = \frac{z_2 - z_1}{P_1P_2}.$$

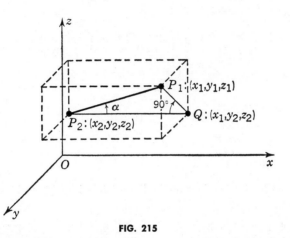

FIG. 215

CASE II. P_1P_2 is negative (Fig. 215).

Through P_2 draw a line parallel to the x-axis and from P_1 draw a perpendicular to this line, intersecting it in Q. The line-segment $\overline{P_1Q}$ is parallel to the yz-plane and therefore the x-coordinate of Q is x_1 (12.1.2). Now

(2)
$$\cos \alpha = \frac{P_2Q}{|P_1P_2|}.$$

But P_1P_2 is negative in Case II and $|P_1P_2| = -P_1P_2$. Also $P_2Q = x_1 - x_2$ (by 12.2.1). Substituting these results in (2),

$$\cos \alpha = \frac{x_1 - x_2}{-P_1P_2} = \frac{x_2 - x_1}{P_1P_2}.$$

Similarly,

$$\cos \beta = \frac{y_2 - y_1}{P_1P_2} \quad \text{and} \quad \cos \gamma = \frac{z_2 - z_1}{P_1P_2}.$$

Example. Find the direction cosines of the line joining the points $(0, 2, 3)$ and $(4, -1, 3)$.

Solution. If we denote the first of the given points by P_1 and the second by P_2, then $P_1P_2 = -5$ (see the Example in Section 12.3). Therefore (by 12.4.4)

$$\cos \alpha = \frac{4 - 0}{-5} = \frac{-4}{5}, \qquad \cos \beta = \frac{-1 - 2}{-5} = \frac{3}{5}, \qquad \cos \gamma = \frac{3 - 3}{-5} = 0.$$

The direction cosines of a line are not all independent but are connected by the following useful identity.

12.4.5 Theorem. *If* $\cos \alpha$, $\cos \beta$, *and* $\cos \gamma$ *are the direction cosines of a line, then*

$$\cos^2 \alpha + \cos^2 \beta + \cos^2 \gamma = 1.$$

Proof.

$$\cos^2 \alpha + \cos^2 \beta + \cos^2 \gamma$$

$$= \left(\frac{x_2 - x_1}{P_1P_2}\right)^2 + \left(\frac{y_2 - y_1}{P_1P_2}\right)^2 + \left(\frac{z_2 - z_1}{P_1P_2}\right)^2 \qquad \text{(by 12.4.4)}$$

$$= \frac{(x_2 - x_1)^2 + (y_2 - y_1)^2 + (z_2 - z_1)^2}{(P_1P_2)^2}$$

$$= \frac{|P_1P_2|^2}{(P_1P_2)^2} = 1 \qquad \text{(by 12.2.4)}.$$

EXERCISES

1. Find the direction cosines of the lines determined by each of the following pairs of points:

(a) $(3, 4, 1)$, $(-1, 8, 3)$;   (b) $(0, -1, 7)$, $(-6, 2, 5)$;
(c) $(-1, 2, 3)$, $(3, 5, 3)$;   (d) $(3, -1, 0)$, $(6, -1, 4)$.

2. Find the direction cosines of the lines determined by each of the following pairs of points:

(a) $(2, 5, 4)$, $(-6, 9, 3)$;   (b) $(1, 6, -2)$, $(-3, 6, -2)$;
(c) $(5, -1, 2)$, $(2, 3, -3)$;   (d) $(0, 4, 1)$, $(-2, 6, 2)$.

3. Find the direction cosines of the lines determined by each of the following pairs of points:

(a) $(2, 0, -1)$, $(-3, 1, 5)$;   (b) $(7, 6, -1)$, $(-3, 2, 0)$;
(c) $(0, 11, 1)$, $(4, -5, 2)$;   (d) $(2, 2, 2)$, $(-1, -1, -1)$.

4. What are the direction angles of each of the coordinate axes? The direction cosines?

5. Given that $\cos \alpha = 3/7$ and $\cos \beta = -6/7$. Find $\cos \gamma$.

6. Given that $\cos \alpha = -1/3$ and $\cos \gamma = 2/3$. Find $\cos \beta$. (Two solutions.)

7. Given that $\alpha = 120°$ and $\gamma = 45°$. Find β. (Two solutions.)

8. Given that $\alpha = 3\pi/4$ and $\beta = \pi/3$. Find γ.

9. Find the direction angles of the line through the points $(-3, 0, 5)$ and $(-7, 4\sqrt{2}, 9)$. Make a sketch.

10. Find the direction angles of the line through the points $(\frac{5}{2}\sqrt{3} + 2, 3, \frac{3}{2})$ and $(2, 3, -1)$. Make a sketch.

12.5 DIRECTION NUMBERS

In many problems it is easier to work with direction numbers of a line than with its direction cosines.

12.5.1 Definition.   *Any set of three numbers which are proportional to the direction cosines of a line are called **direction numbers** of the line.*

Thus any set of three numbers, a, b, c, which may be obtained by multiplying the respective direction cosines, $\cos \alpha$, $\cos \beta$, $\cos \gamma$, of a line by a non-zero constant are direction numbers of the line.   They are always written in the same order as the direction cosines and will be enclosed in brackets. Thus if $\frac{6}{7}$, $\frac{2}{7}$, $\frac{3}{7}$ are the direction cosines of a line, some sets of direction numbers of the same line are $[6, 2, 3]$, $[-12, -4, -6]$, and $[.6, .2, .3]$.

A line has just one set of direction cosines but indefinitely many sets of direction numbers.   Of course the direction cosines themselves are one particular set of direction numbers of the line.

From 12.4.3 and 12.5.1 we have the

12.5.2 Corollary.   *Lines having proportional direction numbers are parallel, and conversely.*

12.4.4 and 12.5.1 imply the

12.5.3 Corollary.   *A set of direction numbers for the line through the points $P_1:(x_1, y_1, z_1)$ and $P_2:(x_2, y_2, z_2)$ is $[x_2 - x_1, y_2 - y_1, z_2 - z_1]$.*

And from 12.5.3 we have the

12.5.4 Corollary.   *Direction numbers of the line joining the origin to the point $P_1:(x_1, y_1, z_1)$ are $[x_1, y_1, z_1]$.*

Example 1.   Draw the line through the point $(2, 2, 4)$ with direction numbers $[3, -1, 1]$.

Solution.   Draw l' through the origin and the point $(3, -1, 1)$.   By 12.5.4, l' has direction numbers $[3, -1, 1]$.   Through the given point, $(2, 2, 4)$, draw l parallel to l'.   Then l is the desired line (by 12.5.2) (Fig. 216).

It is desirable to be able to find the direction cosines of a line when we know a set of its direction numbers.

12.5.5 Theorem. *The direction cosines of a line having* $[a, b, c]$ *for direction numbers are*

$$\cos \alpha = \frac{a}{\pm \sqrt{a^2 + b^2 + c^2}},$$

$$\cos \beta = \frac{b}{\pm \sqrt{a^2 + b^2 + c^2}},$$

$$\cos \gamma = \frac{c}{\pm \sqrt{a^2 + b^2 + c^2}},$$

where the sign before the radical is chosen to agree with the sign of the first of the quantities c, b, a, *which is not zero.*

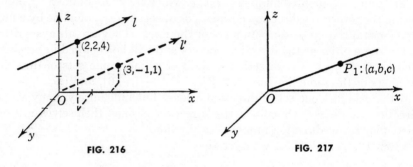

FIG. 216   **FIG. 217**

Proof. The line joining the origin to the point P_1:(a, b, c) has $[a, b, c]$ for direction numbers (by 12.5.4) (Fig. 217). The direction cosines of $\overline{OP}_1$ are

$$\cos \alpha = \frac{a}{OP_1}, \quad \cos \beta = \frac{b}{OP_1} \quad \text{and} \quad \cos \gamma = \frac{c}{OP_1} \qquad \text{(by 12.4.4)}.$$

But

$$OP_1 = \pm \sqrt{a^2 + b^2 + c^2},$$

where the sign before the radical is chosen to agree with the sign of the first of the quantities c, b, a, which is not zero (by 12.3.7).

Therefore

$$\cos \alpha = \frac{a}{\pm \sqrt{a^2 + b^2 + c^2}},$$

$$\cos \beta = \frac{b}{\pm \sqrt{a^2 + b^2 + c^2}},$$

$$\cos \gamma = \frac{c}{\pm \sqrt{a^2 + b^2 + c^2}},$$

All other lines having $[a, b, c]$ for direction numbers are parallel to $\overline{OP}_1$ (by 12.5.2) and therefore have the same direction cosines (by 12.4.3).

Example 2. Find the direction cosines of a line having $[2, -1, -4]$ for direction numbers.

Solution. By 12.5.5,

$$\cos \alpha = \frac{2}{-\sqrt{4+1+16}} = \frac{-2}{\sqrt{21}}, \quad \cos \beta = \frac{-1}{-\sqrt{21}} = \frac{1}{\sqrt{21}}, \quad \cos \gamma = \frac{-4}{-\sqrt{21}} = \frac{4}{\sqrt{21}},$$

where the negative sign before the radical was chosen to agree with the sign of $c = -4$.

We will now prove the

12.5.6 Theorem. *Two lines with direction numbers $[a_1, b_1, c_1]$ and $[a_2, b_2, c_2]$ are perpendicular if and only if*

$$a_1 a_2 + b_1 b_2 + c_1 c_2 = 0.$$

Proof. Join the origin to the points $P_1:(a_1, b_1, c_1)$ and $P_2:(a_2, b_2, c_2)$ (Fig. 218). Then $\overline{OP}_1$ and $\overline{OP}_2$ have for direction numbers $[a_1, b_1, c_1]$ and

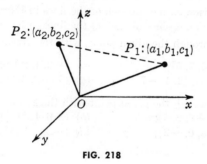

FIG. 218

$[a_2, b_2, c_2]$, respectively (by 12.5.4). Therefore $\overline{OP}_1$ and $\overline{OP}_2$ are respectively parallel to the given lines (by 12.5.2).

Now $\overline{OP}_1$ and $\overline{OP}_2$ are perpendicular if and only if

$$|P_1P_2|^2 = |OP_1|^2 + |OP_2|^2. \qquad \text{(Appendix, 6, 7).}$$

But $|P_1P_2|^2 = (a_2 - a_1)^2 + (b_2 - b_1)^2 + (c_2 - c_1)^2$, $|OP_1|^2 = a_1^2 + b_1^2 + c_1^2$, and $|OP_2|^2 = a_2^2 + b_2^2 + c_2^2$ (by 12.2.4). Substituting above, we have

$$(a_2 - a_1)^2 + (b_2 - b_1)^2 + (c_2 - c_1)^2 = a_1^2 + b_1^2 + c_1^2 + a_2^2 + b_2^2 + c_2^2.$$

If we remove parentheses and collect terms, this becomes

$$a_1 a_2 + b_1 b_2 + c_1 c_2 = 0.$$

EXERCISES

1. Find direction numbers of the lines determined by each of the following pairs of points:

(a) $(2, 3, 5)$ and $(4, 5, 6)$;   (b) $(-2, 0, -4)$ and $(-3, 5, 0)$;

(c) $(5, -3, 3)$ and $(8, -7, 3)$;   (d) $(-4, 2, -4)$ and $(0, 6, -2)$;

(e) $(7, 2, -3)$ and $(6, 7, 1)$;   (f) $(0, 0, 6)$ and $(1, 4, 14)$;

(g) $(3, -1, 2)$ and $(7, 2, 2)$;   (h) $(-2, 1, 5)$ and $(-5, 3, 7)$.

2. Find direction numbers of the lines determined by each of the following pairs of points:

(a) $(-4, 0, 1)$ and $(-1, 0, 2)$;   (b) $(2, 5, 8)$ and $(4, 9, 2)$;

(c) $(-1, -3, -1)$ and $(2, -42, -19)$;   (d) $(11, -5, 2)$ and $(10, -7, 5)$;

(e) $(0, 1, 0)$ and $(4, 5, 5)$;   (f) $(3, -7, 2)$ and $(3, -3, 9)$;

(g) $(1, 0, -2)$ and $(0, 13, 4)$;   (h) $(8, -4, -6)$ and $(5, -1, -5)$.

3. Which lines in Exercise 1 are parallel to each other?

4. Which lines in Exercise 2 are parallel to each other?

5. Which lines in Exercise 1 are perpendicular to each other?

6. Which lines in Exercise 2 are perpendicular to each other?

7. Find the direction cosines of each of the lines in Exercise 1.

8. Find the direction cosines of each of the lines in Exercise 2.

9. Draw a line through the given point, with the given direction numbers:

(a) $(2, 1, 3)$, $[3, 2, 5]$;   (b) $(-3, 1, 2,)$ $[4, -2, 3]$;

(c) $(-4, -2, 4)$, $[2, 1, -7]$;   (d) $(5, -2, 3)$, $[4, 2, -3]$.

10. Draw a line through the given point with the given direction numbers:

(a) $(3, 1, 5)$, $[-2, 2, 5]$;   (b) $(-6, 1, 2)$, $[1, 1, 2]$;

(c) $(1, 1, 2)$, $[5, 0, -2]$;   (d) $(-2, -3, 4)$, $[-4, 4, 6]$.

13

The Plane

13.1 THE TWO FUNDAMENTAL PROBLEMS IN SPACE

Now that we have developed the basic tools, it is time to begin applying them to the geometry of three-dimensional space. We will find that the same two fundamental problems as in plane analytic geometry appear over and over again in space—namely, finding the equation (or equations) of a locus from its geometric description, and discussing and sketching a locus when its equation is known. In this connection we state the

13.1.1 Definition. *A point lies on the locus of an equation (or of a set of simultaneous equations) if and only if its coordinates satisfy the equation (or equations).*

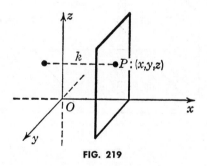

FIG. 219

It is natural to start with a simple locus—a plane. We seek an equation in x, y, and z, satisfied by the coordinates of all points on the plane and by no others.

13.2 EQUATION OF A PLANE PARALLEL TO A COORDINATE PLANE

The locus of points which are k units distant from the yz-plane is a plane parallel to the yz-plane (Fig. 219). But the directed distance from the yz-plane to a point was defined as the x-coordinate of that point (12.1.1).

Therefore the locus of points whose x-coordinates are equal to a constant k is a plane parallel to the yz-plane and k units from it.   The equation of such a plane is

$$x = k.$$

In our diagrams, the plane $x = k$ is to the right of the yz-plane when k is positive, and to the left when k is negative.

Similar equations hold for planes parallel to either of the other coordinate planes.

This is summarized in the

13.2.1 Theorem.   *The equation of the plane parallel to the yz-plane and k units distant from it is*

$$x = k;$$

the equation of the plane parallel to the zx-plane and l units from it is

$$y = l;$$

and the equation of the plane parallel to the xy-plane and m units from it is

$$z = m.$$

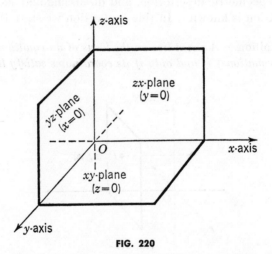

FIG. 220

13.2.2 Corollary.   *The equations of the coordinate planes are $x = 0$, $y = 0$, and $z = 0$.*

A point on the x-axis is on both the zx- and xy-planes (Fig. 220).   Therefore both its y- and z-coordinates are zero (13.2.2).   Analogous statements hold for points on the other coordinate axes.

13.2.3 Corollary.   *Any point on the x-axis has its y- and z-coordinates zero.   Any point on the y-axis has its z- and x-coordinates zero.   Any point on the z-axis has its x- and y-coordinates zero.*

13.3 NORMAL EQUATION OF A PLANE

By a **normal** to a plane is meant any line perpendicular to the plane.

13.3.1 Theorem. *An equation of the plane whose directed distance from the origin is d and whose normals have direction cosines, cos α, cos β, and cos γ, is*

$$x \cos \alpha + y \cos \beta + z \cos \gamma - d = 0.$$

Proof. Indicate by n the line through the origin and normal to the plane (Figs. 221 and 222). Let $P_1:(x_1, y_1, z_1)$ be the point of intersection of the

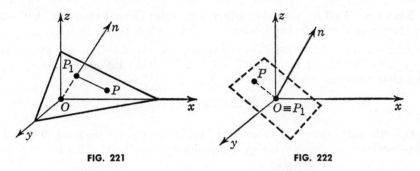

FIG. 221   **FIG. 222**

plane and the normal n. Let $P:(x, y, z)$ be any other point. Then direction numbers of $\overline{P_1P}$ are $[x - x_1, y - y_1, z - z_1]$ (by 12.5.3).

P is on the plane if and only if n and $\overline{P_1P}$ are perpendicular to each other; that is, if and only if

$$(x - x_1) \cos \alpha + (y - y_1) \cos \beta + (z - z_1) \cos \gamma = 0 \qquad \text{(by 12.5.6)},$$

or

(1) $x \cos \alpha + y \cos \beta + z \cos \gamma - (x_1 \cos \alpha + y_1 \cos \beta + z_1 \cos \gamma) = 0.$

If the plane does not go through the origin (Fig. 221), P_1 is distinct from O and

$$\cos \alpha = \frac{x_1}{OP_1}, \quad \cos \beta = \frac{y_1}{OP_1}, \quad \cos \gamma = \frac{z_1}{OP_1} \qquad \text{(by 12.4.4)}.$$

Substituting in (1), we have

$$x \cos \alpha + y \cos \beta + z \cos \gamma - \frac{(x_1^2 + y_1^2 + z_1^2)}{OP_1} = 0,$$

or, since $\qquad x_1^2 + y_1^2 + z_1^2 = (OP_1)^2 \qquad$ (by 12.2.4),

(2) $\qquad\qquad x \cos \alpha + y \cos \beta + z \cos \gamma - OP_1 = 0.$

But $OP_1 = d$ (given). Therefore

(3) $x \cos \alpha + y \cos \beta + z \cos \gamma - d = 0.$

This is called the **normal form** of the equation of the plane.

On the other hand, if the plane does go through the origin (Fig. 222), $x_1 = y_1 = z_1 = 0$, and (1) becomes

(4) $x \cos \alpha + y \cos \beta + z \cos \gamma = 0.$

But when the plane goes through the origin, $OP_1 = 0$ and (3) becomes (4). Therefore (3) is the normal equation of the plane whether it goes through the origin or not.

13.3.2 Corollary. *Every plane has an equation of the first degree.*

Example.   Find the normal equation of the plane through the point $(9, 0, -3)$ and perpendicular to the line joining the points $(-1, 5, 4)$ and $(2, -1, 6)$.

Solution. By 12.4.4, the direction cosines of the line through the points $(-1, 5, 4)$ and $(2, -1, 6)$ are $[3/7, -6/7, 2/7]$. Thus the normal equation of any plane perpendicular to this line is

$$\frac{3x}{7} - \frac{6y}{7} + \frac{2z}{7} - d = 0 \qquad \text{(by 13.3.1)}.$$

Since the particular plane we are interested in goes through the point $(9, 0, -3)$, the coordinates of the point satisfy the equation of the plane. That is,

$$\frac{3(9)}{7} - \frac{6(0)}{7} + \frac{2(-3)}{7} - d = 0,$$

from which $d = 3$.   Therefore the desired equation is

$$\frac{3x}{7} - \frac{6y}{7} + \frac{2z}{7} - 3 = 0$$

EXERCISES

Make a sketch for each exercise.

1. Write the equation of the plane through the point $(-5, 7, -2)$ and
  (*a*) parallel to the zx-plane;
  (*b*) perpendicular to the x-axis;
  (*c*) parallel to both the x- and y-axes.

2. Find the equation of the plane through the point $(4, -1, 6)$ and
  (*a*) perpendicular to the y-axis;
  (*b*) parallel to the yz-plane;
  (*c*) perpendicular to the z-axis.

3. Find the equation of a plane if a normal to it has direction cosines $[2/3, -1/3, 2/3]$, and if the directed distance from the origin to the plane is 6.

4. Find the equation of the plane whose normals have the direction cosines $[4/5, 0, 3/5]$, and whose directed distance from the origin is -2.

5. Direction numbers of a normal to a certain plane are $[-2, 1, 3]$, and the directed distance from the origin to the plane is -5. Find the equation of the plane.

6. A normal to a plane has direction numbers $[4, -2, 5]$, and the directed distance from the origin to the plane is 11. Find the equation of the plane.

7. The line through the origin perpendicular to a plane intersects the plane in the point $(1, -1, -2)$. Find the equation of the plane.

8. The foot of the perpendicular from the origin to a certain plane is $(-1, 5, 2)$. Find the normal equation of the plane.

9. Direction cosines of a normal to a certain plane are $[-3/7, 6/7, 2/7]$. If the plane goes through the point $(5, 2, -1)$, find the normal equation of the plane.

10. Direction cosines of a normal to a plane are $[8/9, -4/9, 1/9]$. If the plane goes through the point $(1, -2, -7)$, find the normal equation of the plane.

11. Find the equation of the plane through the point $(4, 1, -6)$ and perpendicular to the line joining the points $(-1, 6, 2)$ and $(-8, 10, -2)$.

12. Find the equation of the plane through the point $(-4, 1, 3)$ and perpendicular to the line joining the points $(-7, 4, 1)$ and $(-6, 2, 3)$.

13. A line through the point $(4, -2, 3)$ and perpendicular to a certain plane intersects that plane in $(2, 3, 6)$. Find the equation of the plane.

14. The line through the point $(4, 2, 5)$ and perpendicular to a plane intersects the plane in the point $(3, 1, 2)$. Find the equation of the plane.

13.4 LOCUS OF A FIRST DEGREE EQUATION

We have just seen that every plane has a first degree equation. Is it true, conversely that the locus of an equation of the first degree is always a plane?

The most general equation of the first degree in three-dimensional rectangular Cartesian coordinates is

(1)
$$Ax + By + Cz + D = 0,$$

where not all of A, B, and C are zero. Dividing both members by $\pm\sqrt{A^2 + B^2 + C^2}$ (where the sign before the radical is chosen to agree with the first of the numbers C, B, A which is different from zero), we have

(2)
$$\frac{A}{\pm\sqrt{A^2 + B^2 + C^2}}x + \frac{B}{\pm\sqrt{A^2 + B^2 + C^2}}y$$
$$+ \frac{C}{\pm\sqrt{A^2 + B^2 + C^2}}z + \frac{D}{\pm\sqrt{A^2 + B^2 + C^2}} = 0.$$

Since the coefficients of x, y and z in (2) are the direction cosines of a line having direction number $[A, B, C]$ (by 12.5.5), (2) is the normal equation of the plane whose directed distance from the origin is $-D/\pm\sqrt{A^2 + B^2 + C^2}$ and whose normals have direction cosines $A/\pm\sqrt{A^2 + B^2 + C^2}$, $B/\pm\sqrt{A^2 + B^2 + C^2}$, and $C/\pm\sqrt{A^2 + B^2 + C^2}$ (by 13.3.1). This proves the

13.4.1 Theorem. *In space, the locus of a first degree equation in Cartesian coordinates is always a plane.*

Equation (1) is called the **general form** of the equation of a plane. Incidentally, in proving 13.4.1 we learned how to reduce the general equation (1) of any plane to its normal form (2). This is summarized in the

13.4.2 Corollary. *The normal form of the equation of the plane*

$$Ax + By + Cz + D = 0$$

is

$$\frac{A}{\pm\sqrt{A^2 + B^2 + C^2}}x + \frac{B}{\pm\sqrt{A^2 + B^2 + C^2}}y$$

$$+ \frac{C}{\pm\sqrt{A^2 + B^2 + C^2}}z + \frac{D}{\pm\sqrt{A^2 + B^2 + C^2}} = 0,$$

where the sign before the radical is chosen to agree with the sign of C. In the event $C = 0$, the sign of the radical must agree with that of B. If $C = B = 0$, the sign of the radical must agree with that of A.

Example. Find the normal form of the equation of the plane whose general equation is $3x + y - 5z - 70 = 0$. What is its directed distance from the origin?

Solution. By 13.4.2, the normal form of the equation of the given plane is

$$\frac{3}{-\sqrt{35}}x + \frac{y}{-\sqrt{35}} - \frac{5}{-\sqrt{35}}z - \frac{70}{-\sqrt{35}} = 0,$$

where the sign before the radical is negative to agree with the sign of the coefficient of z. The directed distance from the origin to the plane is

$$-\frac{D}{\pm\sqrt{A^2 + B^2 + C^2}} = -\frac{-70}{-\sqrt{35}} \text{ or } -2\sqrt{35} \qquad \text{(by 13.3.1).}$$

Since the coefficients

$$\frac{A}{\pm\sqrt{A^2 + B^2 + C^2}}, \quad \frac{B}{\pm\sqrt{A^2 + B^2 + C^2}}, \quad \frac{C}{\pm\sqrt{A^2 + B^2 + C^2}}$$

in the normal equation of a plane (13.4.2) are the direction cosines of the normals to the plane, the coefficients A, B, C in the general equation of the same plane are a set of direction numbers of every line perpendicular to that plane (12.5.5).

13.4.3 Corollary. *The coefficients of x, y, and z in the equation of a plane are a set of direction numbers of every line perpendicular to the plane.*

For example, a set of direction numbers of any line perpendicular to the plane $x - 5y + 7z + 2 = 0$ is $[1, -5, 7]$.

Now a plane is parallel to the x-axis if and only if its normals are perpendicular to the x-axis. But in that case $\alpha = 90°$ and $\cos \alpha = 0$ in the normal equation of the plane. Therefore a plane is parallel to the x-axis if and only if its equation contains no term in x. Similar statements hold for planes parallel to either of the other coordinate axes.

13.4.4 Corollary. *A plane is parallel to the x-axis if and only if its equation contains no term in x; a plane is parallel to the y-axis if and only if its equation has no term in y; and a plane is parallel to the z-axis if and only if its equation contains no term in z.*

For example, the plane $x + 4z - 1 = 0$ is parallel to the y-axis, and the plane $3y - 11z - 4 = 0$ is parallel to the x-axis.

The lines of intersection of a plane with the coordinate planes are called the **traces** of the plane. Usually the easiest way to sketch a plane is to draw its traces.

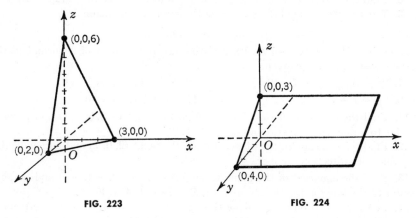

FIG. 223   FIG. 224

To draw the traces of a plane not through the origin and not parallel to a coordinate axis, simply find the points of intersection of the plane with the coordinate axes and connect them by straight lines. For example, the plane $2x + 3y + z - 6 = 0$ intersects the x-axis in the point $(3, 0, 0)$, found by substituting $y = 0$ and $z = 0$ (13.2.3) in the given equation and solving for x. Similarly, the plane intersects the y-axis in the point $(0, 2, 0)$ and the z-axis in the point $(0, 0, 6)$. The triangle formed by these points is a good representation of part of the plane (Fig. 223).

When a plane, not through the origin, is parallel to the x-axis, its traces are still easy to draw. For example, the plane $3y + 4z - 12 = 0$ intersects the y-axis in the point $(0, 4, 0)$ and the z-axis in $(0, 0, 3)$. The line joining these points is the trace of the given plane in the yz-plane. Since the plane is parallel to the x-axis (13.4.4), its trace in the xy-plane, through the point $(0, 4, 0)$, is parallel to the x-axis. The trace in the zx-plane goes through the point $(0, 0, 3)$ and is parallel to the x-axis (Fig. 224).

EXERCISES

Make a sketch for each exercise.

1. Find the coordinates of the points of intersection of the plane

$$3x - 4y + 2z - 12 = 0$$

with the coordinate axes.

2. Find the coordinates of the points of intersection of the plane

$$7x + 2y - 5z + 10 = 0$$

with the coordinate axes.

3. Find the normal equations of the planes $2x + 2y - z - 27 = 0$ and $2x - 3y + 6z + 8 = 0$.

4. Find the normal equations of the planes $3x - y + 7z + 2 = 0$ and $x + 5y - z - 9 = 0$.

5. Find the directed distance from the origin to the plane $5x - 12y - 26 = 0$.

6. What is the directed distance from the origin to the plane

$$x + 6y - 2z - 14 = 0?$$

In each of the Exercises 7 to 10, find the direction cosines of a normal to the plane whose equation is given.

7. $2x - 4y - 4z + 7 = 0$.   **8.** $8x - 4y - z + 7 = 0$.

9. $2y - z + 5 = 0$.   **10.** $3x + 2y - 6 = 0$.

11. Find the equation of the plane through the point $(-3, 8, -1)$ and perpendicular to a line with direction numbers $[-1, 0, 11]$.

12. Find the equation of the plane through the point $(2, 0, 7)$ and perpendicular to a line with direction numbers $[6, -1, -1]$.

13. Find the equation of the plane through the point $(2, -4, -5)$ and perpendicular to the line joining the points $(-1, 5, -7)$ and $(4, 1, 1)$.

14. Find the equation of the plane through the point $(-3, 1, 4)$ and perpendicular to the line joining the points $(5, 11, -2)$ and $(5, 15, -7)$.

15. A line through the origin, perpendicular to a certain plane, intersects that plane in the point $(-1, 5, 4)$. Find the equation of the plane.

16. The foot of the perpendicular from the origin to a plane is $(3, -2, 6)$. Find the equation of the plane.

13.5 PARALLEL AND PERPENDICULAR PLANES

Two planes are parallel if and only if their normals are parallel (Fig. 225). Therefore from 12.5.2 and 13.4.3 we have the

13.5.1 Theorem. *Two   planes, $A_1x + B_1y + C_1z + D_1 = 0$ and $A_2x + B_2y + C_2z + D_2 = 0$, are parallel if and only if A_1, B_1, C_1 are pro-*

portional to A_2, B_2, C_2; that is, if and only if there is a number k (different from zero) such that $A_1 = kA_2$, $B_1 = kB_2$, and $C_1 = kC_2$.

For example, the planes $2x - 3y + z - 1 = 0$ and $4x - 6y + 2z + 4 = 0$ are parallel. But notice that the equations $2x - 3y + z - 1 = 0$ and $4x - 6y + 2z - 2 = 0$ represent the same plane, not two parallel planes, since the second equation can be obtained by multiplying both members of the first by 2 (see 3.4.3).

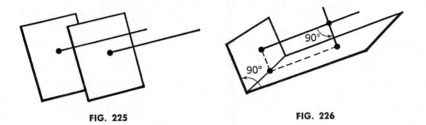

FIG. 225   FIG. 226

If two planes are perpendicular, their normals are perpendicular, and conversely (Fig. 226). Thus, as an immediate consequence of 12.5.6 and 13.4.3, we have the

13.5.2 Theorem. *Two planes,* $A_1x + B_1y + C_1z + D_1 = 0$ *and* $A_2x + B_2y + C_2z + D_2 = 0$, *are perpendicular if and only if*

$$A_1A_2 + B_1B_2 + C_1C_2 = 0.$$

For example, the planes $4x - 2y + z + 7 = 0$ and $x + 3y + 2z - 1 = 0$ are perpendicular because $4(1) - 2(3) + 1(2) = 0$.

Since the equation of the xy-plane is $z = 0$ (by 13.2.2), the plane $Ax + By + Cz + D = 0$ is perpendicular to the xy-plane if and only if $A(0) + B(0) + C(1) = 0$ (by 13.5.2); that is, if and only if $C = 0$. Similar statements are true for planes perpendicular to the yz- or zx-plane. Therefore

13.5.3 Corollary. *A plane is perpendicular to the xy-plane if and only if its equation contains no term in z; it is perpendicular to the yz-plane if and only if its equation contains no term in x; it is perpendicular to the zx-plane if and only if its equation contains no term in y.*

For example, $2x + 3y - 7 = 0$ is perpendicular to the xy-plane, and the plane $y - 2z + 1 = 0$ is perpendicular to the yz-plane. The plane $y = 7$ is perpendicular to the yz-plane because it contains no term in x, and it is also perpendicular to the xy-plane because it contains no term in z. Thus it is parallel to the zx-plane.

Since a plane is perpendicular to the xy-plane if and only if it is parallel to the z-axis, the above corollary gives the same result as that stated in 13.4.4 but approached in a different manner.

EXERCISES

1. Which of the following planes are identical, which are parallel to each other, and which are perpendicular to each other?

     (a) $3x - 5y + z + 12 = 0$;   (b) $7x + y - 16z + 11 = 0$;
     (c) $6x - 10y + 2z - 1 = 0$;   (d) $x - 7y - 7 = 0$;
     (e) $2z + 13 = 0$;   (f) $6x - 10y + 2z + 24 = 0$.

2. Which of the following planes are identical, which are parallel to each other, and which are perpendicular to each other?

     (a) $x + 5z - z - 1 = 0$;   (b) $7x - y - 2z + 4 = 0$;
     (c) $2x - 3y + 4z + 2 = 0$;   (d) $3x + 15y - 3z - 3 = 0$;
     (e) $14x - 2y - 4z + 4 = 0$;   (f) $5x + 2y - z + 13 = 0$.

3. Find the equation of the plane through the origin and parallel to the plane $4x + 2y - 7z + 10 = 0$. Make a sketch.

4. Write the equation of the plane through the origin and parallel to the plane $8x - 6y - 12z + 25 = 0$. Make a sketch.

5. Find the equation of the plane through the point $(0, 0, 1)$ and parallel to the plane $x - 2y + z + 4 = 0$. Make a sketch.

6. Find the equation of the plane through the point $(1, -2, 4)$ and parallel to the plane $6x + 3y - z + 10 = 0$. Make a sketch.

7. Find the value of B if the plane $2x + By - z + 8 = 0$ is perpendicular to the plane $3x - 2y + 10z + 1 = 0$.

8. Find the value of C if the plane $x + 5y + Cz + 6 = 0$ is perpendicular to the plane $4x - y + z - 17 = 0$.

13.6   DIRECTED DISTANCE FROM A PLANE TO A POINT

It is often useful to be able to find the directed (perpendicular) distance from a given plane to a given point.

13.6.1 Theorem. *The directed distance from the plane*

$$x \cos \alpha + y \cos \beta + z \cos \gamma - d = 0$$

to the point P_1:(x_1, y_1, z_1) is

$$x_1 \cos \alpha + y_1 \cos \beta + z_1 \cos \gamma - d.$$

Proof. Denote the given plane by π (Fig. 227). From P_1 draw a perpendicular to π, intersecting it in Q. We seek the value of QP_1.

Through P_1 pass a plane π_1, parallel to π. From O draw a normal to π and π_1, intersecting them in R and S respectively. Then $OR + RS = OS$

(by 1.2.3), whence

(1) $RS = OS - OR.$

But $RS = QP_1$, the desired directed distance from π to P_1, and $OR = d$ (by 13.3.1). Substituting in (1), we have

(2) $QP_1 = OS - d,$

where OS is still to be evaluated.

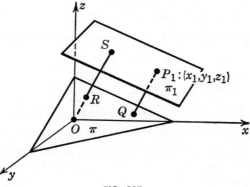

FIG. 227

The parallel planes, π and π_1, have the same normals and therefore the equation of π_1 is $x \cos \alpha + y \cos \beta + z \cos \gamma - OS = 0$ (by 13.3.1). But P_1 lies on π_1 and hence the coordinates of P_1 satisfy the equation of π_1. That is,

$$x_1 \cos \alpha + y_1 \cos \beta + z_1 \cos \gamma - OS = 0,$$

or

(3) $OS = x_1 \cos \alpha + y_1 \cos \beta + z_1 \cos \gamma.$

Substituting (3) in (2) we obtain

$$QP_1 = x_1 \cos \alpha + y_1 \cos \beta + z_1 \cos \gamma - d,$$

which completes the proof.

The student should observe that the directed distance from a plane to a point may be found by substituting the coordinates of the point in the *left-hand member* of the normal form of the equation of the plane.

Example. Find the directed distance from the plane $2x + y - 2z - 5 = 0$ to the point $(3, 8, 0)$.

Solution. By 13.4.2, the normal form of the equation of the plane is

$$\frac{2x + y - 2z - 5}{-3} = 0.$$

By 13.6.1, the directed distance from this plane to the point $(3, 8, 0)$ is

$$\frac{2(3) + (8) - 2(0) - 5}{-3} = -3.$$

EXERCISES

1. Find the directed distance from the given plane to the given point:

(a) $2x - y + 2z - 7 = 0$, $(5, 6, 6)$;
(b) $5x + y - 7z + 2 = 0$, $(-1, 7, 2)$;
(c) $x - y = 0$, $(-6, 2, -11)$.

2. Find the directed distance from the given plane to the given point:

(a) $3x - 2y - 6z + 5 = 0$, $(2, 5, -1)$;
(b) $2z + 7 = 0$, $(-5, 0, -6)$;
(c) $3x - 2y - 8z - 9 = 0$, $(4, 1, 2)$.

3. Find the undirected distance between the parallel planes

$$x + 5y - 2z + 3 = 0 \quad \text{and} \quad x + 5y - 2z - 7 = 0.$$

Make a sketch.   (Hint: Find the coordinates of a point in one plane, for example its intersection with a coordinate axis, and then determine the distance from the other plane to this point.)

4. Find the undirected distance between the parallel planes

$$4x + y - 2z - 6 = 0 \quad \text{and} \quad 4x + y - 2z + 15 = 0.$$

Make a sketch.

5. Find the directed distance from the plane $4x - y + z - 1 = 0$ to the plane $4x - y + z + 8 = 0$.   Make a sketch.

6. Find the directed distance from the plane $2x - 3y - z + 5 = 0$ to the plane $2x - 3y - z - 4 = 0$.   Make a sketch.

7. Are the points $(2, -7, -4)$ and $(7, -6, 2)$ on the same side of the plane $8x + 5y - 7z - 8 = 0$ or on opposite sides?

8. Are the points $(2, 4, -7)$ and $(3, -2, 5)$ on the same side of the plane $6x - y + 15z + 13 = 0$ or on opposite sides?

9. Find the equation of the locus of points whose undirected distances from the plane $3x + 2y + \sqrt{3}z - 7 = 0$ are equal to 2.   Make a sketch.   (Two solutions.)

10. Find the equation of the locus of points whose undirected distances from the plane $3x - 6y + 2z + 7 = 0$ are equal to 5.   Make a sketch.   (Two solutions.)

13.7   CONDITIONS THAT DETERMINE A PLANE

The familiar technique of determining the coefficients in the equation of a locus by means of given geometric conditions serves equally well in three-dimensional geometry.   This is shown in the following examples.

Example 1.   Find the equation of the plane through the three points $(2, -1, 4)$, $(1, 3, -2)$ and $(-3, 1, 2)$.

Solution.   Let the equation of the plane be

(1) $$Ax + By + Cz + D = 0.$$

We must determine values for A, B, C, and D in this equation.

The plane goes through the given points if and only if the coordinates of the points satisfy (1) (by 13.1.1).   Successively substituting each set of coordinates for x, y and z in (1), we obtain

(2) $$2A - B + 4C + D = 0,$$

(3) $$A + 3B - 2C + D = 0,$$

(4) $$-3A + B + 2C + D = 0.$$

This is a system of three simultaneous homogeneous linear equations in the four variables A, B, C, and D.   We can solve for their ratios.   Eliminating D by subtracting (3) from (2), member by member, we obtain

(5) $$A - 4B + 6C = 0.$$

Similarly, subtracting (4) from (2) gives

(6) $$5A - 2B + 2C = 0.$$

We now eliminate C between the equations (5) and (6), and obtain

(7) $$-14A + 2B = 0.$$

From (7),

$$\frac{A}{B} = \frac{1}{7}.$$

Substituting $A = 1$, $B = 7$ in (5), we find $C = \frac{9}{2}$.   The substitution of $A = 1$, $B = 7$, $C = \frac{9}{2}$ in (1) gives $D = -13$.

Putting $A = 1$, $B = 7$, $C = \frac{9}{2}$, and $D = -13$ in (1) we obtain

$$x + 7y + \tfrac{9}{2}z - 13 = 0,$$

or

(8) $$2x + 14y + 9z - 26 = 0,$$

which is the desired equation.   The student should verify that the coordinates of all the given points satisfy (8).

Example 2.   Find the equation of the plane through the point $(2, 0, 3)$ and perpendicular to the line joining the points $(1, 4, -1)$ and $(6, 3, 5)$ (Fig. 228).

Solution.   Direction numbers of the line joining $(1, 4, -1)$ and $(6, 3, 5)$ are $[5, -1, 6]$ (by 12.5.3).   The equation of any plane perpendicular to this line is

(1) $$5x - y + 6z + D = 0 \qquad \text{(by 13.4.3)}.$$

We must determine the value of D so that the plane will go through the point

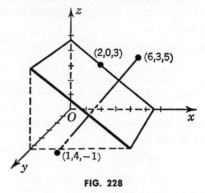

FIG. 228

$(2, 0, 3)$.   But this point is on the plane if and only if its coordinates satisfy the equation of the plane.   Substituting 2, 0, 3 for x, y, z in (1), we obtain $D = -28$. Therefore the desired equation is

$$5x - y + 6z - 28 = 0.$$

EXERCISES

1. Find the equation of the plane through the **three points:**

(a) $(0, 5, -2)$, $(3, 4, 4)$, $(2, -6, -1)$;
(b) $(2, 3, -1)$, $(-1, 5, 2)$, $(-4, -2, 2)$.

2. Find the equation of the plane through the point $(-1, 5, 3)$ and perpendicular to the line joining the points $(2, -4, 5)$ and $(7, 3, -2)$.

3. Find the equation of the plane through the point $(2, 3, -1)$ and perpendicular to the line joining the points $(-1, 4, 5)$ and $(6, 3, 2)$.

4. Find the equation of the plane through the point $(5, 7, 1)$ and parallel to the plane $3x - 4y + 2z + 12 = 0$.

5. Find the equation of the plane through the point $(-2, 1, 3)$ and perpendicular to both of the planes $x + 5y - z + 2 = 0$ and $2x - 4y - 5z + 3 = 0$.

6. Find the equation of the plane through the point $(2, -1, 6)$ and perpendicular to the line of intersection of the planes $5x + 4y - z - 11 = 0$ and

$$2x - y + 7z + 2 = 0.$$

7. Find the equation of the plane which intersects the coordinate axes in the points $(3, 0, 0)$, $(0, 7, 0)$, and $(0, 0, -4)$.

8. Find the equation of the plane through the point $(-1, 7, 2)$ and having the same trace in the xy-plane as the plane $5x + y - 2z + 4 = 0$.

9. Find the point of intersection of the planes $x - 4y + 3z + 4 = 0$,

$$2x + y - z + 4 = 0 \quad \text{and} \quad 3x + y + 5z - 6 = 0.$$

10. Find the equation of the plane through the origin and perpendicular to the trace of the plane $7x + 4y - 11z - 5 = 0$ in the xy-plane.

14

The Straight Line in Space

~~~~~~

We know that in plane analytic geometry one equation of the first degree in Cartesian coördinates always represents a line (4.2.1). But we also know that in three-dimensional space the locus of one equation of the first degree is a plane (13.4.1). How, then, can a straight line be represented analytically in three-dimensional space?

Two methods are in common use—by the intersection of two planes, and by means of parametric equations.

14.1 GENERAL EQUATIONS OF A LINE IN SPACE

The fact that two non-parallel planes always intersect in a straight line suggests one way of representing a line in space.

14.1.1 Theorem. *The locus of points whose coordinates satisfy the equations*

$$\begin{cases} A_1 x + B_1 y + C_1 z + D_1 = 0, \\ A_2 x + B_2 y + C_2 z + D_2 = 0, \end{cases}$$

simultaneously *is the line of intersection of the planes* $A_1 x + B_1 y + C_1 z + D_1 = 0$ *and* $A_2 x + B_2 y + C_2 z + D_2 = 0.$

Proof. The coordinates of a point P satisfy both the given equations simultaneously if and only if P lies on both planes (13.1.1), that is, if and only if P is on the line of intersection of the two planes. This completes the proof.

The simultaneous equations in 14.1.1 are called **general equations** of the line.

It is important to remember that the brace before the equations in 14.1.1 means that they are simultaneous in the sense that their locus consists of those points and only those points whose coordinates satisfy *both equations simultaneously.*

229

For example, the equations

$$2x - 3y + z - 5 = 0,$$
$$x + 4y + 2z + 1 = 0,$$

represent two planes, but the simultaneous equations

$$\begin{cases} 2x - 3y + z - 5 = 0, \\ x + 4y + 2z + 1 = 0, \end{cases}$$

represent a straight line (the line of intersection of the two preceding planes).

The **piercing points** of a line are the points in which it intersects the co-ordinate planes. To draw a line whose general equations are given, find the coordinates of two piercing points and connect them by a straight line. Any other points on the line would have served equally well, but the piercing points are the easiest to find.

Example. Draw the line whose general equations are

$$\begin{cases} 2x - y - 5z + 14 = 0, \\ 4x + 5y + 4z - 28 = 0, \end{cases}$$

and find direction numbers for it.

Solution. The piercing point of the given line in the yz-plane is $(0, 4, 2)$, found by solving simultaneously with the given equations of the line the equation $x = 0$

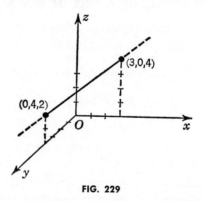

FIG. 229

of the yz-plane. Similarly, the piercing point in the zx-plane is $(3, 0, 4)$. The line l joining these two points is the desired line (Fig. 229). From the two piercing points, direction numbers of the line are $[3 - 0, 0 - 4, 4 - 2]$ or $[3, -4, 2]$ (by 12.5.3).

EXERCISES

Find two piercing points for each of the following lines. Then draw the line and find direction numbers for it.

1. $\begin{cases} x - 2y + 4z - 14 = 0, \\ x + 20y - 18z + 30 = 0. \end{cases}$
2. $\begin{cases} x - 3y - 8z + 1 = 0, \\ x - 7y - 28z + 21 = 0. \end{cases}$

3. $\begin{cases} 2x + 5y + 4z - 4 = 0, \\ 28x - 4y + 19z + 92 = 0. \end{cases}$
4. $\begin{cases} 15x + 5y - 3z = 0, \\ 3x + 4y - 6z + 18 = 0. \end{cases}$

5. $\begin{cases} 4x - 3y + 16z - 36 = 0, \\ 6x + 3y + 9z - 39 = 0. \end{cases}$
6. $\begin{cases} 5x - y - 5z + 5 = 0, \\ 18x + 15y + 13z - 75 = 0. \end{cases}$

14.2 PROJECTING PLANES OF A LINE

There are, of course, infinitely many planes through a line, and any two of them will serve to determine the line. However, those planes through a line which are perpendicular to a coordinate plane have the simplest equations, since each lacks a variable (by 13.5.3).

14.2.1 Definition. *Those planes through a line which are perpendicular to the coordinate planes are called the **projecting planes** of the line.*

In general, a line has three projecting planes (Fig. 230). But if the line is parallel to a coordinate plane, two of the projecting planes coincide.

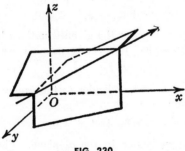

FIG. 230

To find the projecting plane, perpendicular to the xy-plane, of the line

(1) $\qquad \begin{cases} A_1x + B_1y + C_1z + D_1 = 0, \\ A_2x + B_2y + C_2z + D_2 = 0, \end{cases}$

eliminate z between these equations by the method of multiplication and subtraction. We get

(2) $\quad C_2(A_1x + B_1y + C_1z + D_1) - C_1(A_2x + B_2y + C_2z + D_2) = 0,$

or, upon collecting terms,

(3) $\qquad (C_2A_1 - C_1A_2)x + (C_2B_1 - C_1B_2)y + (C_2D_1 - C_1D_2) = 0.$

Equation (3) represents a plane perpendicular to the xy-plane (by 13.5.3). Moreover, it contains the line (1) because the coordinates of every point on the line satisfy the simultaneous equations (1) and therefore cause equation (2) to become $C_2(0) - C_1(0) = 0$. That is, they satisfy (2), and consequently (3). Thus (3) is the equation of the projecting plane, perpendicular to the xy-plane, of the line (1).

14.2.2 Rule. *To find the equation of the projecting plane, perpendicular to the xy-plane, of a line whose general equations are given, eliminate z between the given equations.*

Similarly,

14.2.3 Rule. *To find the projecting plane, perpendicular to the yz-plane, of a line whose general equations are known, eliminate x between the given equations.*

14.2.4 Rule. *To find the projecting plane, perpendicular to the zx-plane, of a line whose general equations are given, eliminate y between the given equations.*

Example. Find the projecting planes of the line whose general equations are

$$\begin{cases} 3x + y - z + 1 = 0, \\ x + 2y + 2z - 4 = 0. \end{cases}$$

Solution. Eliminating x between the given equations by subtracting the first equation from 3 times the second, member by member, we obtain

$$5y + 7z - 13 = 0,$$

which is the projecting plane perpendicular to the yz-plane. Similarly, elimination of y between the given equations yields

$$5x - 4z + 6 = 0,$$

the projecting plane perpendicular to the zx-plane. Finally, elimination of z between the given equations gives

$$7x + 4y - 2 = 0,$$

the equation of the projecting plane of the line, perpendicular to the xy-plane.

Any two of these three equations, taken simultaneously, are called **projecting equations** of the given line.

EXERCISES

In Exercises 1 to 6 find the projecting planes of the lines whose general equations are given.

1. $\begin{cases} 2x - 3y + 4z + 5 = 0, \\ x + 5y - z - 2 = 0. \end{cases}$ 2. $\begin{cases} 3x + 5y - 2z + 1 = 0, \\ 4x - 2y + z + 6 = 0. \end{cases}$

3. $\begin{cases} 2x + y - z + 4 = 0, \\ x - 5y + 2z = 0. \end{cases}$ 4. $\begin{cases} 4x + 4y - z - 5 = 0, \\ 3x + y + 7z + 1 = 0. \end{cases}$

5. $\begin{cases} x - 7y - z - 3 = 0, \\ 5x + y - 2z + 4 = 0. \end{cases}$ **6.** $\begin{cases} 6x + y + 2z + 3 = 0, \\ 2x - y + z - 4 = 0. \end{cases}$

7. Find projecting equations of the line joining the points $(-3, 1, 7)$ and $(4, 6, -5)$. Make a sketch. (Hint: The equation of a plane perpendicular to the xy-plane is of the form $Ax + By + D = 0$. Determine values for A, B, and D as in Example 1, Section 13.7.)

8. Find projecting equations of the line joining the points $(2, -2, 1)$ and $(-1, -7, 3)$. Make a sketch.

9. Find projecting equations of the line joining the points $(-1, 4, 2)$ and $(-2, 6, 6)$. Make a sketch.

10. Find projecting equations of the line joining the points $(4, 1, -1)$ and $(-6, -5, -2)$. Make a sketch.

14.3 SYMMETRIC EQUATIONS OF A LINE

Consider a line l through the point $P_1:(x_1, y_1, z_1)$, and having non-zero direction numbers $[a, b, c]$ (Fig. 231). Let $P:(x, y, z)$ be any other point.

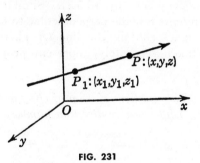

FIG. 231

By 12.5.3, a set of direction numbers of the line joining P_1 and P are $[x - x_1, y - y_1, z - z_1]$. Then P is on l if and only if the direction numbers $[x - x_1, y - y_1, z - z_1]$ are proportional to the given direction numbers $[a, b, c]$; that is, if and only if

(1) $$x - x_1 = ka, \quad y - y_1 = kb, \quad z - z_1 = kc,$$

where k is a factor of proportionality.

Solving each of the equations (1) for k, we obtain

$$\frac{x - x_1}{a} = k, \quad \frac{y - y_1}{b} = k, \quad \frac{z - z_1}{c} = k,$$

from which

(2) $$\begin{cases} \dfrac{x - x_1}{a} = \dfrac{y - y_1}{b}, \\[2ex] \dfrac{y - y_1}{b} = \dfrac{z - z_1}{c}. \end{cases}$$

It was assumed above that P was distinct from P_1.   But it is obvious that the coordinates of P_1 satisfy the equations (2).   Therefore, without exception, a point P is on the line l if and only if the coordinates of P satisfy the equations (2) simultaneously.   Thus the equations (2) are equations of the line l.   They are called the **symmetric equations** of the line.

This proves the

14.3.1 Theorem.   *Symmetric equations of the line through the point $P_1:(x_1, y_1, z_1)$, having non-zero direction numbers $[a, b, c]$, are*

$$\begin{cases} \dfrac{x - x_1}{a} = \dfrac{y - y_1}{b}, \\[2ex] \dfrac{y - y_1}{b} = \dfrac{z - z_1}{c}. \end{cases}$$

Since the first of the symmetric equations (14.3.1) is of the first degree in the variables, yet contains no term in z, it *separately* represents a plane perpendicular to the xy-plane (by 13.5.3).   Similarly, the second symmetric equation represents a plane perpendicular to the yz-plane.

Moreover, both planes contain the line l.   Therefore the symmetric equations (14.3.1), taken separately, represent projecting planes of the line l.

14.3.2 Corollary.   *The equations of the projecting planes of the line through the point $P_1:(x_1, y_1, z_1)$ with non-zero direction numbers $[a, b, c]$ are*

$$\frac{x - x_1}{a} = \frac{y - y_1}{b},$$

$$\frac{y - y_1}{b} = \frac{z - z_1}{c},$$

$$\frac{z - z_1}{c} = \frac{x - x_1}{a}.$$

The first projecting plane is perpendicular to the xy-plane, the second is perpendicular to the yz-plane, and the third is perpendicular to the zx-plane.

Example 1.   Find symmetric equations of the line whose general equations are

$$\begin{cases} 7x - 3y - 7z + 19 = 0, \\ x - y + z - 7 = 0. \end{cases}$$

First Solution.   One method of solution is to reduce the given equations to the symmetric form (14.3.1).

Eliminating z between the given equations, we obtain

(1) $7x - 5y - 15 = 0.$

Similarly, eliminating y between the given equations, we have

(2) $$2x - 5z + 20 = 0.$$

Equations (1) and (2) represent projecting planes of the given line. Solving each for x, we obtain

$$x = \frac{5y + 15}{7}, \quad x = \frac{5z - 20}{2},$$

or, dividing both equations by 5,

(3) $$\frac{x}{5} = \frac{y + 3}{7}, \quad \frac{x}{5} = \frac{z - 4}{2}.$$

Equations (3), *taken simultaneously*, are symmetric equations of the line (by 14.3.1). They indicate that the line goes through the point $(0, -3, 4)$ and has direction numbers $[5, 7, 2]$.

Second Solution. Another method is to find the coordinates of two points on the given line and from them direction numbers of the line. Then substitute in the symmetric equations (14.3.1).

Two piercing points of the line are $(-10, -17, 0)$ and $(0, -3, 4)$. From them, direction numbers of the line are $[10, 14, 4]$ or $[5, 7, 2]$ (by 12.5.3). If we substitute this result in 14.3.1, using $(0, -3, 4)$ for the point (x_1, y_1, z_1), we find the symmetric equations of the given line to be

$$\begin{cases} \dfrac{x}{5} = \dfrac{y + 3}{7}, \\[2mm] \dfrac{x}{5} = \dfrac{z - 4}{2}. \end{cases}$$

Our definition of symmetric equations, Theorem 14.3.1, and its Corollary, all fail if any one of the given direction numbers is zero. The meaning of the symmetric equations of a line, one of whose direction numbers is zero, and the procedure to be followed are shown in the following example.

Example 2. Find symmetric equations of the line through the point $(2, -3, 5)$ with direction numbers $[-4, 0, 1]$.

Solution. Since one of the given direction numbers is zero, 14.3.1 does not apply.

Let $P{:}(x, y, z)$ be any other point on the line. Then a set of direction numbers of the line through $P_1{:}(2, -3, 5)$ and P are $[x - 2, y + 3, z - 5]$ (by 12.5.3). But these direction numbers must be proportional to the given direction numbers. Therefore

$$x - 2 = -4k, \qquad y + 3 = 0, \qquad z - 5 = k.$$

Eliminating k between the first and third of these equations, we have

$$\frac{x - 2}{-4} = z - 5.$$

Thus we call

$$\begin{cases} \dfrac{x-2}{-4} = \dfrac{z-5}{1}, \\ y+3 = 0, \end{cases}$$

symmetric equations of the given line.

EXERCISES

Make a sketch for each exercise.

In Exercises 1 to 6, find symmetric equations of the line through the given point and having the given direction numbers.

1. $(-4, 2, 1)$, $[3, 5, -8]$.   **2.** $(2, 7, -5)$, $[-1, 4, 2]$.

3. $(3, -6, 4)$, $[6, -1, 7]$.   **4.** $(0, 2, -1)$, $[-4, 4, 9]$.

5. $(1, 2, 4)$, $[0, -2, 3]$.   **6.** $(-3, 1, -2)$, $[-6, 1, 0]$.

7. Find symmetric equations of the line through the point $(-2, 1, 5)$ and perpendicular to the plane $3x + 7y - 6z + 19 = 0$.

8. Find symmetric equations of the line through the point $(4, 0, 6)$ and perpendicular to the plane $x - 5y + 2z + 10 = 0$.

9. Find symmetric equations of each of the lines whose general equations are given in the Exercises of Section 14.1.

10. Find symmetric equations for the line in Exercise 1, Section 14.2.

11. Find symmetric equations for the line in Exercise 6, Section 14.2.

12. Find symmetric equations for the line through the points $(7, 4, 6)$ and $(-1, 3, -5)$.

13. Find symmetric equations of the line through the point $(2, 4, 5)$ and intersecting the x-axis at right angles. Make the sketch first.

14. Find symmetric equations of the line through the point $(1, 5, -3)$, parallel to the plane $4x - 6y + z + 13 = 0$, and perpendicular to the line

$$\begin{cases} \dfrac{x+1}{7} = \dfrac{y+6}{2}, \\ \dfrac{y+6}{2} = \dfrac{z-11}{3}. \end{cases}$$

15. Show that the two lines

$$\begin{cases} \dfrac{x+2}{3} = \dfrac{y-4}{2}, \\ \dfrac{y-4}{2} = \dfrac{z+1}{6}, \end{cases} \quad \text{and} \quad \begin{cases} \dfrac{x+1}{-1} = \dfrac{y+1}{5}, \\ \dfrac{y+1}{5} = z+2, \end{cases}$$

lie in the same plane.

16. Show that the two lines

$$\begin{cases} \dfrac{x-1}{5} = \dfrac{y-3}{4}, \\ \dfrac{y-3}{4} = \dfrac{z-1}{3}, \end{cases} \quad \text{and} \quad \begin{cases} \dfrac{x-1}{10} = \dfrac{y-4}{9}, \\ \dfrac{y-4}{9} = \dfrac{z-3}{8}, \end{cases}$$

lie in the same plane.

14.4 PARAMETRIC EQUATIONS OF A LINE IN SPACE

A second way of representing a straight line in space is by means of parametric equations.

Consider the line through the fixed point $P_1:(x_1, y_1, z_1)$, with direction cosines $\cos \alpha$, $\cos \beta$, $\cos \gamma$ (Fig. 232). Let $P:(x, y, z)$ be any other point.

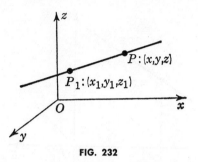

FIG. 232

Then P is on the line if and only if the line segment $\overline{P_1P}$ has the given direction cosines. That is, if and only if

(1) $$\cos \alpha = \frac{x - x_1}{d}, \quad \cos \beta = \frac{y - y_1}{d}, \quad \cos \gamma = \frac{z - z_1}{d},$$

where d is the directed distance P_1P (by 12.4.4). From (1) we obtain

(2) $$x = x_1 + d \cos \alpha, \quad y = y_1 + d \cos \beta, \quad z = z_1 + d \cos \gamma,$$

which are called **parametric equations** of the line.

It was assumed above that P and P_1 were distinct points, but it is obvious that equations (2) yield the coordinates of $P \equiv P_1$ when $d = 0$.

We have proved the

14.4.1 Theorem. *Parametric equations of the line through the point $P_1:(x_1, y_1, z_1)$, with direction cosines $\cos \alpha$, $\cos \beta$, $\cos \gamma$, are*

$$x = x_1 + d \cos \alpha, \quad y = y_1 + d \cos \beta, \quad z = z_1 + d \cos \gamma.$$

In these equations, x_1, y_1, z_1, $\cos \alpha$, $\cos \beta$, and $\cos \gamma$ are constants and d is the variable parameter. For each position of P on the line there is a unique directed distance P_1P and thus a unique value of d, and conversely.

To draw a line whose parametric equations are known, find the coordinates of any two points on the line by assigning any two convenient values to the parameter. Then plot the points and draw the line through them.

Example 1. Draw the line through the point $(-4, 2, 5)$, with direction cosines $[2/3, -2/3, 1/3]$.

Solution. By 14.4.1, parametric equations of the line are

$$x = -4 + \tfrac{2}{3}d, \quad y = 2 - \tfrac{2}{3}d, \quad z = 5 + \tfrac{1}{3}d.$$

When $d = 0$, the corresponding point on the line is $(-4, 2, 5)$.   When $d = 3$, the point is $(-2, 0, 6)$.   Joining these points is the desired line (Fig. 233).

When direction numbers of a line are given instead of its direction cosines, we can, of course, compute the direction cosines (12.5.5) and then

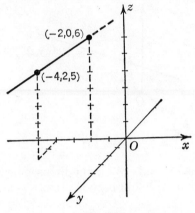

FIG. 233

find parametric equations of the line (by 14.4.1).   But it is more convenient to obtain other parametric equations directly by means of the

14.4.2 Theorem.   *Parametric equations of the line having direction numbers* $[a, b, c]$ *and passing through the point* $P_1:(x_1, y_1, z_1)$ *are*

$$x = x_1 + ka, \quad y = y_1 + kb, \quad z = z_1 + kc,$$

where k is the variable parameter.

Proof.   Let $P:(x, y, z)$ be any point other than P_1 (Fig. 232).   Then P is on the line if and only if the line segment $\overline{P_1P}$ has direction numbers proportional to the given direction numbers (by 12.5.1).   Therefore P is on the line if and only if

$$ka = x - x_1, \quad kb = y - y_1, \quad kc = z - z_1,$$

where k is a factor of proportionality.   Whence

$$x = x_1 + ka, \quad y = y_1 + kb, \quad z = z_1 + kc.$$

Notice that x_1, y_1, z_1, a, b, and c are constants and k is the variable parameter.   If $P \equiv P_1$, $k = 0$ and conversely.   Unlike the parameter d in equations (2), k does not in general equal the distance from (x_1, y_1, z_1) to (x, y, z).

Clearly, 14.4.1 is a special case of 14.4.2.

Example 2.   Find parametric equations of the line whose general equations are

$$\begin{cases} 2x - y - 5z + 14 = 0, \\ 4x + 5y + 4z - 28 = 0. \end{cases}$$

Solution.   We found in the Example, Section 14.1, that one (piercing) point on this line is (0, 4, 2) and that direction numbers of the line are [3, −4, 2]. Therefore, by 14.4.2, parametric equations of the line are

$$x = 3k, \quad y = 4 - 4k, \quad z = 2 + 2k.$$

EXERCISES

1. Find parametric equations of the line through the point $(-1, 5, 4)$ and with direction cosines $[3/\sqrt{14}, -1/\sqrt{14}, 4/\sqrt{14}]$.

2. Find parametric equations of the line through the point $(-7, -6, 2)$ and having direction angles $\beta = 120°$, $\gamma = 45°$. Then sketch the line. (Two solutions.)

3. Find the direction cosines of the line with parametric equations

$$x = 2 + 3k, \quad y = -3 + 4k, \quad z = 5 - k.$$

4. Find the direction cosines of the line with parametric equations

$$x = -1 - 6k, \quad y = 4 + k, \quad z = 2 - 5k.$$

In Exercises 5 to 10, find parametric equations of the lines whose general equations are given. (See the Exercises, Section 14.1.)

5. $\begin{cases} x - 2y + 4z - 14 = 0, \\ x + 20y - 18z + 30 = 0. \end{cases}$

6. $\begin{cases} x - 3y - 8z + 1 = 0, \\ x - 7y - 28z + 21 = 0. \end{cases}$

7. $\begin{cases} 2x + 5y + 4z - 4 = 0, \\ 28x - 4y + 19z + 92 = 0. \end{cases}$

8. $\begin{cases} 15x + 5y - 3z = 0, \\ 3x + 4y - 6z + 18 = 0. \end{cases}$

9. $\begin{cases} 4x - 3y + 16z - 36 = 0, \\ 6x + 3y + 9z - 39 = 0. \end{cases}$

10. $\begin{cases} 5x - y - 5z + 5 = 0, \\ 18x + 15y + 13z - 75 = 0. \end{cases}$

11. Find parametric equations of the line whose general equations are

$$\begin{cases} 2x + 4y - z - 4 = 0, \\ x - 5y + 3z + 5 = 0. \end{cases}$$

Then sketch the line.

12. Find parametric equations of the line through the points $(2, 4, -3)$ and $(-5, 1, 2)$. Sketch the line.

13. Find parametric equations of the line through the origin and perpendicular to the plane $7x - 5y + z + 11 = 0$. Then sketch the line.

14. Find parametric equations of the line through the point $(-7, 2, 6)$ and perpendicular to the plane $3x + 5y - z + 12 = 0$. Then sketch the line.

15. Find parametric equations of the line through the point $(-4, -2, 6)$ and parallel to the z-axis. Draw the line.

16. Find parametric equations of the line through the point $(1, 5, -3)$ and parallel to the y-axis. Make a sketch.

17. Find parametric equations of the line through the point $(4, 0, -3)$ and parallel to the line whose general equations are

$$\begin{cases} 2x + y - 5z + 1 = 0, \\ 3x - 3y + z - 10 = 0. \end{cases}$$

Then sketch the line.

18. Find parametric equations of the line through the point $(2, 3, 4)$ and parallel to the line whose general equations are

$$\begin{cases} 2x + 2y - z + 4 = 0, \\ 4x + 15y + 9z - 3 = 0. \end{cases}$$

Then sketch the line.

15

Surfaces

15.1 THE SPHERE

In Chapter 13 we studied planes, which are the simplest surfaces. We now continue our brief study of surfaces by considering the familiar sphere.

15.1.1 Definition. *A sphere is the locus of points in space whose undirected distances from a fixed point, called the center, are equal to a constant called the radius.*

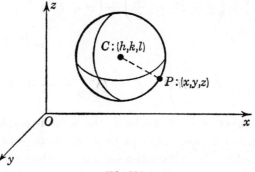

FIG. 234

Denote the center by $C:(h, k, l)$ and the radius by r, a positive number (Fig. 234). Then $P:(x, y, z)$ is on the locus if and only if $|CP| = r$. That is,

$$\sqrt{(x - h)^2 + (y - k)^2 + (z - l)^2} = r \qquad \text{(by 12.2.4)},$$

or

(1) $$(x - h)^2 + (y - k)^2 + (z - l)^2 = r^2.$$

This proves the

15.1.2 Theorem. *The equation of the sphere whose center is (h, k, l) and whose radius is r is*

$$(x - h)^2 + (y - k)^2 + (z - l)^2 = r^2.$$

241

This is called the **center-radius form** of the equation of the sphere.

15.1.3 Corollary. *The equation of the sphere with radius r and center at the origin is*

$$x^2 + y^2 + z^2 = r^2.$$

Expanding equation (1) and rearranging its terms, we have

(2) $x^2 + y^2 + z^2 - 2hx - 2ky - 2lz + (h^2 + k^2 + l^2 - r^2) = 0,$

which is in the form

(3) $x^2 + y^2 + z^2 + Gx + Hy + Iz + J = 0,$

where G, H, I, and J are constants.   Thus every sphere has an equation of the form (3).   This is the **general form** of the equation of a sphere.
   Conversely, (3) can be rewritten

(4) $(x^2 + Gx) + (y^2 + Hy) + (z^2 + Iz) = -J.$

Completing the squares in the parentheses by adding $G^2/4$, $H^2/4$ and $I^2/4$ to both sides of this equation, we get

$$\left(x^2 + Gx + \frac{G^2}{4}\right) + \left(y^2 + Hy + \frac{H^2}{4}\right) + \left(z^2 + Iz + \frac{I^2}{4}\right)$$
$$= \frac{G^2 + H^2 + I^2 - 4J}{4},$$

or

(5) $\left(x + \dfrac{G}{2}\right)^2 + \left(y + \dfrac{H}{2}\right)^2 + \left(z + \dfrac{I}{2}\right)^2 = \dfrac{G^2 + H^2 + I^2 - 4J}{4}.$

If the right member of (5) is positive, the locus is a sphere with center $(-G/2, -H/2, -I/2)$ and radius $\frac{1}{2}\sqrt{G^2 + H^2 + I^2 - 4J}$ (by 15.1.2).   If the right member of (5) is zero, the only point whose coordinates satisfy it is the center, $(-G/2, -H/2, -I/2)$.   This is called a **point sphere.** When the right member of (5) is negative, there is no locus.   Hence the

15.1.4 Theorem.   *The locus, if any, of*

$$x^2 + y^2 + z^2 + Gx + Hy + Iz + J = 0$$

is a sphere, and every sphere has an equation of this form.

The student should not memorize the formulas for the center and radius of the sphere (3) but should apply the method of completing the squares.

Example.   Sketch the locus of $x^2 + y^2 + z^2 - 10x - 6y + 4z + 29 = 0.$

Solution.   Since the coefficients of x^2, y^2 and z^2 are equal and the equation contains no term in xy, yz, or zx, its locus is a sphere, if it is real (15.1.4).   To find its center and radius, we rearrange the terms,

$$(x^2 - 10x) + (y^2 - 6y) + (z^2 + 4z) = -29.$$

Completing the squares in the parentheses by adding 25, 9, and 4 to both sides of the equation, we have

$$(x^2 - 10x + 25) + (y^2 - 6y + 9) + (z^2 + 4z + 4) = 9,$$

or

$$(x - 5)^2 + (y - 3)^2 + (z + 2)^2 = 9.$$

By 15.1.2, the coordinates of the center are $(5, 3, -2)$ and the radius is 3. It is now easy to draw it (Fig. 235).

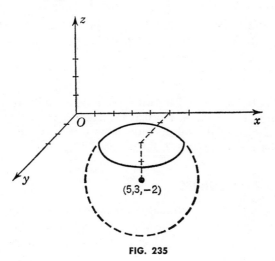

FIG. 235

EXERCISES

Make a sketch for each exercise.

1. Write the equation of the sphere whose center and radius are:

(a) $(-5, 2, 4)$, 6; (b) $(1, 6, -3)$, 4;

(c) $(3, 0, 4)$, 5; (d) $(8, -1, -7)$, 2.

2. Write the equation of the sphere whose center and radius are:

(a) $(2, 4, 1)$, 3; (b) $(-4, 6, 0)$, 7;

(c) $(-6, 2, -3)$, 1; (d) $(8, 0, -1)$, 2.

In Exercises 3 to 8, find the center and radius of the sphere whose equation is given.

3. $x^2 + y^2 + z^2 + 2x - 6y + 22z + 122 = 0.$

4. $x^2 + y^2 + z^2 - 12x + 14y - 8z + 1 = 0.$

5. $x^2 + y^2 + z^2 + 26y + 120 = 0.$

6. $36x^2 + 36y^2 + 36z^2 - 48x + 36y - 360z - 1379 = 0.$

7. $x^2 + y^2 + z^2 - 8x - 6y + 4z + 40 = 0.$

8. $x^2 + y^2 + z^2 + 8x - 4y - 22z + 77 = 0.$

9. Find the equation of the sphere with center on the z-axis and passing through the points $(3, 4, 3)$ and $(-2, -1, 1)$.

10. Find the equation of the sphere with center on the y-axis and passing through the points $(7, 1, -2)$ and $(1, 3, 6)$.

11. Find the equation of the sphere which is tangent to the plane

$$x - 8y + 4z + 7 = 0$$

and which has the same center as $x^2 + y^2 + z^2 - 12x - 4y - 6z + 33 = 0.$

12. Find the equation of the sphere which is tangent to the plane

$$2x + 3y - 6z - 2 = 0$$

and which has the same center as $x^2 + y^2 + z^2 + 14x + 2y - 10z - 6 = 0.$

13. Find the equation of the sphere which has its center on the x-axis and passes through the points $(0, 5, 0)$ and $(-2, 1, 0)$.

14. Find the equation of the sphere which has its center on the z-axis and goes through the points $(3, -1, 2)$ and $(1, -3, 0)$.

15. Find the equation of the sphere with center in the zx-plane and which is tangent to the plane $2x - y + z - 4 = 0$ at the point $(1, 5, 7)$.

16. Find the equation of the sphere with center in the yz-plane and which is tangent to the plane $x + 3y - 2z + 1 = 0$ at the point $(5, 0, 3)$.

15.2 SURFACES AND CURVES

We have seen that in three-dimensional geometry one equation of the first degree always represents a plane and one equation of the second degree, if in the form $x^2 + y^2 + z^2 + Gx + Hy + Iz + J = 0$, represents a spherical surface. More generally,

15.2.1 Definition. *The locus (if any) of points in space whose coordinates satisfy a single equation is called a* **surface.**

The simplest surface is a plane. Its equation is of the first degree.

The locus of points whose coordinates satisfy two simultaneous equations is the curve of intersection of the surfaces represented by the individual equations. It consists of those points and only those points which are on both surfaces simultaneously. For example, the locus of

$$\begin{cases} x^2 + y^2 + z^2 = 9, \\ x = 2, \end{cases}$$

is the circle in which the plane $x = 2$ intersects the sphere $x^2 + y^2 + z^2 = 9$ (Fig. 236).

15.2.2 Definition. *The locus (if any) of points in space whose coordinates satisfy two independent equations simultaneously is called a* **curve.**

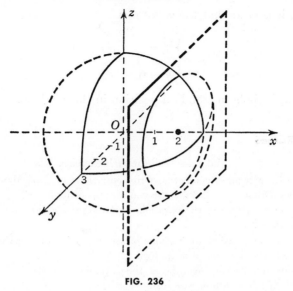

FIG. 236

The simplest curve is a straight line.   It can always be represented by two simultaneous equations of the first degree.

15.2.3 Corollary.   *The locus of two independent simultaneous equations, one of which is of the first degree, is a plane curve lying in the plane represented by the first degree equation.*

We know that in plane analytic geometry the equation $y^2 = 4fx$ represents a parabola (6.2.2).   But in space a single equation always represents a surface (15.2.1).   How can a parabola be represented in three-dimensional geometry?   If we think of the parabola as lying in the xy-plane, the x- and y-coordinates of any point on the parabola must be related in exactly the same way as in plane analytic geometry.   That is, they must satisfy the equation $y^2 = 4fx$.   Moreover, the z-coordinate of every point on the parabola must be zero since it lies in the xy-plane.   Therefore the simultaneous equations

$$\begin{cases} y^2 = 4fx, \\ z = 0, \end{cases}$$

represent the parabola in standard position in the xy-plane.

15.2.4 Corollary.   *In three-dimensional geometry, to represent in the xy-plane a curve whose two dimensional equation is known, make the known equation simultaneous with $z = 0$.*

Similarly, it is clear that the equations

$$\begin{cases} \dfrac{x^2}{a^2} - \dfrac{z^2}{c^2} = 1, \\ y = 0, \end{cases}$$

represent a hyperbola in standard position in the zx-plane.

EXERCISES

Make a sketch for each exercise.

1. In three-dimensional geometry, write equations of a parabola in standard position in the yz-plane. What are the coordinates of its focus?

2. Write the equations of the parabola in standard position in the zx-plane, if its focus is $(0, 0, -2)$.

3. Write three-dimensional equations of an ellipse in standard position in the zx-plane. Find the coordinates of its foci.

4. Find the equations of the ellipse in the yz-plane whose vertices are $(0, \pm 5, 0)$ and the length of whose minor axis is 8.

5. Write three-dimensional equations of a hyperbola in standard position in the xy-plane. Find equations for each of its asymptotes.

6. Find the equations of the hyperbola whose vertices are $(0, \pm 3, 0)$ and which passes through the point $(0, 3\sqrt{2}, 2)$.

7. Write three-dimensional equations for each of the plane cubic curves shown in Figures 137 and 141.

8. Name and describe the locus of

$$\begin{cases} x^2 + y^2 + z^2 = 16, \\ z = -3. \end{cases}$$

9. What is the locus of

$$\begin{cases} x^2 + y^2 + z^2 = 25, \\ y = 5? \end{cases}$$

10. What is the locus of

$$\begin{cases} x^2 + y^2 + z^2 = 4, \\ x = -3? \end{cases}$$

15.3   CYLINDERS

The student is familiar with the right circular cylinder from his high school geometry (Fig. 237). In analytic geometry the word **cylinder** denotes a much more extensive class of surfaces.

15.3.1 Definition. *The surface generated by a moving line which is always parallel to a fixed direction and intersects a fixed curve is called a* **cylinder.**

The various positions of the moving line are **generators** of the cylinder, and the fixed curve is its **directrix.** In the examples considered in this book, the directrix is always a plane curve lying in a coordinate plane and the generators are straight lines perpendicular to that plane. A cylinder is said to be perpendicular to a plane if its generators are perpendicular to the plane.

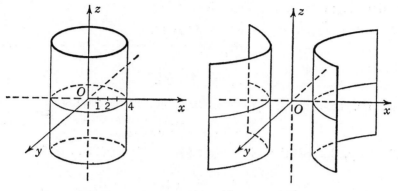

FIG. 237　　　　　　　　　FIG. 238

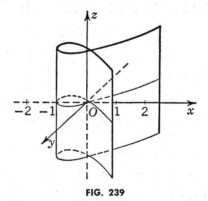

FIG. 239

Fig. 237 shows a circular cylinder whose directrix is a circle in the xy-plane with center at the origin and radius 4. Its generators are perpendicular to the xy-plane. Figs. 238 and 239 show a hyperbolic cylinder and a cubic cylinder. They are named after their directrices.

Each of these cylinders may be thought of as composed of straight lines perpendicular to the xy-plane and intersecting the xy-plane in the directrix.

To find the equation of the circular cylinder shown in Fig. 237, let $P_1 : (x_1, y_1, z_1)$ be an arbitrary point in space and denote the foot of the perpendicular from P_1 to the xy-plane by Q. Then P_1 is on the cylinder if and only if Q is on the directrix.

By 12.1.5, the coordinates of Q are $(x_1, y_1, 0)$. Since the directrix of the

circular cylinder is a circle lying in the xy-plane, with center at the origin
and radius 4, its equations are

(1)
$$\begin{cases} x^2 + y^2 = 16, \\ z = 0 \end{cases} \quad \text{(by 15.2.4)}.$$

Thus P_1 is on the cylinder if and only if the coordinates of Q satisfy the
equations (1); that is, if and only if

$$\begin{cases} x_1{}^2 + y_1{}^2 = 16, \\ 0 = 0, \end{cases}$$

or

$$x_1{}^2 + y_1{}^2 = 16.$$

Therefore, the equation of the circular cylinder (Fig. 237) is

$$x^2 + y^2 = 16.$$

Similarly, the equation of the hyperbolic cylinder (Fig. 238) is

$$\frac{x^2}{a^2} - \frac{y^2}{b^2} = 1,$$

and the equation of the cubic cylinder (Fig. 239) is

$$y^2 = (x + 1)x^2.$$

Since the above discussion applies to any equation in x and y, its results
may be generalized in the

15.3.2 Theorem. *In three-dimensional space, an equation in x and y
represents a cylinder perpendicular to the xy-plane, and conversely,*

More generally,

15.3.3 Theorem. *In three-dimensional space, an equation in only two of
the three variables x, y, z represents a cylinder whose generators are parallel
to the axis of the missing variable.*

For example,

$$\frac{y^2}{a^2} + \frac{z^2}{c^2} = 1$$

represents an elliptic cylinder whose generators are parallel to the x-axis.

In 15.2 we said that the simultaneous equations

(2)
$$\begin{cases} y^2 = 4fx, \\ z = 0, \end{cases}$$

represent a parabola. It is now clear that the first equation alone represents a parabolic cylinder perpendicular to the xy-plane, and the two equations simultaneously represent the intersection of the parabolic cylinder and the xy-plane. That is, they represent the directrix of the parabolic cylinder.

At this point the student should observe that while equations

(3)
$$\begin{cases} x^2 + y^2 + z^2 = 9, \\ x = 2, \end{cases}$$

represent the circle of intersection of the sphere $x^2 + y^2 + z^2 = 9$ and the plane $x = 2$ (Fig. 236), simpler and more useful equations of the same circle are readily available. Eliminating x between the equations (3) by substituting $x = 2$ from the second equation into the first equation, we have

(4)
$$y^2 + z^2 = 5,$$

which represents a circular cylinder perpendicular to the yz-plane. Clearly, every set of coordinates that satisfy the simultaneous equations (3) also satisfy (4). That is, the circle (3) is on the cylinder (4). But the circle is also on the plane $x = 2$. Therefore, new equations of the circle (3) are

(5)
$$\begin{cases} y^2 + z^2 = 5, \\ x = 2. \end{cases}$$

It is obvious from the equations (5) (but not from the equations (3)) that the radius of the circle is $\sqrt{5}$ and that its center is on the x-axis. Equation (4) represents a **projecting cylinder** of the circle (3).

This method is general and the student should use it to obtain the simplest possible equations when sketching a curve in space.

Example. Find simpler equations of the curve
$$\begin{cases} 45x^2 - 180y^2 - 4z^2 = 36, \\ z = 6, \end{cases}$$

and draw it.

Solution. The projecting cylinder of this curve perpendicular to the xy-plane is
$$\frac{x^2}{4} - \frac{y^2}{1} = 1,$$

found by eliminating z between the given equations (by substituting $z = 6$ from the second equation into the first) and simplifying. Therefore simpler equations of the given curve are

(6)
$$\begin{cases} \dfrac{x^2}{4} - \dfrac{y^2}{1} = 1, \\ z = 6. \end{cases}$$

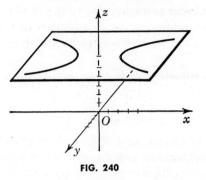

FIG. 240

It is a hyperbola in standard position in the plane $z = 6$ (Fig. 240). The length of its semi-transverse axis is 2 and the length of its semi-conjugate axis is 1.

EXERCISES

Make a sketch for each exercise.

1. Name the locus of each of the following equations:

(a) $x^2 + y^2 = 81$;   (b) $x^2 + y^2 + z^2 = 81$;

(c) $x^2 = 4z$;   (d) $3y - 6z + 4 = 0$;

(e) $9y^2 - 4z^2 = 36$;   (f) $4y^2 + 9z^2 + 36 = 0$.

2. Name the locus of each of the following equations:

(a) $25x^2 + 16y^2 = 400$;   (b) $y^2 + z^2 = 9$;

(c) $2x + 5z - 12 = 0$;   (d) $z^2 = 6y$;

(e) $x^2 + y^2 - 8x + 2y + 13 = 0$;   (f) $z^2 = y^3$.

3. Write the equation of a parabolic cylinder whose generators are parallel to the y-axis.

4. Find the equation of a parabolic cylinder whose generators are parallel to the x-axis.

5. Write the equation of the circular cylinder whose generators are parallel to the x-axis, if its directrix has its center at $(0, -2, 5)$ and radius equal to 3.

6. Write the equation of the circular cylinder whose generators are parallel to the y-axis, if its directrix has its center at $(4, 0, -2)$ with radius equal to 5.

7. Find a projecting cylinder of the curve whose equations are

$$\begin{cases} x^2 + 2y^2 - z - 50 = 0, \\ y = 5. \end{cases}$$

8. Find a projecting cylinder of the curve whose equations are

$$\begin{cases} 3x^2 + z^2 + 3y - 27 = 0, \\ x = -3. \end{cases}$$

9. Find simpler equations for the ellipse

$$\begin{cases} \dfrac{x^2}{27} + \dfrac{y^2}{9} + \dfrac{z^2}{3} = 1, \\ x = 3. \end{cases}$$

10. Find simpler equations of the hyperbola

$$\begin{cases} \dfrac{x^2}{4} - \dfrac{y^2}{16} + \dfrac{z^2}{64} = 1, \\ z = 4. \end{cases}$$

11. Find the equations of two projecting cylinders of the space curve

$$\begin{cases} y^2 + z^2 = x, \\ 2x^2 + z^2 = 3y, \end{cases}$$

and use them to write new equations of the curve. No sketch required.

12. Find the equations of two projecting cylinders of the space curve

$$\begin{cases} x^2 + y^2 + z^2 = 16, \\ \dfrac{x^2}{9} + \dfrac{y^2}{4} - \dfrac{z^2}{16} = 1, \end{cases}$$

and use them to write new equations of the curve. No sketch is required.

15.4   SURFACES OF REVOLUTION

Another extensive class of surfaces, which are used in the applications of mathematics, are **surfaces of revolution.** Such a surface can be thought of as swept out by a plane curve revolving about a fixed line lying in the plane of the curve. The fixed line is called the **axis** of the surface of revolution.

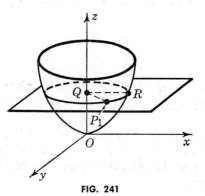

FIG. 241

For example, a sphere can be generated by revolving a circle about one of its diameters. A surface of revolution generated by revolving a parabola about its principal axis is shown in Fig. 241. Clearly, all plane sections of a surface of revolution, which are perpendicular to its axis, are circles.

To derive the equation of the surface of revolution generated by revolving the parabola

(1)
$$\begin{cases} x^2 = 4z, \\ y = 0, \end{cases}$$

about the z-axis (Fig. 241), let P_1:(x_1, y_1, z_1) be any point on the surface. Pass a plane, π, through P_1 perpendicular to the z-axis, indicating its intersection with the z-axis by Q and one of its intersections with the given parabola by R.   The coordinates of Q are $(0, 0, z_1)$.   Since the plane π cuts the surface in a circle, P_1 is on the surface if and only if

$$(2) \hspace{4cm} |QP_1| = |QR|.$$

But $|QP_1| = \sqrt{x_1^2 + y_1^2}$ (by 12.2.4) and QR is the x-coordinate of R, a point on the given parabola.   From the first of the equations (1) we obtain $QR = x = \pm 2\sqrt{z_1}$.   Substituting these values of $|QP_1|$ and QR in (2), we have $\sqrt{x_1^2 + y_1^2} = \pm 2\sqrt{z_1}$, or

$$(3) \hspace{4cm} x_1^2 + y_1^2 = 4z_1.$$

Therefore P_1 is on the surface if and only if its coordinates satisfy the equation

$$(4) \hspace{4cm} x^2 + y^2 = 4z.$$

This is the desired equation of the surface of revolution.

The method of derivation is perfectly general and applies when the given parabola is replaced by any other curve in the xz-plane.   This is stated in the

15.4.1 Theorem.   *The equation of the surface of revolution generated by revolving the curve*

$$\begin{cases} f(x, z) = 0^* \\ y = 0 \end{cases}$$

about the z-axis is $f(\pm\sqrt{x^2 + y^2}, z) = 0$, and the surface generated by revolving the given curve about the x-axis is $f(x, \pm\sqrt{y^2 + z^2}) = 0$.

Analogous statements hold when a curve lying in any coordinate plane is revolved about one of the coordinate axes that lie in the plane.

For example, the equation of the surface of revolution generated by revolving the hyperbola

$$\begin{cases} \dfrac{x^2}{a^2} - \dfrac{y^2}{b^2} = 1, \\ z = 0, \end{cases}$$

about the y-axis is found by replacing x by $\pm\sqrt{x^2 + z^2}$ in the first of the given equations, yielding

---

* The notation $f(x, z) = 0$ here means an equation in x and z.   It is read "a function of x and z equated to zero."   Then $f(\pm\sqrt{x^2 + y^2}, z) = 0$ means that $\pm\sqrt{x^2 + y^2}$ has been substituted for x throughout the equation $f(x, z) = 0$.

$$\frac{x^2 + z^2}{a^2} - \frac{y^2}{b^2} = 1.$$

The surface generated by revolving the given hyperbola about the x-axis is found by replacing y in the first of the given equations by $\pm\sqrt{y^2 + z^2}$, obtaining

$$\frac{x^2}{a^2} - \frac{(y^2 + z^2)}{b^2} = 1.$$

EXERCISES

In Exercises 1–10, find the equation of the surface of revolution generated by revolving the given plane curve about the indicated axis. Make a sketch.

1. $\begin{cases} z^2 = 6x, \\ y = 0, \end{cases}$ about the x-axis.

2. The same curve as in Exercise 1, about the z-axis.

3. $\begin{cases} 9x^2 + 16y^2 = 144, \\ z = 0, \end{cases}$ about the x-axis.

4. Same curve as in Exercise 3, but about the y-axis.

5. $\begin{cases} 25x^2 - 4z^2 = 100, \\ y = 0, \end{cases}$ about the z-axis.

6. $\begin{cases} x^2 = y^3, \\ z = 0, \end{cases}$ about the y-axis.

7. $\begin{cases} (x - 7)^2 + z^2 = 4, \\ y = 0, \end{cases}$ about the z-axis.

8. $\begin{cases} xz = 1, \\ y = 0, \end{cases}$ about the x-axis.

9. $\begin{cases} z = \sin y, \\ x = 0, \end{cases}$ about the y-axis.

10. $\begin{cases} z = e^x, \\ y = 0, \end{cases}$ about the x-axis.

11. Some of the following equations represent surfaces of revolution. Find the axis and the generating curve for each such surface of revolution.

(a) $x^2 + y^2 + z^2 = 25$;   (b) $2x^2 + 3y^2 - 4z^2 = 24$;

(c) $x^2 + z^2 - 2y = 0$.

12. Find the axis and the generating curve for each of the following surfaces of revolution:

(a) $x^2 + y^2 - z^6 = 0$;   (b) $x^2y^2 + y^2z^2 = 1$.

(c) $9x^2 + 9y^2 - 4z^2 + 24z - 36 = 0$;

15.5 SYMMETRY, TRACES, AND PLANE SECTIONS OF A SURFACE

It is desirable to be able to draw a surface when its equation is known. Several of the ideas used in discussing plane curves can readily be extended to space.

Two points are said to be symmetric with respect to a plane if the plane bisects perpendicularly the line segment joining the points.   Clearly, two points are symmetric with respect to the xy-plane if and only if their x-coordinates are the same and their y-coordinates are the same but the

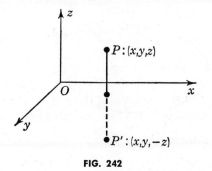

FIG. 242

z-coordinate of one is the negative of the z-coordinate of the other (Fig. 242).   This leads to the

15.5.1 Corollary.   *A surface is symmetric with respect to the xy-plane if its equation is unaffected by replacing z by $-z$ throughout.*

Similar statements hold for surfaces symmetric with respect to either of the other coordinate planes.

For example, the surface $x^2 + y^2 = 4z$ is symmetric with respect to the yz-plane, since the equation contains no odd power of x and therefore is unaffected when we replace x by $-x$.   It is also symmetric with respect to the zx-plane, since it contains no odd power of y.   Because the surface is symmetric with respect to both the yz- and zx-planes, it is symmetric with respect to the z-axis.

The curve of intersection of a surface with a coordinate plane is called a **trace** of the surface.   The three traces of a surface are of great help in sketching it.   To find the trace of a surface in the xy-plane, set $z = 0$ simultaneously with the given equation of the surface.   We proceed similarly in finding the other traces.

For example, the trace of the surface $x^2 + y^2 - z^2 = 1$ in the xy-plane is the plane curve

$$\begin{cases} x^2 + y^2 - z^2 = 1, \\ z = 0. \end{cases}$$

As in 15.3, we obtain simpler equations of this curve by finding its projecting cylinder.   Eliminating z between the two equations, we obtain $x^2 + y^2 = 1$.   Thus equivalent but simpler equations of the trace of the given surface in the xy-plane are

$$\begin{cases} x^2 + y^2 = 1, \\ z = 0, \end{cases}$$

which represent a circle with center at the origin and radius 1 (Fig. 243).

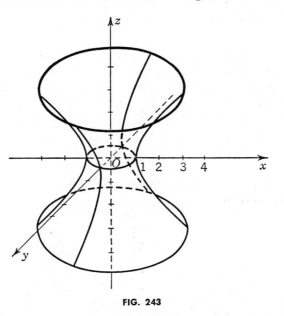

FIG. 243

Similarly the trace of the surface $x^2 + y^2 - z^2 = 1$ in the zx-plane is

$$\begin{cases} x^2 + y^2 - z^2 = 1, \\ y = 0, \end{cases} \quad \text{or} \quad \begin{cases} x^2 - z^2 = 1, \\ y = 0, \end{cases}$$

which is an equilateral hyperbola in standard position in the zx-plane. The trace of the surface in the yz-plane is the equilateral hyperbola

$$\begin{cases} y^2 - z^2 = 1, \\ x = 0. \end{cases}$$

If further information is needed to sketch the surface, we resort to a series of plane sections of the surface parallel to a coordinate plane. For example, the plane $z = 1$ cuts the surface (Fig. 243) in the curve

$$\begin{cases} x^2 + y^2 - z^2 = 1, \\ z = 1, \end{cases} \quad \text{or} \quad \begin{cases} x^2 + y^2 = 2, \\ z = 1, \end{cases}$$

which is a circle with radius $\sqrt{2}$, lying in the plane $z = 1$, and with its center on the z-axis. The plane $z = -5$ cuts the surface in the circle

$$\begin{cases} x^2 + y^2 - z^2 = 1, \\ z = -5, \end{cases} \quad \text{or} \quad \begin{cases} x^2 + y^2 = 26, \\ z = -5. \end{cases}$$

Similarly, all plane sections parallel to the zx-plane are hyperbolas. For example, the plane $y = 3$ cuts the surface in the hyperbola

$$\begin{cases} x^2 + y^2 - z^2 = 1, \\ y = 3, \end{cases} \quad \text{or} \quad \begin{cases} \dfrac{z^2}{8} - \dfrac{x^2}{8} = 1, \\ y = 3. \end{cases}$$

Example. Sketch the surface whose equation is $x^2 - 2y^2 - 2z^2 + 2x = 1$.

Solution. Our tests show that the surface is symmetric with respect to the zx-plane and also to the xy-plane. Therefore the surface is symmetric with respect to the x-axis.

The trace in the xy-plane is

$$\begin{cases} x^2 - 2y^2 + 2x = 1, \\ z = 0, \end{cases} \quad \text{or} \quad \begin{cases} \dfrac{(x + 1)^2}{2} - \dfrac{y^2}{1} = 1, \\ z = 0, \end{cases}$$

which is a hyperbola in the xy-plane, symmetric with respect to the x-axis and with center at $(-1, 0, 0)$.

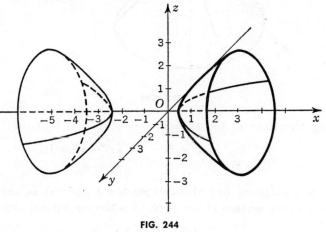

FIG. 244

Similarly, the trace in the yz-plane is

$$\begin{cases} 2y^2 + 2z^2 = -1, \\ x = 0, \end{cases}$$

which is imaginary. Thus the surface does not intersect the yz-plane.

The trace in the zx-plane is

$$\begin{cases} x^2 - 2z^2 + 2x = 1, \\ y = 0, \end{cases} \quad \text{or} \quad \begin{cases} \dfrac{(x + 1)^2}{2} - \dfrac{z^2}{1} = 1, \\ y = 0, \end{cases}$$

which is a hyperbola, symmetric with respect to the x-axis and with center at $(-1, 0, 0)$.

The intersections of the surface with planes perpendicular to the x-axis, and to the right of $x = -1 + \sqrt{2}$ (or approximately $x = .4$), are circles which get larger and larger as we move to the right. Similarly, the sections perpendicular to the x-axis and to the left of $x = -1 - \sqrt{2}$ (or approximately $x = -2.4$) are circles which increase in size as we move to the left. Thus it is a surface of revolution about the x-axis. It is now easy to sketch it (Fig. 244).

EXERCISES

Sketch the surfaces whose equations follow.

1. $x^2 + y^2 - z^2 - 1 = 0$.
2. $9x^2 + 36y^2 + 16z^2 - 144 = 0$.
3. $3x^2 + 4y^2 + 9z^2 - 24 = 0$.
4. $16x^2 - 100y^2 - 25z^2 - 400 = 0$.
5. $y^2 + z^2 + x = 0$.
6. $4x^2 + 9y^2 - 12z = 0$.
7. $x^2 + y^2 - z^2 = 0$.
8. $400x^2 - 144y^2 - 225z^2 + 3600 = 0$.
9. $9x^2 + 9y^2 - 4z^2 + 36 = 0$.
10. $9x^2 - 36y^2 - 4z^2 - 36 = 0$.
11. $y^2 + z^2 - 4y = 0$.
12. $x^2 - y^2 = 0$.
13. $x^2 + 4y^2 + 4z^2 - 4 = 0$.
14. $x^2 - y^2 + z^2 + 16 = 0$.
15. $x^2 + z^2 - y = 0$.
16. $y = \sin x$.

15.6 QUADRIC SURFACES

The locus, if any, of an equation of the second degree in three-dimensional Cartesian coordinates is called a **quadric surface**. All plane sections of a quadric surface are conics.

It is shown in more advanced treatises that any equation of the second degree in x, y, and z can be reduced, by rotation and translation of the coordinate axes, to one of the two forms

(1) $$Ax^2 + By^2 + Cz^2 + J = 0$$

and

(2) $$Ax^2 + By^2 + Iz = 0.$$

The quadric surfaces represented by equation (1) are symmetric with respect to all three coordinate planes (by 15.5) and therefore symmetric with respect to the origin. For this reason the loci of (1) are called **central quadrics** and the origin is their center. If the coefficients in (1) are all different from zero, it can be rewritten

(3) $$\pm \frac{x^2}{a^2} \pm \frac{y^2}{b^2} \pm \frac{z^2}{c^2} = 1,$$

which represents the following three types of central quadrics.

1. **Ellipsoid** (Fig. 245).

Its equation is

(4) $$\frac{x^2}{a^2} + \frac{y^2}{b^2} + \frac{z^2}{c^2} = 1.$$

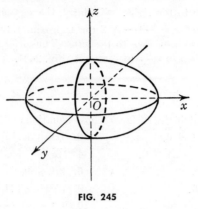

FIG. 245

The ellipsoid intersects the x-axis in the points $(\pm a, 0, 0)$, found by substituting $y = 0$ and $z = 0$ in (4) (see 13.2.3). Similarly, it intersects the y-axis in $(0, \pm b, 0)$, and the z-axis in $(0, 0, \pm c)$.

The trace of the ellipsoid in the xy-plane is the ellipse

$$\begin{cases} \dfrac{x^2}{a^2} + \dfrac{y^2}{b^2} = 1, \\ z = 0. \end{cases}$$

All plane sections of the surface parallel to the xy-plane are ellipses which become smaller as the cutting plane recedes from the origin. For, the equations of curve of intersection of the ellipsoid and the plane $z = k$ are

$$\begin{cases} \dfrac{x^2}{a^2} + \dfrac{y^2}{b^2} + \dfrac{k^2}{c^2} = 1, \\ z = k, \end{cases}$$

or

$$\begin{cases} \dfrac{x^2}{a^2} + \dfrac{y^2}{b^2} = 1 - \dfrac{k^2}{c^2}, \\ z = k, \end{cases}$$

which may be rewritten

(5)
$$\begin{cases} \dfrac{x^2}{a^2\left(1 - \dfrac{k^2}{c^2}\right)} + \dfrac{y^2}{b^2\left(1 - \dfrac{k^2}{c^2}\right)} = 1, \\ z = k. \end{cases}$$

When $|k| < c$, the equations (5) represent an ellipse, the lengths of whose semi-axes are $a\sqrt{1 - \dfrac{k^2}{c^2}}$ and $b\sqrt{1 - \dfrac{k^2}{c^2}}$. The ellipse is largest when $k = 0$, that is, when it is the trace of the ellipsoid in the plane $z = 0$. As $|k|$

increases, the ellipses grow smaller, and reduce to a point when $|k| = c$. For $|k| > c$, the ellipse is imaginary.

Similarly, the traces of the ellipsoid in the yz- and zx-planes are also ellipses and every real plane section of the surface, parallel to either of those planes, is an ellipse.

If two of the three quantities a, b, c are equal, the ellipsoid is a surface of revolution, and if all three are equal, the ellipsoid is a sphere.

2. Hyperboloid of One Sheet (Fig. 246).

Its equation is

$$(5) \qquad \frac{x^2}{a^2} + \frac{y^2}{b^2} - \frac{z^2}{c^2} = 1.$$

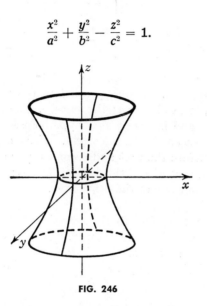

FIG. 246

Its trace in the xy-plane is an ellipse and all plane sections parallel to the xy-plane are ellipses which become larger as the cutting plane recedes from the origin. The trace of this hyperboloid in the yz- or zx-plane is a hyperbola and all plane sections parallel to either of those coordinate planes are hyperbolas. If $a = b$, the hyperboloid of one sheet is a surface of revolution. If the negative sign in (5) had been before the first or second term instead of the third, the locus would still have been a hyperboloid of one sheet, but about one of the other axes.

3. Hyperboloid of Two Sheets (Fig. 247).

Its equation is

$$(6) \qquad \frac{x^2}{a^2} - \frac{y^2}{b^2} - \frac{z^2}{c^2} = 1.$$

The traces of this surface in the xy- and zx-planes are hyperbolas, as are all plane sections parallel to either of them. The transverse axis of these

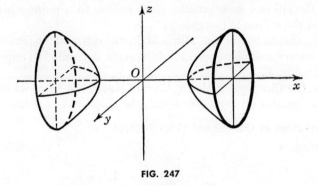

FIG. 247

hyperbolas gets longer as the cutting plane recedes from the origin.   This hyperboloid of two sheets does not intersect the yz-plane and thus there is no trace in that plane.   Planes parallel to the yz-plane, between the vertices $(\pm a, 0, 0)$, fail to intersect the surface.   All other planes that are parallel to the yz-plane intersect this hyperboloid in ellipses which get larger as their plane recedes from the origin.   If the negative signs in equation (6) had been before the first and second terms or the first and third terms, instead of the second and third terms, the hyperboloid of two sheets would have been about one of the other axes.

We now turn our attention to the equation (2) which represents the **non-central quadrics.**   They are symmetric with respect to the yz- and zx-planes but not the xy-plane.   Thus, they are symmetric with respect to the z-axis.   If all of the coefficients in (2) are different from zero, it can be rewritten

$$(7) \qquad \pm \frac{x^2}{a^2} \pm \frac{y^2}{b^2} = z.$$

This represents the following two distinct types of non-central quadric surfaces.   (For simplicity of language we shall assume that the coordinate axes are oriented as in our diagrams.)

1. **Elliptic Paraboloid** (Fig. 248).

Its equation is

$$(8) \qquad \frac{x^2}{a^2} + \frac{y^2}{b^2} = z.$$

Its trace in the xy-plane is a single point—the origin.   Planes parallel to and above the xy-plane cut the surface in ellipses which are larger when the cutting plane is higher.   The surface does not extend below the xy-plane.   The traces in the yz- and zx-planes are parabolas and so are all plane sections of the surface parallel to either of those coordinate planes.

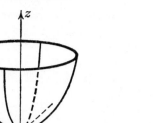

FIG. 248

If there had been a negative sign before z in (8), the elliptic paraboloid would have opened downward. Of course, the equation $x^2/a^2 + z^2/b^2 = y$ also represents an elliptic paraboloid—one that opens toward us along the y-axis.

2. **Hyperbolic Paraboloid** (Fig. 249).

Its equation is

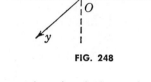

(9)
$$\frac{x^2}{a^2} - \frac{y^2}{b^2} = z.$$

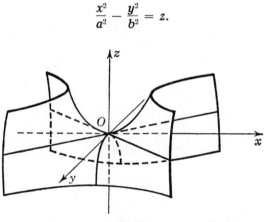

FIG. 249

The trace of this surface in the xy-plane is

$$\begin{cases} \dfrac{x^2}{a^2} - \dfrac{y^2}{b^2} = 0, \\ z = 0, \end{cases}$$

which consists of two straight lines through the origin since the first of the two simultaneous equations can be factored. All plane sections parallel to the xy-plane and above it are hyperbolas whose transverse axes are parallel to the x-axis.   All plane sections parallel to and below the xy-plane are hyperbolas whose transverse axes are parallel to the y-axis.   The trace of the hyperbolic paraboloid in the yz-plane is a parabola opening downward, as are all plane sections parallel to the yz-plane.   The trace in the zx-plane is a parabola opening upward and so are all plane sections of the surface parallel to the zx-plane.

Singular or degenerate quadric surfaces may occur when one or more of the coefficients in equations (1) or (2) are zero.   The most important are the **quadric cone** and the **quadric cylinders.**

Quadric Cone (Fig. 250).

Its equation can be written

(10)
$$\frac{x^2}{a^2} + \frac{y^2}{b^2} - \frac{z^2}{c^2} = 0.$$

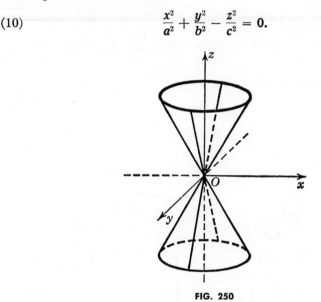

FIG. 250

Its trace in the xy-plane is a single point—the origin.   All plane sections parallel to the xy-plane are ellipses which get larger as they recede from the origin.   The trace in the yz-plane is a pair of intersecting lines through the origin.   All plane sections parallel to the yz-plane are hyperbolas.   The trace in the zx-plane is also a pair of intersecting lines through the origin and plane sections parallel to the zx-plane are hyperbolas.

Quadric Cylinders

The equations

$$\frac{x^2}{a^2} \pm \frac{y^2}{b^2} = 1$$

represent an elliptic cylinder and a hyperbolic cylinder (Fig. 238) perpendicular to the xy-plane (by 15.3.2).   The equation $y^2 = kx$ has for its locus a parabolic cylinder perpendicular to the xy-plane.

15.7 PROCEDURE FOR SKETCHING A SURFACE

It may be helpful to outline a systematic procedure for sketching a surface when its equation is known.

1. If the equation is of the first degree, the surface is a plane.   When the plane does not go through the origin, that is, when its equation has a constant term, find its points of intersection with the coordinate axes and connect them by straight lines.   When the plane does go through the origin, as shown by the absence of any constant term in the equation, find two traces of the plane and draw a triangular portion of the plane.

2. If the equation is of the second degree, the locus, if any, is a quadric surface.   If the second degree equation is similar to one of those discussed in 15.6, the quadric is in standard position and is readily sketched from its traces.   Otherwise, proceed as follows.

3. If the equation lacks one of the variables, its locus is a cylinder perpendicular to a coordinate plane (15.3).

4. Test the given equation for symmetry with respect to the coordinate planes (15.5).

5. Find and draw its traces (15.5).

6. If further information is necessary, draw a series of plane sections of the surface parallel to a coordinate plane (15.5).

EXERCISES

1. By inspection of the equations in Exercises 1 to 8, Section 15.5, name their loci.

2. By inspection of the equations in Exercises 9 to 15, Section 15.5, name their loci.

In Exercises 3 to 14, name and sketch the quadric surfaces whose equations are given.

3. $4x^2 + 36y^2 + 9z^2 - 1 = 0.$ **4.** $100x^2 + 225y^2 - 36z^2 = 0.$

5. $4x^2 - y^2 + 4z^2 - 4 = 0.$ **6.** $16x^2 - 25y^2 - 400z = 0.$

7. $144x^2 + 16y^2 - 9z^2 - 144 = 0.$ **8.** $x^2 - z^2 - y = 0.$

9. $36x^2 + 4y^2 + 9z = 0.$ **10.** $400x^2 + 25y^2 + 16z^2 - 400 = 0.$

11. $9x^2 + 36y^2 - 4z^2 + 36 = 0.$ **12.** $4y^2 + z^2 - 8x = 0.$

13. $x^2 - 4y^2 - 4z^2 + 4 = 0.$ **14.** $225x^2 - 100y^2 - 144z^2 = 0.$

In Exercises 15 to 22, sketch the surfaces whose equations are given.

15. $x - \log_e z = 0.$ **16.** $2x + 5y - z = 0.$

17. $y = e^{-x^2}.$ **18.** $yz + x = 0.$

19. $\pm\sqrt{y^2 + z^2} = \cos x.$ **20.** $y^2 + z^2 = (x - 1)x(x + 1).$

21. $z = 2 \sin y.$ **22.** $z = \tan 2y.$

APPENDIX

APPENDIX

SQUARES, CUBES, ROOTS

n	n^2	$\sqrt{n}$	n^3	$\sqrt[3]{n}$	n	n^2	$\sqrt{n}$	n^3	$\sqrt[3]{n}$
1	1	1.000	1	1.000	51	2,601	7.141	132,651	3.708
2	4	1.414	8	1.260	52	2,704	7.211	140,608	3.732
3	9	1.732	27	1.442	53	2,809	7.280	148,877	3.756
4	16	2.000	64	1.587	54	2,916	7.348	157,464	3.780
5	25	2.236	125	1.710	55	3,025	7.416	166,375	3.803
6	36	2.449	216	1.817	56	3,136	7.483	175,616	3.826
7	49	2.646	343	1.913	57	3,249	7.550	185,193	3.848
8	64	2.828	512	2.000	58	3,364	7.616	195,112	3.871
9	81	3.000	729	2.080	59	3,481	7.681	205,379	3.893
10	100	3.162	1,000	2.154	60	3,600	7.746	216,000	3.915
11	121	3.317	1,331	2.224	61	3,721	7.810	226,981	3.936
12	144	3.464	1,728	2.289	62	3,844	7.874	238,328	3.958
13	169	3.606	2,197	2.351	63	3,969	7.937	250,047	3.979
14	196	3.742	2,744	2.410	64	4,096	8.000	262,144	4.000
15	225	3.873	3,375	2.466	65	4,225	8.062	274,625	4.021
16	256	4.000	4,096	2.520	66	4,356	8.124	287,496	4.041
17	289	4.123	4,913	2.571	67	4,489	8.185	300,763	4.062
18	324	4.243	5,832	2.621	68	4,624	8.246	314,432	4.082
19	361	4.359	6,859	2.668	69	4,761	8.307	328,509	4.102
20	400	4.472	8,000	2.714	70	4,900	8.367	343,000	4.121
21	441	4.583	9,261	2.759	71	5,041	8.426	357,911	4.141
22	484	4.690	10,648	2.802	72	5,184	8.485	373,248	4.160
23	529	4.796	12,167	2.844	73	5,329	8.544	389,017	4.179
24	576	4.899	13,824	2.884	74	5,476	8.602	405,224	4.198
25	625	5.000	15,625	2.924	75	5,625	8.660	421,875	4.217
26	676	5.099	17,576	2.962	76	5,776	8.718	438,976	4.236
27	729	5.196	19,683	3.000	77	5,929	8.775	456,533	4.254
28	784	5.291	21,952	3.037	78	6,084	8.832	474,552	4.273
29	841	5.385	24,389	3.072	79	6,241	8.888	493,039	4.291
30	900	5.477	27,000	3.107	80	6,400	8.944	512,000	4.309
31	961	5.568	29,791	3.141	81	6,561	9.000	531,441	4.327
32	1,024	5.657	32,768	3.175	82	6,724	9.055	551,368	4.344
33	1,089	5.745	35,937	3.208	83	6,889	9.110	571,787	4.362
34	1,156	5.831	39,304	3.240	84	7,056	9.165	592,704	4.380
35	1,225	5.916	42,875	3.271	85	7,225	9.220	614,125	4.397
36	1,296	6.000	46,656	3.302	86	7,396	9.274	636,056	4.414
37	1,369	6.083	50,653	3.332	87	7,569	9.327	658,503	4.431
38	1,444	6.164	54,872	3.362	88	7,744	9.381	681,472	4.448
39	1,521	6.245	59,319	3.391	89	7,921	9.434	704,969	4.465
40	1,600	6.325	64,000	3.420	90	8,100	9.487	729,000	4.481
41	1,681	6.403	68,921	3.448	91	8,281	9.539	753,571	4.498
42	1,764	6.481	74,088	3.476	92	8,464	9.592	778,688	4.514
43	1,849	6.557	79,507	3.503	93	8,649	9.643	804,357	4.531
44	1,936	6.633	85,184	3.530	94	8,836	9.695	830,584	4.547
45	2,025	6.708	91,125	3.557	95	9,025	9.747	857,375	4.563
46	2,116	6.782	97,336	3.583	96	9,216	9.798	884,736	4.579
47	2,209	6.856	103,823	3.609	97	9,409	9.849	912,673	4.595
48	2,304	6.928	110,592	3.634	98	9,604	9.899	941,192	4.610
49	2,401	7.000	117,649	3.659	99	9,801	9.950	970,299	4.626
50	2,500	7.071	125,000	3.684	100	10,000	10.000	1,000,000	4.642
n	n^2	$\sqrt{n}$	n^3	$\sqrt[3]{n}$	n	n^2	$\sqrt{n}$	n^3	$\sqrt[3]{n}$

COMMON LOGARITHMS

n	0	1	2	3	4	5	6	7	8	9
10	0000	0043	0086	0128	0170	0212	0253	0294	0334	0374
11	0414	0453	0492	0531	0569	0607	0645	0682	0719	0755
12	0792	0828	0864	0899	0934	0969	1004	1038	1072	1106
13	1139	1173	1206	1239	1271	1303	1335	1367	1399	1430
14	1461	1492	1523	1553	1584	1614	1644	1673	1703	1732
15	1761	1790	1818	1847	1875	1903	1931	1959	1987	2014
16	2041	2068	2095	2122	2148	2175	2201	2227	2253	2279
17	2304	2330	2355	2380	2405	2430	2455	2480	2504	2529
18	2553	2577	2601	2625	2648	2672	2695	2718	2742	2765
19	2788	2810	2833	2856	2878	2900	2923	2945	2967	2989
20	3010	3032	3054	3075	3096	3118	3139	3160	3181	3201
21	3222	3243	3263	3284	3304	3324	3345	3365	3385	3404
22	3424	3444	3464	3483	3502	3522	3541	3560	3579	3598
23	3617	3636	3655	3674	3692	3711	3729	3747	3766	3784
24	3802	3820	3838	3856	3874	3892	3909	3927	3945	3962
25	3979	3997	4014	4031	4048	4065	4082	4099	4116	4133
26	4150	4166	4183	4200	4216	4232	4249	4265	4281	4298
27	4314	4330	4346	4362	4378	4393	4409	4425	4440	4456
28	4472	4487	4502	4518	4533	4548	4564	4579	4594	4609
29	4624	4639	4654	4669	4683	4698	4713	4728	4742	4757
30	4771	4786	4800	4814	4829	4843	4857	4871	4886	4900
31	4914	4928	4942	4955	4969	4983	4997	5011	5024	5038
32	5051	5065	5079	5092	5105	5119	5132	5145	5159	5172
33	5185	5198	5211	5224	5237	5250	5263	5276	5289	5302
34	5315	5328	5340	5353	5366	5378	5391	5403	5416	5428
35	5441	5453	5465	5478	5490	5502	5514	5527	5539	5551
36	5563	5575	5587	5599	5611	5623	5635	5647	5658	5670
37	5682	5694	5705	5717	5729	5740	5752	5763	5775	5786
38	5798	5809	5821	5832	5843	5855	5866	5877	5888	5899
39	5911	5922	5933	5944	5955	5966	5977	5988	5999	6010
40	6021	6031	6042	6053	6064	6075	6085	6096	6107	6117
41	6128	6138	6149	6160	6170	7180	6191	6201	6212	6222
42	6232	6243	6253	6263	6274	6284	6294	6304	6314	6325
43	6335	6345	6355	6365	6375	6385	6395	6405	6415	6425
44	6435	6444	6454	6464	6474	6484	6493	6503	6513	6522
45	6532	6542	6551	6561	6571	6580	6590	6599	6609	6618
46	6628	6637	6646	6656	6665	6675	6684	6693	6702	6712
47	6721	6730	6739	6749	6758	6767	6776	6785	6794	6803
48	6812	6821	6830	6839	6848	6857	6866	6875	6884	6893
49	6902	6911	6920	6928	6937	6946	6955	6964	6972	6981
50	6990	6998	7007	7016	7024	7033	7042	7050	7059	7067
51	7076	7084	7093	7101	7110	7118	7126	7135	7143	7152
52	7160	7168	7177	7185	7193	7202	7210	7218	7226	7235
53	7243	7251	7259	7267	7275	7284	7292	7300	7308	7316
54	7324	7332	7340	7348	7356	7364	7372	7380	7388	7396
n	0	1	2	3	4	5	6	7	8	9

Prop. Parts

	43	42	41	40
1	4.3	4.2	4.1	4.0
2	8.6	8.4	8.2	8.0
3	12.9	12.6	12.3	12.0
4	17.2	16.8	16.4	16.0
5	21.5	21.0	20.5	20.0
6	25.8	25.2	24.6	24.0
7	30.1	29.4	28.7	28.0
8	34.4	33.6	32.8	32.0
9	38.7	37.8	36.9	36.0

	39	38	37	36
1	3.9	3.8	3.7	3.6
2	7.8	7.6	7.4	7.2
3	11.7	11.4	11.1	10.8
4	15.6	15.2	14.8	14.4
5	19.5	19.0	18.5	18.0
6	23.4	22.8	22.2	21.6
7	27.3	26.6	25.9	25.2
8	31.2	30.4	29.6	28.8
9	35.1	34.2	33.3	32.4

	35	34	33	32
1	3.5	3.4	3.3	3.2
2	7.0	6.8	6.6	6.4
3	10.5	10.2	9.9	9.6
4	14.0	13.6	13.2	12.8
5	17.5	17.0	16.5	16.0
6	21.0	20.4	19.8	19.2
7	24.5	23.8	23.1	22.4
8	28.0	27.2	26.4	25.6
9	31.5	30.6	29.7	28.8

	31	30	29	28
1	3.1	3.0	2.9	2.8
2	6.2	6.0	5.8	5.6
3	9.3	9.0	8.7	8.4
4	12.4	12.0	11.6	11.2
5	15.5	15.0	14.5	14.0
6	18.6	18.0	17.4	16.8
7	21.7	21.0	20.3	19.6
8	24.8	24.0	23.2	22.4
9	27.9	27.0	26.1	25.2

	27	26	25	24
1	2.7	2.6	2.5	2.4
2	5.4	5.2	5.0	4.8
3	8.1	7.8	7.5	7.2
4	10.8	10.4	10.0	9.6
5	13.5	13.0	12.5	12.0
6	16.2	15.6	15.0	14.4
7	18.9	18.2	17.5	16.8
8	21.6	20.8	20.0	19.2
9	24.3	23.4	22.5	21.6

COMMON LOGARITHMS (Continued)

n	0	1	2	3	4	5	6	7	8	9
55	7404	7412	7419	7427	7435	7443	7451	7459	7466	7474
56	7482	7490	7497	7505	7513	7520	7528	7536	7543	7551
57	7559	7566	7574	7582	7589	7597	7604	7612	7619	7627
58	7634	7642	7649	7657	7664	7672	7679	7686	7694	7701
59	7709	7716	7723	7731	7738	7745	7752	7760	7767	7774
60	7782	7789	7796	7803	7810	7818	7825	7832	7839	7846
61	7853	7860	7868	7875	7882	7889	7896	7903	7910	7917
62	7924	7931	7938	7945	7952	7959	7966	7973	7980	7987
63	7993	8000	8007	8014	8021	8028	8035	8041	8048	8055
64	8062	8069	8075	8082	8089	8096	8102	8109	8116	8122
65	8129	8136	8142	8149	8156	8162	8169	8176	8182	8189
66	8195	8202	8209	8215	8222	8228	8235	8241	8248	8254
67	8261	8267	8274	8280	8287	8293	8299	8306	8312	8319
68	8325	8331	8338	8344	8351	8357	8363	8370	8376	8382
69	8388	8395	8401	8407	8414	8420	8426	8432	8439	8445
70	8451	8457	8463	8470	8476	8482	8488	8494	8500	8506
71	8513	8519	8525	8531	8537	8543	8549	8555	8561	8567
72	8573	8579	8585	8591	8597	8603	8609	8615	8621	8627
73	8633	8639	8645	8651	8657	8663	8669	8675	8681	8686
74	8692	8698	8704	8710	8716	8722	8727	8733	8739	8745
75	8751	8756	8762	8768	8774	8779	8785	8791	8797	8802
76	8808	8814	8820	8825	8831	8837	8842	8848	8854	8859
77	8865	8871	8876	8882	8887	8893	8899	8904	8910	8915
78	8921	8927	8932	8938	8943	8949	8954	8960	8965	8971
79	8976	8982	8987	8993	8998	9004	9009	9015	9020	9025
80	9031	9036	9042	9047	9053	9058	9063	9069	9074	9079
81	9085	9090	9096	9101	9106	9112	9117	9122	9128	9133
82	9138	9143	9149	9154	9159	9165	9170	9175	9180	9186
83	9191	9196	9201	9206	9212	9217	9222	9227	9232	9238
84	9243	9248	9253	9258	9263	9269	9274	9279	9284	9289
85	9294	9299	9304	9309	9315	9320	9325	9330	9335	9340
86	9345	9350	9355	9360	9365	9370	9375	9380	9385	9390
87	9395	9400	9405	9410	9415	9420	9425	9430	9435	9440
88	9445	9450	9455	9460	9465	9469	9474	9479	9484	9489
89	9494	9499	9504	9509	9513	9518	9523	9528	9533	9538
90	9542	9547	9552	9557	9562	9566	9571	9576	9581	9586
91	9590	9595	9600	9605	9609	9614	9619	9624	9628	9633
92	9638	9643	9647	9652	9657	9661	9666	9671	9675	9680
93	9685	9689	9694	9699	9703	9708	9713	9717	9722	9727
94	9731	9736	9741	9745	9750	9754	9759	9763	9768	9773
95	9777	9782	9786	9791	9795	9800	9805	9809	9814	9818
96	9823	9827	9832	9836	9841	9845	9850	9854	9859	9863
97	9868	9872	9877	9881	9886	9890	9894	9899	9903	9908
98	9912	9917	9921	9926	9930	9934	9939	9943	9948	9952
99	9956	9961	9965	9969	9974	9978	9983	9987	9991	9996

Prop. Parts

	23	22	21	20
1	2.3	2.2	2.1	2.0
2	4.6	4.4	4.2	4.0
3	6.9	6.6	6.3	6.0
4	9.2	8.8	8.4	8.0
5	11.5	11.0	10.5	10.0
6	13.8	13.2	12.6	12.0
7	16.1	15.4	14.7	14.0
8	18.4	17.6	16.8	16.0
9	20.7	19.8	18.9	18.0

	19	18	17	16
1	1.9	1.8	1.7	1.6
2	3.8	3.6	3.4	3.2
3	5.7	5.4	5.1	4.8
4	7.6	7.2	6.8	6.4
5	9.5	9.0	8.5	8.0
6	11.4	10.8	10.2	9.6
7	13.3	12.6	11.9	11.2
8	15.2	14.4	13.6	12.8
9	17.1	16.2	15.3	14.4

	15	14	13	12
1	1.5	1.4	1.3	1.2
2	3.0	2.8	2.6	2.4
3	4.5	4.2	3.9	3.6
4	6.0	5.6	5.2	4.8
5	7.5	7.0	6.5	6.0
6	9.0	8.4	7.8	7.2
7	10.5	9.8	9.1	8.4
8	12.0	11.2	10.4	9.6
9	13.5	12.6	11.7	10.8

	11	10	9	8
1	1.1	1.0	0.9	0.8
2	2.2	2.0	1.8	1.6
3	3.3	3.0	2.7	2.4
4	4.4	4.0	3.6	3.2
5	5.5	5.0	4.5	4.0
6	6.6	6.0	5.4	4.8
7	7.7	7.0	6.3	5.6
8	8.8	8.0	7.2	6.4
9	9.9	9.0	8.1	7.2

	7	6	5	4
1	0.7	0.6	0.5	0.4
2	1.4	1.2	1.0	0.8
3	2.1	1.8	1.5	1.2
4	2.8	2.4	2.0	1.6
5	3.5	3.0	2.5	2.0
6	4.2	3.6	3.0	2.4
7	4.9	4.2	3.5	2.8
8	5.6	4.8	4.0	3.2
9	6.3	5.4	4.5	3.6

TRIGONOMETRIC FUNCTIONS

Angle	Sin	Tan	Cot	Cos	
0.0°	.0000	.0000	——	1.0000	90.0°
0.5°	.0087	.0087	114.59	1.0000	89.5°
1.0°	.0175	.0175	57.290	.9998	89.0°
1.5°	.0262	.0262	38.188	.9997	88.5°
2.0°	.0349	.0349	28.636	.9994	88.0°
2.5°	.0436	.0437	22.904	.9990	87.5°
3.0°	.0523	.0524	19.081	.9986	87.0°
3.5°	.0610	.0612	16.350	.9981	86.5°
4.0°	.0698	.0699	14.301	.9976	86.0°
4.5°	.0785	.0787	12.706	.9969	85.5°
5.0°	.0872	.0875	11.430	.9962	85.0°
5.5°	.0958	.0963	10.385	.9954	84.5°
6.0°	.1045	.1051	9.5144	.9945	84.0°
6.5°	.1132	.1139	8.7769	.9936	83.5°
7.0°	.1219	.1228	8.1443	.9925	83.0°
7.5°	.1305	.1317	7.5958	.9914	82.5°
8.0°	.1392	.1405	7.1154	.9903	82.0°
8.5°	.1478	.1495	6.6912	.9890	81.5°
9.0°	.1564	.1584	6.3138	.9877	81.0°
9.5°	.1650	.1673	5.9758	.9863	80.5°
10.0°	.1736	.1763	5.6713	.9848	80.0°
10.5°	.1822	.1853	5.3955	.9833	79.5°
11.0°	.1908	.1944	5.1446	.9816	79.0°
11.5°	.1994	.2035	4.9152	.9799	78.5°
12.0°	.2079	.2126	4.7046	.9781	78.0°
12.5°	.2164	.2217	4.5107	.9763	77.5°
13.0°	.2250	.2309	4.3315	.9744	77.0°
13.5°	.2334	.2401	4.1653	.9724	76.5°
14.0°	.2419	.2493	4.0108	.9703	76.0°
14.5°	.2504	.2586	3.8667	.9681	75.5°
15.0°	.2588	.2679	3.7321	.9659	75.0°
15.5°	.2672	.2773	3.6059	.9636	74.5°
16.0°	.2756	.2867	3.4874	.9613	74.0°
16.5°	.2840	.2962	3.3759	.9588	73.5°
17.0°	.2924	.3057	3.2709	.9563	73.0°
17.5°	.3007	.3153	3.1716	.9537	72.5°
18.0°	.3090	.3249	3.0777	.9511	72.0°
18.5°	.3173	.3346	2.9887	.9483	71.5°
19.0°	.3256	.3443	2.9042	.9455	71.0°
19.5°	.3338	.3541	2.8239	.9426	70.5°
20.0°	.3420	.3640	2.7475	.9397	70.0°
20.5°	.3502	.3739	2.6746	.9367	69.5°
21.0°	.3584	.3839	2.6051	.9336	69.0°
21.5°	.3665	.3939	2.5386	.9304	68.5°
22.0°	.3746	.4040	2.4751	.9272	68.0°
22.5°	.3827	.4142	2.4142	.9239	67.5°
	Cos	Cot	Tan	Sin	Angle

Angle	Sin	Tan	Cot	Cos	
22.5°	.3827	.4142	2.4142	.9239	67.5°
23.0°	.3907	.4245	2.3559	.9205	67.0°
23.5°	.3987	.4348	2.2998	.9171	66.5°
24.0°	.4067	.4452	2.2460	.9135	66.0°
24.5°	.4147	.4557	2.1943	.9100	65.5°
25.0°	.4226	.4663	2.1445	.9063	65.0°
25.5°	.4305	.4770	2.0965	.9026	64.5°
26.0°	.4384	.4877	2.0503	.8988	64.0°
26.5°	.4462	.4986	2.0057	.8949	63.5°
27.0°	.4540	.5095	1.9626	.8910	63.0°
27.5°	.4617	.5206	1.9210	.8870	62.5°
28.0°	.4695	.5317	1.8807	.8829	62.0°
28.5°	.4772	.5430	1.8418	.8788	61.5°
29.0°	.4848	.5543	1.8040	.8746	61.0°
29.5°	.4924	.5658	1.7675	.8704	60.5°
30.0°	.5000	.5774	1.7321	.8660	60.0°
30.5°	.5075	.5890	1.6977	.8616	59.5°
31.0°	.5150	.6009	1.6643	.8572	59.0°
31.5°	.5225	.6128	1.6319	.8526	58.5°
32.0°	.5299	.6249	1.6003	.8480	58.0°
32.5°	.5373	.6371	1.5697	.8434	57.5°
33.0°	.5446	.6494	1.5399	.8387	57.0°
33.5°	.5519	.6619	1.5108	.8339	56.5°
34.0°	.5592	.6745	1.4826	.8290	56.0°
34.5°	.5664	.6873	1.4550	.8241	55.5°
35.0°	.5736	.7002	1.4281	.8192	55.0°
35.5°	.5807	.7133	1.4019	.8141	54.5°
36.0°	.5878	.7265	1.3764	.8090	54.0°
36.5°	.5948	.7400	1.3514	.8039	53.5°
37.0°	.6018	.7536	1.3270	.7986	53.0°
37.5°	.6088	.7673	1.3032	.7934	52.5°
38.0°	.6157	.7813	1.2799	.7880	52.0°
38.5°	.6225	.7954	1.2572	.7826	51.5°
39.0°	.6293	.8098	1.2349	.7771	51.0°
39.5°	.6361	.8243	1.2131	.7716	50.5°
40.0°	.6428	.8391	1.1918	.7660	50.0°
40.5°	.6494	.8541	1.1708	.7604	49.5°
41.0°	.6561	.8693	1.1504	.7547	49.0°
41.5°	.6626	.8847	1.1303	.7490	48.5°
42.0°	.6691	.9004	1.1106	.7431	48.0°
42.5°	.6756	.9163	1.0913	.7373	47.5°
43.0°	.6820	.9325	1.0724	.7314	47.0°
43.5°	.6884	.9490	1.0538	.7254	46.5°
44.0°	.6947	.9657	1.0355	.7193	46.0°
44.5°	.7009	.9827	1.0176	.7133	45.5°
45.0°	.7071	1.0000	1.0000	.7071	45.0°
	Cos	Cot	Tan	Sin	Angle

References to Algebra, Geometry, and Trigonometry

~~~~~~

ALGEBRA

1. Quadratic formula. The roots of the equation

$$ax^2 + bx + c = 0 \qquad (a \neq 0)$$

are

$$x = \frac{-b \pm \sqrt{b^2 - 4ac}}{2a}.$$

2. Logarithm. The logarithm to the base b of any positive number N is the exponent of the power to which b must be raised to equal N. The base, b, can be any positive number except 1. In symbols, $x = \log_b N$ if and only if $N = b^x$.

GEOMETRY

3. Theorem. If two parallel lines are cut by a transversal, the exterior-interior angles are equal.

4. Theorem. If two lines in the same plane are cut by a transversal so that the exterior-interior angles are equal, the two lines are parallel.

5. Theorem. If a line is drawn through the midpoint of one side of a triangle, parallel to another side, it bisects the third side.

6. Pythagorean theorem. The square on the hypotenuse of a right triangle is equal to the sum of the squares on the other two sides.

7. Converse of the Pythagorean theorem. If the square on one side of a triangle is equal to the sum of the squares on the other two sides, the triangle is a right triangle.

TRIGONOMETRY

8. Definition of the trigonometric functions. Let P be any point, other than the vertex, on the terminal side of an angle θ. Denote the vertex by R (Fig. 251). Drop a perpendicular from P to the initial side (or its extension) and call the foot of the perpendicular Q. Then

$$\sin \theta = \frac{QP}{|RP|}, \quad \cos \theta = \frac{RQ}{|RP|}, \quad \tan \theta = \frac{QP}{RQ}.$$

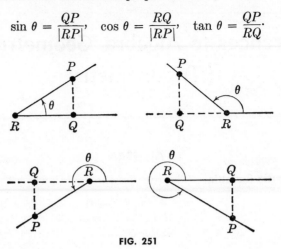

FIG. 251

9. Reduction formulas.

$$\sin (-\theta) = -\sin \theta.$$
$$\cos (-\theta) = \cos \theta.$$
$$\sin (90° + \theta) = \cos \theta.$$
$$\tan (90° + \theta) = -\cot \theta.$$
$$\tan (180° - \theta) = -\tan \theta.$$

10. Theorem. If $\tan \theta = -\cot \varphi$, then $\varphi = \theta \pm \frac{n\pi}{2}$, where n is an odd positive integer.

11. Identities.

$$\sin^2 \theta + \cos^2 \theta = 1.$$
$$1 + \tan^2 \theta = \sec^2 \theta.$$
$$1 + \cot^2 \theta = \csc^2 \theta.$$

12. Addition formulas.

$$\sin (\theta + \varphi) = \sin \theta \cos \varphi + \cos \theta \sin \varphi.$$
$$\cos (\theta + \varphi) = \cos \theta \cos \varphi - \sin \theta \sin \varphi.$$
$$\tan (\theta - \varphi) = \frac{\tan \theta - \tan \varphi}{1 + \tan \theta \tan \varphi}.$$

13. Double-angle formulas.

$$\sin 2\theta = 2 \sin \theta \cos \theta.$$

$$\cos 2\theta = \cos^2 \theta - \sin^2 \theta.$$

14. Half-angle formulas.

$$\sin \tfrac{1}{2}\theta = \pm\sqrt{\frac{1 - \cos \theta}{2}}.$$

$$\cos \tfrac{1}{2}\theta = \pm\sqrt{\frac{1 + \cos \theta}{2}}.$$

15. Law of cosines. If A, B, and C are the interior angles of a triangle and a, b, and c are the sides respectively opposite to these angles, then

$$a^2 = b^2 + c^2 - 2bc \cos A.$$

Answers to Odd-Numbered Exercises

~~~~~~

Page 4

1. $\overline{AB} = 13$ has no meaning because $\overline{AB}$ denotes a line segment itself, not its length. Similarly, $\overline{BA} = -13$ has no meaning.

Page 6

3. No. $\sqrt{-4}$ is an imaginary number.
5. On the y-axis.
7. (a) The x-coordinate is zero;   (b) the y-coordinate is 5;   (c) the x-coordinate is the negative of the y-coordinate.
9. They have equal x-coordinates.   **11.** $AB = 4$; $BA = -4$.
13. $AB = 10$; $|AB| = 10$.   **15.** $|AB| = 3$; $|BC| = 4$; $|AC| = 5$.

Page 11

1. On a straight line parallel to the y-axis and two units to the right of it.
3. $AB = -6$; $BA = 6$.   **5.** $|AC| = 12$; $|CB| = 5$; $|AB| = 13$.
7. 5.

Page 13

1. (a) $2\sqrt{10}$;   (b) $\sqrt{37}$;   (c) $3\sqrt{10}$;   (d) $\sqrt{82}$.
3. $\sqrt{29} + \sqrt{61} + \sqrt{10}$.
5. Undirected distance between $(1, 1)$ and $(5, 4)$ is 5, and the undirected distance between $(1, 1)$ and $(-2, 5)$ is also 5.
7. Length of each side is $\sqrt{17}$.
9. Call the given points A, B, C, D, respectively.   Then $|AB| = \sqrt{58}$, $|AD| = \sqrt{232}$, and $|DB| = \sqrt{290}$.   By the Pythagorean theorem, the angle at A is a right angle. Similarly for the other three angles.
11. Each of the three points is 5 units distant from $(-2, 3)$.
13. Call the three given points A, B, C, respectively.   Then $|AB| = \sqrt{13}$, $|BC| = 3\sqrt{13}$, and $|AC| = 4\sqrt{13}$.   Therefore $|AB| + |BC| = |AC|$.
15. $\sqrt{(x - 3)^2 + (y - 2)^2} = 6$; a circle.
17. None.   Because the formula for P_1Q is valid, no matter how P_1 and Q are situated relative to the coordinate axes if only $\overline{P_1Q}$ is horizontal.   Similarly for QP_2, since $\overline{QP_2}$ is vertical.   The Pythagorean theorem is independent of coordinate systems.

Page 19

3. (a) 2;   (b) $-\frac{3}{5}$;   (c) $-\frac{6}{5}$;   (d) 1.
5. (a) $63°$;   (b) $149°$;   (c) $130°$;   (d) $45°$.
7. $-\frac{7}{5}, \frac{1}{12}, \frac{8}{7}$.   **9.** They do not.
11. $(y - 3)/(x - 1) = 2$; a straight line.
13. $(11, 0)$.   **15.** -4.

Page 22

1. $\frac{3}{4}$.

3. Call the given points A, B, C, D, respectively.   Slope of $\overline{AB} = -1$; slope of $\overline{BC} = \frac{3}{4}$; slope of $\overline{CD} = -\frac{5}{3}$; slope of $\overline{DA} = \frac{4}{5}$; slope of $\overline{AC} = -\frac{1}{8}$; slope of $\overline{BD} = 8$. $\overline{AC}$ and $\overline{BD}$ are perpendicular to each other.

5. Each of the interior base angles of the triangle is equal to arc tan 2.

7. One pair of sides has slope $\frac{5}{3}$ and other pair of sides has slope $\frac{2}{3}$.

Page 24

1. (a) $\frac{1}{8}$;   (b) $-\frac{17}{11}$;   (c) -12.5;   (d) $\frac{14}{23}$.

3. (a) $26°$;   (b) $117°$;   (c) $89°$;   (d) $20°$.

5. $87°, 42°, 52°$.   **7.** 1.1.

9. The tangent of the angle at $(4, 11)$ is 7, and so is the tangent of the angle at $(6, 9)$.

11. $-\frac{1}{3}$ or 3.   **13.** $3 + \sqrt{10}$.

Page 27

1. (a) $(3, 3)$;   (b) $(3, -1)$;   (c) $(-\frac{7}{2}, -\frac{1}{2})$;   (d) $(\frac{3}{2}, -6)$.

3. $(6, -5)$.   **5.** $2\sqrt{5}$.

7. Slopes of sides of triangle are $-3, 1, -\frac{1}{7}$.   Slopes of lines joining midpoints are $-3, 1, -\frac{1}{7}$.

Page 30

15. $(-4, -2)$.   **17.** $(3, \pm 4)$.

Page 33

1. They represent the same straight line.

3. The locus of the first equation consists of all points of the line $y = x$ except the origin.

5. The locus of the second equation contains the locus of the first equation and also the line $y = -2x$.

7. The locus of the first equation is the upper half of the parabola $y^2 = 4x$.

9. 2.   **11.** 4.   **13.** 6.

Page 38

1. Symmetric with respect to both coordinate axes. x-intercepts: ± 8. y-intercepts: ± 8.

3. Symmetric with respect to the x-axis. x-intercepts: $2, -6$. y-intercepts: $\pm 2\sqrt{3}$.

5. Symmetric with respect to both coordinate axes. x-intercepts: ± 2. y-intercepts: none.

7. Not symmetric with respect to either coordinate axis.   No intercepts.

9. Symmetric with respect to the x-axis. x-intercept: 0. y-intercept: 0.

11. Symmetric with respect to the x-axis. x-intercept: 0. y-intercept: 0.

13. Symmetric with respect to both coordinate axes. x-intercepts: ± 3. y-intercepts: ± 3.

15. Not symmetric with respect to either coordinate axis. x-intercepts: 1, 4. y-intercept: 4.

17. Symmetric with respect to both coordinate axes. x-intercepts: 0, ± 4.   The y-axis is part of the locus.

Page 41

1. $x^2 + y^2 = 9$.
5. $x = 6$.   A vertical line.
9. $x + y - 4 = 0$.   A straight line.
13. $y^2 = 8x$.
17. $16x^2 + 15y^2 - 160y + 400 = 0$.
21. $x = 8$ and $y = 0$.   (Two lines.)

3. $x^2 + y^2 - 4y = 0$.
7. $x = k$.
11. $y - b = m(x - a)$.
15. $y^2 = 4kx$.
19. $x^2 - 8y^2 - 8y + 16 = 0$.

Page 46

1. $4x - y - 13 = 0$.
5. $3x + y - 1 = 0$.
9. $7x + 2y - 14 = 0$.
13. $4x - y - 8 = 0$.
17. $(-2, -3)$.

3. $x + 5 = 0$.
7. $x - 3y - 5 = 0$.
11. $7x + 3y = 0$.
15. $6x - 8y - 7 = 0$.

Page 48

1. Slope $\frac{1}{3}$.
4. Slope -2.
7. No slope.

2. Slope $-\frac{1}{2}$.
5. No slope.
8. Slope 0.

3. Slope $\frac{3}{5}$.
6. Slope 0.

Page 50

1. $3x - 4y = 0$.
7. $x - 5y - 17 = 0$.

3. $7x - 4y + 28 = 0$.
9. $5x + y - 7 = 0$.

5. $2x - 3y - 4 = 0$.

Page 55

1. -4.
9. $17/\sqrt{52}$.
15. $6x - 9y - 16 = 0$.

3. 6.
11. $4x + 8y - 7 = 0$.

5. $\frac{39}{2}$.
13. $77x + 21y + 29 = 0$.
17. $x^2 + y^2 - 2xy + 4x + 16y + 14 = 0$.

Page 60

1. Slope 2.
5. x-intercept is -2.
9. $2x - 6y + k = 0$.
13. $31x + 39y - 23 = 0$.
17. $42x - 63y - 116 = 0$.

3. Through $(-5, 2)$.
7. Directed distance from origin is 4.
11. $x - 3y + k = 0$.
15. $295x - 708y + 973 = 0$.
19. $290x - 71y - 284 = 0$.

Page 64

1. $(x - 5)^2 + (y - 2)^2 = 9$; $x^2 + y^2 - 10x - 4y + 20 = 0$.
3. $x^2 + (y + 8)^2 = 64$; $x^2 + y^2 + 16y = 0$.
5. $(x - 11)^2 + y^2 = 25$; $x^2 + y^2 - 22x + 96 = 0$.
7. $(x - 12)^2 + (y + 5)^2 = 169$; $x^2 + y^2 - 24x + 10y = 0$.
9. $x^2 + y^2 - 2x - 8y - 41 = 0$.
13. $5x^2 + 5y^2 - 40x - 1 = 0$.
17. $x^2 + y^2 - 6x + 2y - 15 = 0$.

11. $x^2 + y^2 - 6x - 4y + 4 = 0$.
15. $x^2 + y^2 - 10x = 0$.
19. $x^2 + y^2 + 4x + 2y - 164 = 0$.

Page 66

3. A circle.
7. Center: $(0, -10)$; radius $= 6$.

5. Center: $(-7, 2)$; radius $= 1$.
9. Point—circle at $(2, 6)$.

11. $x - 4y + 1 = 0$. **13.** $x^2 + y^2 + 12x + 23 = 0$.
15. $2x - y - 7 = 0$ and $2x - y + 23 = 0$.
17. $x^2 + y^2 + 8x + 2y - 72 = 0$.

Page 70

1. $x^2 + y^2 + 2x - 4y - 20 = 0$. **3.** $x^2 + y^2 + 6x + 16y - 96 = 0$.
5. $x^2 + y^2 - 8x - 2y + 4 = 0$ and $x^2 + y^2 + 2x - 4y - 8 = 0$.
7. $x^2 + y^2 + 4x + 4y + 4 = 0$ and $9x^2 + 9y^2 - 12x + 12y + 4 = 0$.
9. $4x^2 + 4y^2 - 12x - 12y + 9 = 0$. **11.** $x^2 + y^2 - 4x - 10y + 16 = 0$.
13. $x^2 + y^2 - 20x + 20y + 100 = 0$ and $x^2 + y^2 - 4x + 4y + 4 = 0$.
15. $x^2 + y^2 - 6x - 2y - 39 = 0$ and $x^2 + y^2 + 134x + 110y + 3345 = 0$.

Page 74

3. (a) $(6, 4)$ and $(5, 5)$; (b) none. **5.** $2x^2 + 2y^2 - 19y + 15 = 0$.
7. $x^2 + y^2 - 39x - 22y + 60 = 0$. **9.** $x^2 + y^2 - 3x - 4y + 6 = 0$.

Page 78

1. $(5, -6)$, $(6, 2)$, $(2, 3)$, $(9, 6)$, $(3, -4)$, $(4, 7)$, $(-12, -3)$, $(8, -9)$.
3. $(-10, 4)$. **5.** $x' = 0$.
7. $2x' - 5y' = 0$. **9.** $4x' + y' = 0$.
11. $x'^2 + y'^2 = 4$. **13.** $y'^2 = 4x'$.
15. $4x'^2 + 9y'^2 = 36$.

Page 81

1. $x'^2 + y'^2 = 1$. **3.** $4x'^2 + 9y'^2 = 36$.
5. $5x'^2 = 6y'$. **7.** $y'^2 = 10x'$.
9. $16x'^2 + 5y'^2 = 80$. **11.** $x'y' = 4$.
13. $8x'^3 - y' = 0$.

Page 86

1. Parabola. **3.** Hyperbola.

Page 89

1. $(\frac{1}{2}, 0)$, $x = -\frac{1}{2}$. **3.** $(0, \frac{3}{2})$, $y = -\frac{3}{2}$.
5. $(\frac{5}{4}, 0)$, $x = -\frac{5}{4}$. **7.** $(-\frac{1}{3}, 0)$, $x = \frac{1}{3}$.
9. $y^2 = 12x$. **11.** $x^2 = 16y$.
13. $y^2 = -20x$. **15.** $3y^2 - 16x = 0$.
17. $3y^2 - x = 0$. **19.** $y'^2 = 8x'$.
21. $y'^2 = -2x'$. **23.** Vertex: (h, k).
25. Vertex: $(-5, 1)$. **27.** Vertex: $(7, -3)$.
29. $y^2 - 16x + 8y - 32 = 0$.
31. $9x^2 - 24xy + 16y^2 - 116x - 62y + 121 = 0$.

Page 95

1. $e = \sqrt{5}/3$; foci: $(\pm\sqrt{5}, 0)$; vertices: $(\pm3, 0)$; directrices: $x = \pm9/\sqrt{5}$; lengths of major and minor axes: 6 and 4.
3. $e = \sqrt{3}/2$; foci: $(0, \pm2\sqrt{3})$; vertices: $(0, \pm4)$; directrices: $y = \pm8\sqrt{3}$; lengths of major and minor axes: 8 and 4.
5. $e = \sqrt{3}/2$; foci: $(0, \pm3\sqrt{3})$; vertices: $(0, \pm6)$; directrices: $y = \pm4\sqrt{3}$; lengths of major and minor axes: 12 and 6.
7. $x^2/64 + y^2/48 = 1$. **9.** $x^2/9 + y^2/13 = 1$.

11. $3x^2 + 7y^2 = 75$.   **13.** $8x^2 + 5y^2 = 77$.
15. $x'^2/16 + y'^2/4 = 1$.   **17.** $25x'^2 + 36y'^2 = 900$.
19. Center: (h, k).   **21.** Center: $(3, -1)$.
23. Center: $(4, 2)$.   **25.** Center: $(7, -4)$.
27. $16x^2 - 4xy + 19y^2 - 64x - 132y + 164 = 0$.

Page 99

1. $e = \sqrt{13}/3$; foci: $(\pm\sqrt{13}, 0)$; vertices: $(\pm 3, 0)$; directrices: $x = \pm 9/\sqrt{13}$; lengths of transverse and conjugate axes are 6 and 4.
3. $e = \sqrt{5}/2$; foci: $(0, \pm 2\sqrt{5})$; vertices: $(0, \pm 4)$; directrices: $y = \pm 8/\sqrt{5}$; lengths of transverse and conjugate axes are 8 and 4.
5. $e = \sqrt{\frac{23}{5}}$; foci: $(0, \pm\sqrt{46})$; vertices: $(0, \pm\sqrt{10})$; directrices: $y = \pm\sqrt{\frac{50}{23}}$; lengths of transverse and conjugate axes are $2\sqrt{10}$ and 12.
7. $12x^2 - 4y^2 = 27$.   **9.** $y^2 - x^2 = 8$.
11. $5y^2 - 4x^2 = 45$.   **13.** $7x^2 - 9y^2 = 27$.
15. $9x'^2 - 16y'^2 = 144$.   **17.** $5y'^2 - 3x'^2 = 30$.
19. Center: (h, k).   **21.** Center: $(5, -2)$.
23. Center: $(-4, -11)$.   **25.** Center: $(0, 6)$.
27. $4x^2 - 36xy + 31y^2 + 36x - 32y - 44 = 0$.

Page 103

1. $2x \pm 5y = 0$.   **3.** $5y \pm 4x = 0$.
5. $3x + 4y + 11 = 0$ and $3x - 4y - 29 = 0$.
9. $25x^2 - 9y^2 = 900$.   **11.** $4x^2 - y^2 = 80$.
13. $9x^2 - 16y^2 = 432$.   **15.** $x^2 - 9y^2 = 36$ and $9y^2 - x^2 = 324$.

Page 106

1. $(y - 3)^2 = 8(x + 2)$; directrix: $x = -4$.
3. $(y + 3)^2 = 12(x - 4)$.   **5.** $(x + 2)^2/4 - (y + 3)^2/5 = 1$; $e = \frac{3}{2}$.
7. $(x - 3)^2/25 + (y - 6)^2/1 = 1$; foci: $(3 \pm 2\sqrt{6}, 6)$.
13. $(x - 4)^2 = 8(y - 1)$.
15. $(y + 1)^2 = 4(x - 5)$; $e = 1$; focus: $(6, -1)$; directrix: $x = 4$.
17. $(x + 2)^2 = -12(y + 5)$; $e = 1$; focus: $(-2, -8)$; directrix: $y = -2$.
19. $(x - 3)^2/25 + (y - 4)^2/9 = 1$; $e = \frac{4}{5}$; foci: $(7, 4)$ and $(-1, 4)$; directrices: $x = \frac{37}{4}$ and $x = -\frac{13}{4}$.
21. $(y - 1)^2/4 - (x - 4)^2/3 = 1$; $e = \sqrt{7}/2$; foci: $(4, 1 \pm \sqrt{7})$; directrices:
$$y = 1 \pm 4/\sqrt{7}.$$

Page 109

1. $x^2/9 + y^2/5 = 1$.   **3.** $x^2/11 + y^2/36 = 1$.
5. $220y^2 - 36x^2 = 495$.   **7.** $x^2/a^2 + y^2/a^2(1 - e^2) = 1$.
9. $3x^2 + 4y^2 - 30x - 48y + 171 = 0$.

Page 111

1. $9x^2 - 24xy + 16y^2 + 146x + 72y - 119 = 0$.
3. $x^2 - 4xy + 4y^2 - 54x + 8y + 29 = 0$.
5. $44x^2 - 4xy + 41y^2 - 78x - 66y + 54 = 0$.
7. $79x^2 + 4xy + 76y^2 + 326x - 12y + 311 = 0$.
9. $7x^2 + 18xy + 7y^2 - 26x - 18y + 1 = 0$.
11. $16x^2 + 36xy - 11y^2 + 192x - 4y - 164 = 0$.

Page 117

1. $(2\sqrt{2}, -\sqrt{2})$, $(0, 2\sqrt{2})$, $(1, 1)$, $(1, -3)$.
5. $x' - 1 = 0$.   **7.** $x'^2 + 4y'^2 - 18 = 0$.   **9.** $x'^2 - 3y'^2 - 9 = 0$.

Page 121

1. $2x'^2 + y'^2 - 1 = 0$.   **3.** $5x'^2 - 5y'^2 - 2 = 0$.
5. $3x'^2 - y'^2 - 2x' - 4y' + 6 = 0$.   **7.** $10x'^2 - 3x' + y' + 2 = 0$.
9. $14x'^2 - 11y'^2 - 3x' - y' - 9 = 0$.

Page 124

1. $y'^2 = 3x'$.   **3.** $x'^2 = -9y'$.   **5.** $9x'^2 + 20y'^2 = 180$.
7. $x'^2 = 6y'$.   **9.** $x'^2 - 2y'^2 = 2$.

Page 127

1. $5x''^2 - 2y''^2 - 10 = 0$.   **3.** $y''^2 + 3x'' = 0$.
5. $2x''^2 - 3y''^2 - 6 = 0$.   **7.** $x''^2 - 6y'' = 0$.
9. $4x''^2 + 9y''^2 - 36 = 0$.   **11.** $3x''^2 + 16y''^2 - 48 = 0$.

Page 131

1. Ellipse. Hyperbola. Hyperbola. Ellipse. Hyperbola. Parabola. Parabola. Hyperbola. Hyperbola. Ellipse.
3. Hyperbola. Ellipse. Parabola. Ellipse. Hyperbola. Hyperbola. Parabola. Parabola. Ellipse. Hyperbola. Ellipse. Hyperbola.

Page 137

1. Tangent: $2x + y + 2 = 0$; normal: $x - 2y - 9 = 0$.
3. Tangent: $2\sqrt{5}x + 5y - 10 = 0$; normal: $\sqrt{5}x - 2y - 14 = 0$.
5. Tangent: $2\sqrt{3}x - y - 6 = 0$; normal: $\sqrt{3}x + 6y - 42 = 0$.
7. Tangent: $3x - 2y - 3 = 0$; normal: $2x + 3y + 11 = 0$.
9. $(4, 2\sqrt{5})$.   **11.** $\pm 2x + y + 5 = 0$.
13. $2x - 3y + 18 = 0$ and $2x + y + 2 = 0$.
15. $4\sqrt{13}x - 13y - 52 = 0$.   **19.** $x - y + 8 = 0$.

Page 143

1. Tangent: $2x + 3y - 12 = 0$; normal: $3x - 2y - 5 = 0$.
3. Tangent: $8x - 25y - 133 = 0$; normal: $25x + 8y + 15 = 0$.
5. Tangent: $64x - 45y - 31 = 0$; normal: $45x + 64y - 500 = 0$.
7. Tangent: $9x + 2\sqrt{13}y + 12 = 0$; normal: $4\sqrt{13}x - 18y - 39\sqrt{13} = 0$.
9. $(1, -2)$ and $(-1, 2)$.   **11.** $2x + \sqrt{3}y \pm 3 = 0$.
13. $x + y - 5 = 0$ and $x - y + 5 = 0$.
15. $12x - 5y - 14 = 0$ and $9x - 5y - 7 = 0$.
19. $x + 2y - 15 = 0$.

Page 146

1. Symmetric with respect to the origin. No intercepts.
3. Symmetric with respect to both coordinate axes. x-intercepts: ± 3. y-intercepts: ± 2.
5. x-intercepts: 0, 2. y-intercepts: -1, 0.

7. Symmetric with respect to the origin. x-intercept: 0. y-intercept: 0.
9. Symmetric with respect to the origin. x-intercepts: 0, ± 2. y-intercept: 0.
11. Symmetric with respect to the origin. x-intercepts: 0, $\pm \sqrt{2}$. y-intercept: 0.
13. Symmetric with respect to the y-axis. x-intercept: 0. y-intercepts: 0, 1.
15. Symmetric with respect to the origin. x-intercepts: $\pm \sqrt{3}$. y-intercepts: ± 1.

Page 148

1. $y = 0$.
5. $x \pm y = 0$.
9. None.
13. $y = 0$, $3x + y = 0$ and $x - 6y = 0$.

3. $x \pm 2y = 0$.
7. $x = 0$ and $2x + y = 0$.
11. None.
15. None.

Page 151

1. $y = 0$; $x = 0$.
5. $x = 0$.
9. $y - 3 = 0$; $x = 0$.
13. $x - 1 = 0$.

3. $y = \pm 3$; $x - 2 = 0$.
7. None.
11. $y \pm \sqrt{2} = 0$; $x \pm \sqrt{5} = 0$.
15. $y + 1 = 0$, $y + 4 = 0$; $x - 7 = 0$.

Page 1 3

1. Exclude $-4 < x < 1$.
3. Exclude $x < -1$ and $x > 1$.   Exclude $y < -\frac{1}{2}$ and $y > \frac{1}{2}$.
5. Exclude $-1 \leqslant x \leqslant 1$.   Exclude $-1 \leqslant y \leqslant 1$.
7. Exclude $-3 \leqslant y < \frac{5}{2}$.
9. Exclude $x < \frac{1}{2}$.   Exclude $y < -1$ and $y > 1$.
11. Exclude $x < -2$ and $x > 2$.   Exclude $y < -2$ and $y > 2$.
13. Exclude $x \leqslant 0$.   Exclude $-2 < y < 2$.

Page 155

1. Symmetric with respect to the x-axis. x-intercept: 0; y-intercept: 0.   Tangent at the origin: $y = 0$.   Vertical asymptote: $x - 4 = 0$.   Exclude $x < 0$ and $x \geqslant 4$.
3. Symmetric with respect to both coordinate axes. x-intercepts: ± 2; y-intercepts: ± 2.   Exclude $x < -2$ and $x > 2$; exclude $y < -2$ and $y > 2$.
5. Symmetric with respect to both coordinate axes. x-intercept: 0; y-intercept: 0.   Tangents at origin: $x \pm y = 0$.   Vertical asymptotes: $x \pm 2 = 0$.   Exclude $x \leqslant -2$ and $x \geqslant 2$.
7. Symmetric with respect to the origin. x-intercept: 0; y-intercept: 0.   Tangent at origin: $x = 0$.
9. Symmetric with respect to the x-axis. x-intercepts: 0, ± 2; y-intercept: 0.   Tangent at origin: $x = 0$.   Exclude $0 < x < 2$ and $x < -2$.
11. Symmetric with respect to the y-axis. y-intercept: 2.   Horizontal asymptote: $y = 0$.   Exclude $y \leqslant 0$ and $y > 2$.
13. Symmetric with respect to the y-axis. x-intercept: 0; y-intercepts: 0, 4.   Tangent at origin: $x = 0$.   Exclude $y < 0$ and $y > 4$.
15. Symmetric with respect to the origin. x-intercept: 0; y-intercept: 0.   Tangent at origin: $x - 8y = 0$.   Vertical asymptote: $x = 0$.   Exclude $x < -4$ and $x > 4$.

Page 170

1. $3x - 2y = 0$.
5. $xy - 1 = 0$.
9. $x^3 + y^3 - 3xy = 0$.
13. $(x + 1)^2/9 + (y - 2)^2/4 = 1$.
17. $x^{2/3} + y^{2/3} - a^{2/3} = 0$.

3. $y^2 - 4x = 0$.
7. $8x^3 - y = 0$.
11. $9x^2 - 16y^2 - 144 = 0$.
15. $x^{1/2} + y^{1/2} - 2 = 0$.
19. $x^2y + 2x - y = 0$.

Page 173

1. $x = 128t$, $y = 96t - 16t^2$; 768 feet; 144 feet high.
3. 3 seconds; 36 feet high.   **5.** 19 feet.
7. $x = 4m(1 + m^2)$, $y = 4m^2/(1 + m^2)$.   **9.** $x = 16/m^2$, $y = 16/m$.
11. $x = m^{1/2}/4$, $y = m^{3/2}/4$.

Page 182

1. $(3/\sqrt{2}, 3/\sqrt{2})$, $(0, -5)$, $(\sqrt{3}, 1)$, $(6, 0)$, $(-2, 2\sqrt{3})$.
3. $(2, 30°)$, $(6, 300°)$.
5. $x^2 + y^2 - 4y = 0$; $x - 5 = 0$; $x^2 + y^2 - 9 = 0$; $y - (\tan 2)x = 0$; $y^2 + 6x - 9 = 0$; $3x^2 + 4y^2 - 4x - 4 = 0$.
7. $\rho(2 \cos \theta - 3 \sin \theta) + 4 = 0$.   **9.** $\theta = 0$.
11. $\rho^2 + 2\rho(2 \cos \theta - 3 \sin \theta) - 3 = 0$.   **13.** $\rho \sin^2 \theta - 2k \cos \theta = 0$.
15. $\rho^2(a^2 \sin^2 \theta + b^2 \cos^2 \theta) - a^2 b^2 = 0$.

Page 185

1. $\rho - a \sec \theta = 0$.   **3.** $\rho - 2a \cos \theta = 0$.
5. $\rho - a \cos \theta - b = 0$.   **7.** $\rho - a(\sin \theta + \cos \theta) = 0$.
9. $\rho - a \sin \theta \tan \theta = 0$.

Page 187

1. (a) $\rho \cos \theta - 8 = 0$; (b) $\rho \sin \theta + 3 = 0$; (c) $\theta = 60°$; (d) $\theta = 0$.
3. $\rho \cos \theta - 2 = 0$.   **7.** $\rho(5 \cos \theta - \sin \theta) - (10 + 2\sqrt{3}) = 0$.
9. $\rho(3 \cos \theta - 2 \sin \theta) - 3 = 0$.

Page 189

1. (a) $\rho - 8 = 0$; (b) $\rho - 10 \cos \theta = 0$; (c) $\rho - 12 \sin \theta = 0$; (d) $\rho + 8 \cos \theta = 0$;
(e) $\rho \pm 6 \sin \theta = 0$.
3. (a) $(0, 0°)$, 5; (b) $(3, 0°)$, 3; (c) $(\frac{7}{2}, 270°)$, $\frac{7}{2}$; (d) $(1, 180°)$, 1.
5. $\rho^2 - 6\rho \cos (\theta - 135°) - 55 = 0$.   **7.** $\rho - 10 \cos (\theta + \pi/6) = 0$.
9. $\rho^2 + 2\rho (2 \sin \theta - \cos \theta) + 1 = 0$.

Page 192

1. Parabola.   **3.** Parabola.   **5.** Ellipse.
7. Parabola.   **9.** Parabola.
11. (1) Vertex is $(3, 180°)$, directrix is $\rho \cos \theta + 6 = 0$; (3) vertex is $(\frac{3}{2}, 270°)$, directrix is $\rho \sin \theta + 3 = 0$; (9) vertex is $(\frac{5}{2}, 270°)$, directrix is $7 \rho \sin \theta + 10 = 0$.
13. (4) Vertices are $(3, 0°)$ and $(-15, 180°)$, center is $(9, 0°)$, directrices are $\rho \cos \theta - 5 = 0$ and $\rho \cos \theta - 13 = 0$; (6) vertices are $(\frac{7}{3}, 90°)$ and $(-\frac{7}{5}, 270°)$, center is $(\frac{6 \cdot 42}{6 \cdot 6}, 90°)$, directrices are $\rho \sin \theta - 8 = 0$ and $65\rho \sin \theta - 776 = 0$; (10) vertices are $(1, 90°)$ and $(-7, 270°)$, center is $(4, 90°)$, directrices are $4\rho \sin \theta - 7 = 0$ and $4\rho \sin \theta - 25 = 0$.

Page 202

3. The yz-plane.   **5.** The z-axis.
7. The plane which is parallel to the zx-plane and two units behind it.
9. The plane bisecting the dihedral angle in the first octant formed by the yz- and zx-planes.

Page 204

1. Yes, the z-axis; $PQ = 6$.
3. 3.   **5.** -7.
7. (a) $5\sqrt{3}$;   (b) 7;   (c) $\sqrt{83}$;   (d) $\sqrt{149}$.
9. $\sqrt{(x-2)^2 + (y-3)^2 + (z-1)^2} = 5$; a sphere with center at $(2, 3, 1)$ and radius 5.
11. A sphere with center at $(1, -4, 2)$ and radius 3.
13. $x^2 + y^2 + z^2 = 49$.

Page 207

1. Positive.   **3.** Negative.   **5.** Positive.
7. Positive.   **9.** $6; -7; 5; 5$.

Page 210

1. (a) $[-\frac{2}{3}, \frac{2}{3}, \frac{1}{3}]$;   (b) $[\frac{6}{7}, -\frac{3}{7}, \frac{2}{7}]$;   (c) $[\frac{4}{5}, \frac{3}{5}, 0]$;   (d) $[\frac{3}{5}, 0, \frac{4}{5}]$.
3. (a) $[-5/\sqrt{62}, 1/\sqrt{62}, 6/\sqrt{62}]$;   (b) $[-10/\sqrt{117}, -4/\sqrt{117}, 1/\sqrt{117}]$;
    (c) $[4/\sqrt{273}, -16/\sqrt{273}, 1/\sqrt{273}]$;   (d) $[\sqrt{3}/3, \sqrt{3}/3, \sqrt{3}/3]$.
5. $\frac{2}{7}$.   **7.** $60°$ or $120°$.
9. $\alpha = 120°, \beta = 45°, \gamma = 60°$.

Page 214

1. (a) $[2, 2, 1]$;   (b) $[-1, 5, 4]$;   (c) $[3, -4, 0]$;   (d) $[2, 2, 1]$;   (e) $[-1, 5, 4]$;
    (f) $[1, 4, 8]$;   (g) $[4, 3, 0]$;   (h) $[-3, 2, 2]$.
3. (a) and (d); (b) and (e).
5. (a) and (h); (c) and (g); (d) and (h).
7. (a) $[\frac{2}{3}, \frac{2}{3}, \frac{1}{3}]$;   (b) $[-1/\sqrt{42}, 5/\sqrt{42}, 4/\sqrt{42}]$;   (c) $[-\frac{3}{5}, \frac{4}{5}, 0]$;   (d) $[\frac{2}{3}, \frac{2}{3}, \frac{1}{3}]$;
    (e) $[-1/\sqrt{42}, 5/\sqrt{42}, 4/\sqrt{42}]$;   (f) $[\frac{1}{9}, \frac{4}{9}, \frac{8}{9}]$;   (g) $[\frac{4}{5}, \frac{3}{5}, 0]$;
    (h) $[-3/\sqrt{17}, 2/\sqrt{17}, 2/\sqrt{17}]$.

Page 218

1. (a) $y = 7$;   (b) $x = -5$;   (c) $z = -2$.
3. $2x - y + 2z - 18 = 0$.   **5.** $2x - y - 3z - 5\sqrt{14} = 0$.
7. $x - y - 2z - 6 = 0$.   **9.** $-\frac{3}{7}x + \frac{6}{7}y + \frac{2}{7}z + \frac{9}{7} = 0$.
11. $7x - 4y + 4z = 0$.   **13.** $2x - 5y - 3z + 29 = 0$.

Page 222

1. $(4, 0, 0), (0, -3, 0), (0, 0, 6)$.
3. $-\frac{2}{3}x - \frac{2}{3}y + \frac{1}{3}z + 9 = 0$ and $\frac{2}{3}x - \frac{2}{3}y + \frac{1}{3}z + \frac{9}{3} = 0$.
5. -2.   **7.** $[-\frac{1}{3}, \frac{2}{3}, \frac{2}{3}]$.
9. $[0, -2/\sqrt{5}, 1/\sqrt{5}]$.   **11.** $x - 11z - 8 = 0$.
13. $5x - 4y + 8z + 14 = 0$.   **15.** $x - 5y - 4z + 42 = 0$.

Page 224

1. Identical: (a) and (f); parallel: (a), (c) and (f), (b) and (c), (b) and (f), (d) and (e), (b) and (d).
3. $4x + 2y - 7z = 0$.   **5.** $x - 2y + z - 1 = 0$.   **7.** $B = -2$.

Page 226

1. (a) 3;   (b) $2\sqrt{3}/3$;   (c) $4\sqrt{2}$.   **3.** $\sqrt{30}/3$.
5. $-3\sqrt{2}/2$.   **7.** Same side.
9. $3x + 2y + \sqrt{3}z - 15 = 0; 3x + 2y + \sqrt{3}z + 1 = 0$.

Page 228

1. (a) $65x + 9y - 31z - 107 = 0$;   (b) $7x - 3y + 9z + 4 = 0$.
3. $7x - y - 3z - 14 = 0$.   5. $29x - 3y + 14z + 19 = 0$.
7. $28x + 12y - 21z - 84 = 0$.   9. $(-2, 2, 2)$.

Page 230

1. $(0, 3, 5)$ and $(6, 0, 2)$; $[-2, 1, 1]$.
3. $(0, 4, -4)$ and $(-3, 2, 0)$; $[-3, -2, 4]$.
5. $(0, 4, 3)$ and $(5, 0, 1)$; $[-5, 4, 2]$.

Page 232

1. $13y - 6z - 9 = 0$, $13x + 17z + 19 = 0$, $6x + 17y - 3 = 0$.
3. $11y - 5z + 4 = 0$, $11x - 3z + 20 = 0$, $5x - 3y + 8 = 0$.
5. $36y + 3z + 19 = 0$, $36x - 15z + 25 = 0$, $3x + 15y + 10 = 0$.
7. $\begin{cases} 5x - 7y + 22 = 0, \\ 12x + 7z - 13 = 0. \end{cases}$ 9. $\begin{cases} 4x + z + 2 = 0, \\ 2y - z - 6 = 0. \end{cases}$

Page 236

1. $\begin{cases} (x + 4)/3 = (y - 2)/5, \\ (y - 2)/5 = (z - 1)/-8. \end{cases}$ 3. $\begin{cases} (x - 3)/6 = (y + 6)/-1, \\ (y + 6)/-1 = (z - 4)/7. \end{cases}$
5. $\begin{cases} (y - 2)/-2 = (z - 4)/3, \\ x + 1 = 0. \end{cases}$ 7. $\begin{cases} (x + 2)/3 = (y - 1)/7, \\ (y - 1)/7 = (z - 5)/-6. \end{cases}$
9. $\begin{cases} x/-2 = y - 3, \\ y - 3 = z - 5. \end{cases}$ $\begin{cases} x/-7 = (y + 5)/-5, \\ (y + 5)/-5 = z - 2. \end{cases}$
$\begin{cases} x/-3 = (y - 4)/-2, \\ (y - 4)/-2 = (z + 4)/4. \end{cases}$ $\begin{cases} x/-2 = (y - 3)/9, \\ (y - 3)/9 = (z - 5)/5. \end{cases}$
$\begin{cases} x/-5 = (y - 4)/4, \\ (y - 4)/4 = (z - 3)/2. \end{cases}$ $\begin{cases} x/2 = (y - 5)/-5, \\ (y - 5)/-5 = z/3. \end{cases}$
11. $\begin{cases} (x + 1\frac{1}{2})/-3 = y/2, \\ y/2 = (z - 15)/8. \end{cases}$ 13. $\begin{cases} x = 2, \\ y/4 = z/5. \end{cases}$
15. The lines intersect in the point $(-2, 4, -1)$.

Page 239

1. $x = -1 + 3d/\sqrt{14}$, $y = 5 - d/\sqrt{14}$, $z = 4 + 4d/\sqrt{14}$.
3. $[-3/\sqrt{26}, -4/\sqrt{26}, 1/\sqrt{26}]$.   5. $x = -2k$, $y = 3 + k$, $z = 5 + k$.
7. $x = -3k$, $y = 4 - 2k$, $z = -4 + 4k$.   9. $x = 5 - 5k$, $y = 4k$, $z = 1 + 2k$.
11. $x = -k$, $y = 1 + k$, $z = 2k$.   13. $x = 7k$, $y = -5k$, $z = k$.
15. $x = -4$, $y = -2$, $z = 6 + k$.   17. $x = 4 + 14k$, $y = 17k$, $z = -3 + 9k$.

Page 243

1. (a) $x^2 + y^2 + z^2 + 10x - 4y - 8z + 9 = 0$;
   (b) $x^2 + y^2 + z^2 - 2x - 12y + 6z + 30 = 0$;
   (c) $x^2 + y^2 + z^2 - 6x - 8z = 0$;
   (d) $x^2 + y^2 + z^2 - 16x + 2y + 14z + 110 = 0$.
3. $(-1, 3, 11)$; 3.   5. $(0, -13, 0)$; 7.
7. Imaginary.   9. $x^2 + y^2 + z^2 - 14z + 8 = 0$.
11. $x^2 + y^2 + z^2 - 12x - 4y - 6z + 48 = 0$.
13. $x^2 + y^2 + z^2 - 10x - 25 = 0$.
15. $x^2 + y^2 + z^2 - 22x - 24z + 115 = 0$.

Page 246

1. $\begin{cases} z^2 = 4fy, \\ x = 0. \end{cases}$ Focus: $(0, f, 0)$.

3. $\begin{cases} x^2/a^2 + z^2/b^2 = 1, \\ y = 0. \end{cases}$ Foci: $(\pm\sqrt{a^2 - b^2}, 0, 0)$.

5. $\begin{cases} x^2/a^2 - y^2/b^2 = 1, \\ z = 0. \end{cases}$ Asymptotes: $\begin{cases} bx \pm ay = 0, \\ z = 0. \end{cases}$

7. $\begin{cases} y = x^3, \\ z = 0. \end{cases}$ $\begin{cases} y^2 = kx^2(x + b), \\ z = 0. \end{cases}$

9. The point $(0, 5, 0)$.

Page 250

1. (a) Circular cylinder;   (b) sphere;   (c) parabolic cylinder;   (d) plane;   (e) hyperbolic cylinder;   (f) no locus.

3. $z^2 = 4fx$.

5. $y^2 + z^2 + 4y - 10z + 20 = 0$.

7. $x^2 - z = 0$.

9. $\begin{cases} y^2/6 + z^2/2 = 1, \\ x = 3. \end{cases}$

11. $2x^2 - y^2 + x - 3y = 0$, $2y^4 + 4y^2z^2 + 2z^4 + z^2 - 3y = 0$.

Page 253

1. $y^2 + z^2 - 6x = 0$.

3. $9x^2 + 16y^2 + 16z^2 - 144 = 0$.

5. $25x^2 + 25y^2 - 4z^2 - 100 = 0$.

7. $x^4 + y^4 + z^4 + 2x^2y^2 + 2y^2z^2 + 2x^2z^2 - 106x^2 - 106y^2 + 90z^2 + 2025 = 0$.

9. $x^2 + z^2 = \sin^2 y$.

11. (a) $\begin{cases} x^2 + z^2 = 25, \\ y = 0, \end{cases}$ about the x-axis;

    (c) $\begin{cases} z^2 - 2y = 0, \\ x = 0, \end{cases}$ about the y-axis.

Page 263

1. Hyperboloid of one sheet.   Ellipsoid.   Ellipsoid.   Hyperboloid of two sheets. Elliptic paraboloid.   Elliptic paraboloid.   Quadric cone.   Hyperboloid of one sheet.

3. Ellipsoid.

5. Hyperboloid of one sheet.

7. Hyperboloid of one sheet.

9. Elliptic paraboloid.

11. Hyperboloid of two sheets.

13. Hyperboloid of one sheet.

Index

(*The numbers refer to pages*)